Technology
and Man's Future
Second Edition

Technology
and Man's Future
Second Edition

ALBERT H. TEICH, EDITOR
Graduate Program in Science, Technology,
and Public Policy

The George Washington University

ST. MARTIN'S PRESS   NEW YORK

Contents

3
Toward Assessment and Control

Introduction

When historians in the twenty-first century look back upon the present period, they are certain to be struck by the proximity in time of two enormously significant but very different technological events. To many of us, the landing of the Apollo 11 astronauts on the moon on July 20, 1969, symbolized the culmination of a path of technological development through which man demonstrated his hegemony over the forces of nature. There seemed to be little that a society such as ours could not achieve, given a sufficiently sustained national commitment. Only four years later, however, in the fall of 1973, the precariousness of our technological society became clear to anyone who drove or traveled in an automobile. Our petroleum-based transportation system nearly ground to a halt as a result of the Arab oil embargo. The "energy crisis" was upon us.

Of course, the Apollo moon landing was not the apex of technological civilization, and, contrary to what some would have us believe, the energy crisis does not necessarily mark the beginning of its decline. But it is remarkable that, so soon after witnessing the most impressive demonstration of technology in recorded history, we were rudely awakened to a sense of technology's limitations.

In the introduction to the first edition of this book, published in 1972, I described my childhood images of a technological future. The picture of tomorrow's world that I carried around in my head throughout my childhood years corresponded, more or less, to that which one might have acquired from any number of science-fiction movies or from such monuments to technology as the Museum of Science and Industry in Chicago. My world of the future was characterized by symmetry and neatness, mile upon mile of gleaming chrome, millions of buttons to push, and endless gadgets to do all the work. All of our "old-fashioned" ways of doing things were, I believed, to be replaced by modern, more efficient ones. A nourishment pill in the morning would save us the trouble of consuming three meals during the day. Automated highways would carry us effortlessly from place to place. When I reflected on these images several years ago I was struck by the fact that the technological future always seemed to be an end in itself. When adults in my life spoke of the future, they implied its inevitability—with some interest and some, but not much, enthusiasm. No one seemed to care very much for the prospect, but this was the course of "progress," and only a fool would try to resist its tide.

Influenced by a major theme of social criticism, and to some extent by the political movements of the late 1960s, I was interested in these juvenile images because of what they implied about the relationship between technological progress and human happiness. What, I asked, is the point of making the tools of society more and more efficient and increasing the material affluence of society if the ultimate result is not satisfaction but alienation of a large segment of the population? Is material progress an end in itself, or is it, more properly, a means to some higher end? Is the development of technology leading toward a more desirable state of human affairs, or is it actually producing a decline in the quality of life? Is technology a tool that human beings are capable of using as they choose, or is it, in a basic sense, a system that has gone out of control?

Five years later these questions have neither been answered nor have they disappeared. Their immediate importance has been overshadowed, however, by another, apparently more urgent, complex of technological problems besetting society. To most people, the energy crisis is the most pressing aspect of the complex. Intertwined with it are a variety of more fundamental issues: how long can society continue to grow in the face of limited reserves of natural resources and the limited capacity of the earth to absorb technology's waste products; can inequities between rich and poor nations be resolved by any means short of global upheaval; can our technological civilization survive in anything near its present form when threatened with an exploding population, environmental catastrophe, and a diminishing resource base.

The tone of discussions on technology and society has changed during the 1970s. Although often couched in unnecessarily pessimistic terms, a growing (and healthy) realization exists among national leaders as well as ordinary citizens that ours has been an extravagant age, wasteful of energy and natural resources, careless about environmental side effects. Whether or not one accepts the "limits to growth" thesis and its frightening implications (see the articles by Meadows et al. and Freeman in part one), it is becoming clear that tomorrow's technology will be qualitatively different from today's—not because of abstract notions about ends and means, but because of concrete requirements of survival. The technology of tomorrow will certainly extend our capabilities in transportation, medicine, data processing, and many other areas. More importantly, however, it will perform many of the same functions of today's technology while using less energy and fewer raw materials.

Notions of technology once regarded as radical have gained increasing currency in our society. Advance assessment of technological consequences (see part three) is no longer an issue; it is an accepted procedure. The most "sophisticated" or "advanced" technology, many of us have come to recognize, is not necessarily the best. Technology must first of all be "appropriate" to its use. The United Nations has given official sanction to this concept in its assistance programs for developing countries. And in 1976 California was the first state to establish an Office of Appropriate Technology, implementing Governor Jerry Brown's "small is beautiful" philosophy.*

Futurists are fond of reminding us that the only thing we can say with certainty about the future is that it has in store developments that are completely unanticipated today. The readings in this book—with a couple of exceptions—do not attempt to tell us what the future will be like. Their aim, and the aim of the book as a whole, is to provide the reader with ways of thinking about the future, with an understanding of the forces, particularly the technological forces, that will shape the future, and with a sense of how to deal with those forces.

The book is organized into three parts. The articles in part one reflect the views of those who are primarily responsible for creating new technology, namely scientists and engineers. Part two contains selections from the writings on technology of a number of contemporary philosophers, as well as an extended debate on the place of technology in society between two observers with very different political perspectives. The concept of technology assessment and a variety of associated, recent ideas for the control of technology are presented and criticized in part three.

The literature on technology and society is large and growing rapidly. This book samples but a small part of that literature. If it encourages the reader to explore the field more deeply, this book will have accomplished its purpose.

ALBERT H. TEICH

---

*See E. F. Schumacher, *Small is Beautiful: Economics as if People Mattered* (New York: Harper & Row, 1973).

Technology
and Man's Future
Second Edition

1

Scientists, Technologists, and the Future

Scientific research and development (R&D) are major sectors of intellectual and economic activity in the industrialized regions of the world today. In the United States, for example, in 1975, $35 billion was spent on R&D, an amount equal to approximately 2.3 percent of the nation's entire gross national product. Nearly 530,000 scientists and engineers were employed in R&D, or nearly 25 for every 10,000 persons in the country. There is a spectrum of R&D activities. At one end is basic, or fundamental, research—the pursuit of knowledge without regard to practical application. At the other end is development—the translation of scientific knowledge into products or processes. In the middle of the spectrum is applied research—studies undertaken with the aim of contributing to the solution of practical problems.

Not all technological innovation is a direct result of R&D. But on the whole, the dramatic technological changes that have taken place in the way we live—in food, medicine, transportation, and communication, for example—have been made possible by advances in scientific research. And research conducted today will bring about changes in tomorrow's technology. This we can state with certainty. What we cannot state with certainty is whether the changes in technology will result in net improvements in human life. Although science has given us a better understanding of the physical and biological workings of our world, the ways in which we have used this understanding have, as often as not, brought us mixed blessings.

As part two of this book illustrates, a significant body of thought holds that the application of scientific knowledge through technology is inexorably leading humanity to disaster. Some observers, such as Theodore Roszak, have criticized not just technology but the whole scientific approach, claiming that it has led us to neglect other, equally valid forms of knowledge.

It is unfair and simplistic to characterize critics such as Roszak as "anti-technology," and it is similarly unfair to label those who do not share such views—including most scientists and engineers—as "protechnology." The points of difference among various perspectives are much more subtle and complex, and the articles in parts one and two provide a sense of the subtleties and complexities.

The writers represented in part one all come from scientific or technological backgrounds, yet their perspectives on the technology-society relationship are vastly different. To some degree their differences reflect an evolution of attitudes that has taken place in the 1970s. The first two articles, dating from the late 1960s, express a generally optimistic orientation toward the role of technology in society and see future developments mainly as extensions of the past. In "Forecasts of Some Technological and Scientific Developments and Their Societal Consequences," Theodore Gordon and Robert Ament report on a study carried out by the Institute for the Future—a scientific organization whose main function is developing and applying forecasting tools to aid long-range planning. Gordon and Ament employed the Delphi method to develop a series of forecasts of future events in science and technology. In this technique, a panel of experts is assembled and made to deliberate as a committee without face-to-face contact. Thus, the group brings its collective knowledge and judgment to bear on a problem in a manner free of such extraneous influences as the relative strengths of individual personalities, influences that often shape the course of conventional committee operations. Although there is some dispute over the validity of the Delphi method (and the authors would be the first to caution that their studies are experimental and should be viewed with a critical eye), the result is an intriguing excursion into the future as seen by a panel of recognized scientists. The projected world bears much resemblance to some strains of American science fiction, but the conception of that world is tempered by informed judgment on what is scientifically and technologically feasible. Of course, the future described is not one that the panelists necessarily see as desirable—it is simply one that they believe probable.

Based on the consensus of their panelists, Gordon and Ament sketch three scenarios, describing the technological worlds of 1985, 2000, and 2025. The scenarios are not meant to be complete descriptions of the world in these years; they are more narrowly concerned with technological advances and their consequences. Nevertheless, it is interesting that, except for some discussion of overpopulation, there is no real mention of the possible impact of limited resources for growth on the condition of society. The technological world of the future, as envisioned by these scientists and engineers, is like today's world, only faster paced, more automated, and more efficient.

The second article, "Can Technology Replace Social Engineering?", is similar to the first in some respects. This piece, which has become something of a classic since the mid-1960s, was written by Alvin M. Weinberg, one of the pioneers in large-scale atomic energy R&D and director of Oak Ridge National Laboratory, one of the world's largest R&D institutions, from 1955 through 1973. Weinberg argues that technology is capable of finding short-cuts to the solution of many pressing social problems. He calls such shortcuts "technological fixes." Since technological problems are intrinsically easier to solve than social problems, Weinberg suggests that we transform our social problems into technological ones. For example, faced with a shortage of fresh water, one can either try social engineering—altering life-styles and the ways people use water—or a technological fix, such as the provision of additional fresh water through nuclear-powered desalting of sea water. Technology defines the limits within which society can function. By developing new technologies we can change the limits on society and thereby remove the conditions creating the problem. Weinberg concludes that technology will not ultimately replace social engineering (a concept he uses in a rather narrow sense in this article), but it may in the short term ease some of the pressures society faces and buy time to develop long-term solutions.

Weinberg, like the Delphi panelists in Gordon and Ament's study, regards technology in the traditional sense as the application of knowledge to the solution of practical problems. Sometimes in the evolution of technology, however, solutions actually precede problems. Just as there is pure science, the writer Daedalus suggests, only half tongue-in-cheek, so too is there pure technology—technology for its own sake. The pseudonym "Daedalus" protects the anonymity of an imaginative British scientist who writes regularly for the *New Scientist.* His satirical article "Pure Technology" proposes that the forces that drive technological advance are not just the needs of society. Rather, technology is a creative art form in itself. A prime example of what Daedalus regards as pure technology is the supersonic transport plane. Rational analysis, he says, clearly shows the pointlessness of the project. The real reason for wanting to carry it through must then be the "sheer entertainment of overcoming all the technical problems and finally flying such a thrilling machine." The developers of such pure technologies should be encouraged, in the same way as are sculptors, composers, and poets. Society should recognize, however, that their creations need not all be put to use; many ought to be placed instead in museums.

Steven Weinberg's article "Reflections of a Working Scientist" is concerned not so much with technology as with science. The writer is seeking to respond as a scientist to what he sees as the current challenges to science. The problem he faces is that public attitudes toward science are shaped more by the impact of new technology than by science itself. Weinberg does not refute all the accusations against technology. In fact, he declares himself sympathetic toward some of them and troubled by the role that science appears to play in advancing some types of technology. On issues involving the nature of science itself, however—its supposed closure to new ideas and its coldness, objectivity, and nonhumanity—Weinberg is a stronger advocate for his profession. There is beauty in science, he observes, and there is great aesthetic satisfaction in the process of scientific research.

The last two selections in part one return to the theme of the first selection; that is, they use scientific and technological techniques to forecast the shape of the world in the years to come. The picture they develop, however, barely resembles that which we saw at first. Rather than using the Delphi technique, as Gordon and Ament did in their study, Donella and Dennis Meadows and their colleagues at MIT employed a complex mathematical model describing relationships among five key aspects of the world system: population, industrialization, pollution, food production, and resource depletion. With financial support from an international group of industrialists and technocrats known as the Club of Rome, the authors programed a computer with equations representing their model and with as much data as they were able to obtain concerning the current values and historical trends of these five aspects. Their analysis leads them to conclude that the world is rapidly reaching limits to growth and that if present trends continue, "the most probable result will be a rather sudden and uncontrollable decline in both population and industrial capacity" within the next 100 years.

The selection included here is taken mainly from one chapter in their study entitled *Limits to Growth.* It is concerned with whether new technological breakthroughs can push back present limits and allow growth to continue by such means as controlling pollution, increasing the availability of resources, or increasing agricultural productivity. The authors manipulate their model to simulate the effects of breakthroughs in these and other areas, and they conclude that, although new technologies will be "vital to the future of human society," they cannot substitute for deliberate checks on growth.

According to the authors of the *Limits to Growth,* the purpose of their report was not so much to provide the last word in analyzing the problems of growth as it was to stimulate discussion and further analysis. In this, at least, they have been eminently successful. Their study has been a center of controversy since its publication in 1972, and it has been followed by a variety of critiques and studies. The best-known follow-up study, also sponsored by the Club of Rome, was conducted by Mihajlo Mesarovic and Eduard Pestel and published in 1974 under the title *Mankind at the Turning Point* (Dutton/Reader's Digest Press, 1974). This analysis views the world in terms of a multilevel, regionalized model instead of the Meadows's homogeneous system, and it draws the more hopeful conclusion that balanced, differentiated growth (as opposed to undifferentiated growth or global equilibrium) is not only possible but necessary.

Mankind at the Turning Point is a useful follow-up to *Limits to Growth*, but it is only a partial response to the criticisms that have been leveled at *Limits*. Perhaps the best critique, in detail as well as in overview, was prepared by the staff of the Science Policy Research Unit at the University of Sussex (England) and published under the title *Models of Doom*. We have chosen Christopher Freeman's "Malthus with a Computer" from that study as the final selection of part one. Freeman criticizes the underlying assumptions and biases of the MIT group. In particular, he addresses the issue of technological change and charges that *Limits to Growth* has vastly underestimated its potential for "indefinitely postponing the catastrophes which the model otherwise predicts." Freeman's piece is not unduly optimistic, but it is a strong counterpoint to *Limits*.

Forecasts of Some Technological and Scientific Developments and Their Societal Consequences

THEODORE J. GORDON AND ROBERT H. AMENT

Scientific and technological developments have profoundly altered man's institutions, his life styles, and his aspirations in the last several generations. What is striking about this transformation is not that it has occurred, but rather that it has occurred without preparation. For the consequences have been pervasive, and many of them, favorable and unfavorable alike, have left today's policy makers and policy advisors seriously behind the course of events, with the result that by the time their efforts have been translated into programs for action they have become infeasible or simply irrelevant. Long-range forecasting of scientific and technological developments can provide some of the information decision makers need to accommodate the long lead-times separating the evaluation of opportunities from the implementation of specific plans. The technological Delphi study reported in this article was undertaken to help provide such information.

The immediate objectives of the study were:

- To generate a list of important prospective events and developments in the physical and biological disciplines;
- To determine, using the judgment of experts, when these events and developments might take place;
- To ascertain what societal changes are likely to accompany these scientific and technological innovations;
- To determine whether the anticipated societal consequences appeared likely to be beneficial or detrimental to society as a whole;
- To determine whether intervention in the processes producing these consequences seemed feasible, and if so, through what means; and
- To test the use of the Delphi method for attaining reasonable consensus among groups of experts in dealing with questions of social change, values, and science policy.

THE DELPHI TECHNIQUE

Most decision makers utilize expert advice in forming their judgment. Where the question being examined is so complex and involves such obscure inter-relationships that no single person could be expected to be expert in the many disciplines required, the traditional approach to the answer is to seek a consensus among experts through open discussion or a conference. However, joint committee activity often introduces certain undesirable psychological factors, "such as specious persuasion, unwillingness to abandon publicly expressed opinions, and the bandwagon effect of majority opinion."[1]

The Delphi technique, which was used in this study, makes it possible to avoid some of these difficulties because the experts involved exchange their opinions anonymously and through an intermediary, who controls the feedback of opinion in subsequent rounds of the inquiry. It has been found in previous studies of this type that the Delphi process—involving anonymity, iteration, and controlled feedback—tends to produce a converging group consensus

In a typical Delphi investigation, the participants are sent a series of questionnaires through the mail. In the first, they might be asked to provide their judgment as to likely dates of occurrence of a group of events and developments. The collated responses normally reveal a spread of opinions; these data are presented to the respondents in the second questionnaire. In this round, the respondents are given the opportunity to revise their estimates in light of the group response, and those participants whose estimates have fallen earlier or later than those of the majority are asked to provide reasons for their positions. These reasons, along with the new estimates of the group as a whole, are collated and fed back to the respondents on the third questionnaire, and they are again asked to reassess their earlier estimates in view of the new group response and reasons provided for early and late dates.

The Delphi method has proven useful for long-range forecasting of expected technological and societal developments. Several corporations and government agencies have conducted future-oriented Delphi studies concerned with such subjects as political alliances,[2] technological potentials,[3] war pre-

1. N. C. Dalkey and O. Helmer, "An Experimental Application of the Delphi Method to the Use of Experts," *Management Science,* vol. 9, no. 3 (April 1963).

2. Joseph Matino, *An Experiment with the Delphi Procedure for Long-Range Forecasting* (Washington, D.C.: Office of Scientific Research, US Air Force, 1967), AFOSR Document 670175.

3. Harper Q. North and Donald L. Pyke, *A Probe of TRW's Future, The Next 20 Years,* a TRW proprietary document, 1966.

vention techniques,[4] economic indices,[5] and medical developments.[6] Results generally have been satisfactory; that is, in many cases a reasonable consensus seems to have been achieved and the potential developments described provided a basis for subsequent planning, action, and analysis.

Even though this technique has been used with some success, however, it should not be interpreted as a device that produces "truth about the future." The Delphi method is designed to produce consensus judgments in inexact fields; it would be a mistake to consider such judgments as complete or precise descriptions about the future.

The future will contain events that are totally unanticipated today; perhaps this is the only thing that can be said about the future with absolute certainty. Furthermore, all techniques of forecasting that rely on judgment and opinion (rather than on the more rigid laws of causality of the natural sciences) depend on the imagination and technical adequacy of the forecasters. Nevertheless, forecasting the future seems to be a worthwhile enterprise despite the certainty of the unexpected and despite the limitations imposed by relying on human judgment, however well informed. Forecasts, even hazy forecasts, based on careful judgment can provide a seemingly coherent structure for testing alternative contemplated actions, for warning that certain other actions may be needed or should be avoided, and for defining the scope of reasonable expectations in a world where expectations sometimes seem unbounded.

OUTLINE OF THE STUDY

As in all Delphi studies, the value of the results depends largely on the excellence and cooperation of the participants. Since this study dealt with scientific and technological events and their implications for society, the experimenters invited respondents who had, in the aggregate, skills which included the following:

Aerospace technology	Industrialization
Agriculture	Manufacturing
Bacteriology	Mathematics
Biochemistry	Microbiology

4. See, for example, T. J. Gordon and O. Helmer, *Report on a Long-Range Forecasting Study,* The Rand Corporation, Paper P-2982 (September 1964).
5. Robert M. Campbell, "Methodological Study of the Utilization of Experts in Business Forecasting," Ph.D. thesis, University of California, Los Angeles, September, 1966.
6. Alan Sheldon, Laboratory of Community Psychiatry, Boston, 1969.

Brain physiology	Molecular biology
Computer sciences	Natural resources
Cytogenetics	Pediatrics
Electron physics	Philosophy
Engineering	Psychiatry
Finance	Public administration
Genetics	Science journalism
Gerontology	Transportation
History of science	

Four questionnaires were used in this study. The first presented a list of forty technological developments selected by the experimenters and asked that the respondents estimate the dates at which the item had, in their judgment, a 10 percent, a 50 percent, and a 90 percent chance of occurrence. The respondents were also asked to suggest additional scientific and technical developments which they believed might have significant social impact and to indicate how familiar they felt they were with each item. The responses to this questionnaire were collated. In all, forty-three additional items were suggested by the respondents and added to the study.

The new items were presented to the respondents in Questionnaire 2, along with a request that they provide estimates of the dates by which they judged the items to have a 10 percent, a 50 percent, and a 90 percent probability of occurrence. A second part of this questionnaire asked the respondent to list what they considered to be socially important consequences likely to result from all of the technological and scientific events. The questionnaire suggested that the respondents consider a full spectrum of consequences—technological, demographic, political, personal, social.

Questionnaires 3 and 4 further refined the results of the study by informing respondents of items upon which agreement had been reached and asking them to reconsider their responses on other items, as well as (in certain cases) to state the reasons for their opinions. Questionnaire 4 also asked respondents to suggest specific policy strategies that might be used to intervene in the consequences of the events being discussed.

FORECASTS AND CONSEQUENCES

The full range of results obtained from this study tells a fascinating story. Unfortunately, we are unable to present complete tabulations in the limited space afforded by the context of this article.[7] In the next section, these tabulations are used to delineate a series of scenarios, describing possible technological futures. Here, to give the reader a feeling for the type of findings upon which the scenarios were based, we present a number of sample tabulations. Some examples of the forecasts of the time of occurrence of events discussed by the panelists are presented in Figure 1. The polygons are used to depict the final range of opinions generated by the group. The high point on the bar indicates the median date at which the panelists judged there was a 50 percent chance the event would occur. The shorter legs of the polygon define the limits of the upper and lower quartiles, and the bar itself the interquartile range.

For each item in these figures, the asterisk denotes the median date of occurrence forecasted by the subset of respondents who rated themselves "expert" or "generally familiar" with the event in question.

The respondents also developed an extensive list of prospective consequences which they felt might be expected as a result of the forecasted technological and scientific developments. Each of these consequences was judged as to its likelihood of being a result of the event and, assuming it should occur, whether it was favorable or unfavorable.

The list of consequences for those items shown in Figure 1 is given in Figure 2; the polygons again indicate the interquartile range of the responses.

7. See the report from which this article was condensed for a full presentation of the results.

Figure 1. Potential Physical and Biological Developments

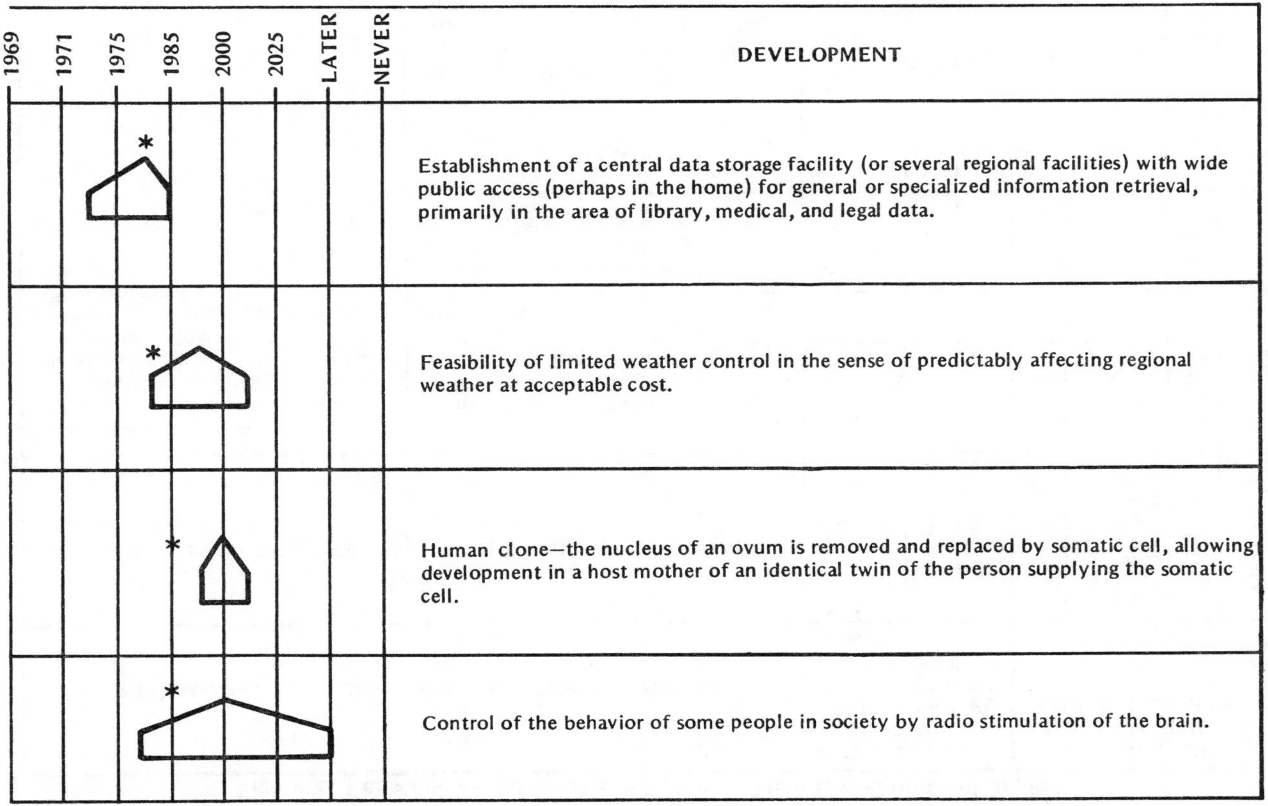

Figure 2. Consequences of Forecasted Events: Their Likelihood and Impact

NEW AUTOMATION AND COMMUNICATION TECHNIQUES

IF THESE DEVELOPMENTS WERE TO OCCUR,

Establishment of a central data storage facility (or several regional or disciplinary facilities) with wide public access (perhaps in the home) for general or specialized information retrieval primarily in the areas of library, medical and legal data.

THEY MIGHT RESULT IN:	HOW LIKELY IS IT THAT THE RESULT WILL BE A CONSEQUENCE OF THE DEVELOPMENT?				WHAT WILL THE EFFECT OF THE CONSEQUENCE BE?				
	VIRTUALLY CERTAIN	PROBABLE	POSSIBLE	ALMOST IMPOSSIBLE	VERY FAVORABLE	FAVORABLE	LITTLE OR NO IMPORTANCE	DETRIMENTAL	VERY DETRIMENTAL
Use of home terminals for education; transformation of the home into a part-time school; growing competition between traditional teaching profession and advocates of programmed instruction.		●				●			
Information storage becoming a salable service, resulting in widespread revision to business practices.	●					●			
Improvement in social science research.		●				●			
Individual citizens becoming proficient in law and medicine, through easy availability of the relevant data in the home.			●			●	●		

Figure 2 (continued)

IF THESE DEVELOPMENTS WERE TO OCCUR,	THEY MIGHT RESULT IN:	HOW LIKELY IS IT THAT THE RESULT WILL BE A CONSEQUENCE OF THE DEVELOPMENT?				WHAT WILL THE EFFECT OF THE CONSEQUENCE BE?				
		VIRTUALLY CERTAIN	PROBABLE	POSSIBLE	ALMOST IMPOSSIBLE	VERY FAVORABLE	FAVORABLE	LITTLE OR NO IMPORTANCE	DETRIMENTAL	VERY DETRIMENTAL
NEW AUTOMATION AND COMMUNICATION TECHNIQUES (con't)	The rise of new methods of computer-aided crime.									
	Information overload; the problem will be to select from the available plethora of information that which is important and relevant to the individual.									
	Great revolutions in library sciences, including greatly improved methods of searching for particular subjects.									
	Invasion of privacy (assuming data associated with individual people can be retrieved).									

Figure 2 (continued)

NEW METHODS OF MODIFYING THE ENVIRONMENT		HOW LIKELY IS IT THAT THE RESULT WILL BE A CONSEQUENCE OF THE DEVELOPMENT?				WHAT WILL THE EFFECT OF THE CONSEQUENCE BE?				
IF THESE DEVELOPMENTS WERE TO OCCUR,	THEY MIGHT RESULT IN:	VIRTUALLY CERTAIN	PROBABLE	POSSIBLE	ALMOST IMPOSSIBLE	VERY FAVORABLE	FAVORABLE	LITTLE OR NO IMPORTANCE	DETRIMENTAL	VERY DETRIMENTAL
Feasibility of limited weather control in the sense of predictably affecting regional weather at acceptable cost.	Great improvements in agricultural efficiency by creating rain on demand, avoidance of floods, and minimizing the number of clouds over farms during sunlight hours.									
	Disruption in ecological balance leading to extinction of some plant and animal species.									
	Weather being used as a military or economic weapon.									
	Great increase in the number of civil suits alleging damage caused by weather manipulation.									
	Emergence of a new power elite: "the weather makers."									

Figure 2 (continued)

NEW REPRODUCTIVE TECHNIQUES		HOW LIKELY IS IT THAT THE RESULT WILL BE A CONSEQUENCE OF THE DEVELOPMENT?				WHAT WILL THE EFFECT OF THE CONSEQUENCE BE?				
IF THESE DEVELOPMENTS WERE TO OCCUR,	THEY MIGHT RESULT IN:	VIRTUALLY CERTAIN	PROBABLE	POSSIBLE	ALMOST IMPOSSIBLE	VERY FAVORABLE	FAVORABLE	LITTLE OR NO IMPORTANCE	DETRIMENTAL	VERY DETRIMENTAL
Human Clone—the nucleus of an ovum is removed and replaced by somatic cells, allowing development in a host mother of an identical twin of the person supplying the somatic cell.	A replication of essential or great men, resulting in a kind of immortality.			⟨	⟩		⟨		⟩	
	Creation of a super race, an effective way to preserve and distribute good genotypes.			⟨	⟩	⟨			⟩	
	New animal breeding practices.	⟨	⟩			⟨	⟩			

Figure 2 (continued)

NEW BEHAVIOR MANIPULATION TECHNIQUES

IF THESE DEVELOPMENTS WERE TO OCCUR,	THEY MIGHT RESULT IN:	HOW LIKELY IS IT THAT THE RESULT WILL BE A CONSEQUENCE OF THE DEVELOPMENT?				WHAT WILL THE EFFECT OF THE CONSEQUENCE BE?				
		VIRTUALLY CERTAIN	PROBABLE	POSSIBLE	ALMOST IMPOSSIBLE	VERY FAVORABLE	FAVORABLE	LITTLE OR NO IMPORTANCE	DETRIMENTAL	VERY DETRIMENTAL
Control of the behavior of some people in society by radio stimulation of the brain.	Decisive tool for control of abnormal (including criminal) behavior.									
	A substitution for penal institutions.									
	Development of protective and jamming systems.									
	Stimulation of socially useful responses, such as the wish to work.									
	Use in medicine as a form of sedation.									

SCENARIOS

The forecasts of events and their consequences can be used to form a number of scenarios which may be useful in a variety of long-range planning contexts. The scenarios presented here were written using group median dates as a basis for sorting the events into the various time intervals described; the important consequences of these events were then included.

The Technological World of 1985. Solution of the foreign-body rejection problem will have greatly improved the process of organ transplantation, and to meet the need for natural transplantable organs, "parts" banks will be operating. Competition for organs will have encouraged black markets, although the importance of these markets will have been diminished by legislative regulation of transplantations within the hospital-physician community and by the development of artificial organs, including, for example, implantable artificial hearts with power sources capable of lasting five years. Research will be continuing into the use of tissue-compatible animals to provide yet another source of organs. This activity will have changed the emphasis in medicine from repair to replacement, a development accompanied by the rise of new industries, technologies, and classes of medical personnel.

Several other biological technologies will have significantly affected the world of 1985. Contraceptive drugs will have been developed which will lower fertility rates, being mass-administered as aerosols or as additions to water supplies or staples (as iodine is added to table salt). Societal acceptance of this practice will result from extensive public education about the consequences of overpopulation. But this development will have led to the possibility of a new form of warfare: surreptitious contraception. Research and development projects will have been implemented to create an anticontraceptive pill and detection system. The drug will form only one more addition to the arsenal of biological and chemical weapons.

There will have been an enormous increase in information-handling machines and in the complexities and pervasiveness of their operations. The importance of skilled programmers will have been enhanced. Central data storage facilities with wide public access will have been established and will provide library, medical, and legal data. Privacy will have been challenged by the large data banks, and new methods of computer-aided crime will have come on the scene. New computer and automation uses will include automated language translation capable of coping with idiomatic syntactical complexities and sophisticated teaching machines which will utilize adaptive programs responding not only to the students' answers but also to certain physiological responses, such as extreme tensions.

Perhaps most startling will be new opportunities and innovations in human reproduction. Nonsurgical techniques permitting the choice of the sex of offspring (with 90-percent certainty) will have been demonstrated, and chromosome typing will be used to discover human abnormalities within weeks of conception. There will be concern about the very detrimental effects of fads for sexes, and regulation of the sex ratio may take the form of legislation or financial incentives to those parents who help to maintain a socially desirable sex equilibrium.

Immunizing agents will have been developed to protect against most bacterial and viral diseases. Inexpensive nonnarcotic drugs for producing specific personality changes, such as euphoria, antiaggression, and increased attention, will be available to the public, and these will have led to improvements in mental therapy, education, and criminal control.

A primitive form of artificial life will have been created and protein usable for food will have been produced, spawning new industries and offering the hopeful prospect of specialized diet additives for protein-deficient populations. Conventional agriculture will be augmented by the advent of large-scale desalination plants which may, through their method of distribution, be instruments of international power politics.

Various high-speed transportation systems—such as VTOL-STOL, 200 mph trains, ground-effects machines—will be in wide use, but air traffic control problems and transit congestion in major urban city centers will still exist. Automobile engines, fuels, and accessories will have been produced that will permit operation of vehicles without harmful exhaust. While these devices will have eased the problems of air pollution, traffic congestion will still be with us.

A manned space station of relatively long duration will be orbiting the earth. It will have brought advances in meteorology, cartography, geology, resources mapping, astronomy, geophysics, and military intelligence. Satellite-derived weather forecasting will allow regular and reliable forecasts fourteen days in advance for areas as small as 100 square miles.

The Technological World of 2000. Between 1985 and 2000, biological research and development will have led to many results, including the development of new methods of behavior control, new reproductive techniques, and advances in medical technology. Apparently the threat of starvation will have lent impetus to the development of several new food-producing techniques. There is some fear that these techniques will offer only a short-term reprieve in the onset of world starvation, that the catastrophe of large-scale starvation will yet occur, since these advances will remove some incentives to the limiting of family size. To minimize this threat, some governments will have enacted legislation designed to limit family size; others may have used or encouraged the use of antifertility drugs. World food production will have been expanded through the development of techniques which bring 50 percent more arable acreage under cultivation. Microbial systems converting petroleum to protein will contribute significantly to world food supplies, and ocean fish farming and aquaculture will also be in extensive use. Population pressures will demand all the food the world can produce.

New methods of behavior control which stem from biological research will have included (1) the development and use of LSD-like drugs to heighten perception and learning speed of retardates, (2) knowledge of how to stimulate cognitive growth to a maximum ability in preschool children, (3) brain surgery or psychochemicals for modifying the behavior of criminals, and (4) radio stimulation of the brains of some people in society. These forms of control will have been accompanied by break-throughs concerning our understanding of human behavior and motivation, including knowledge of the significance of dreams and REM (rapid-eye-movement) sleep in human cognitive development.

New reproductive techniques also will have been developed by 2000. For example, human ova will have been fertilized *in vitro* with subsequent implantation into a surrogate mother. The therapeutic uses of this technique will have allowed some mothers to bear children without their former fear of undesirable gene combinations resulting. Human beings will have been successfully cloned, and the technique will be used routinely for the breeding of other animals, especially in cattle farming.

The nations of the world will be using the oceans not only as a major source of food, as mentioned earlier, but also as a source of minerals through mining of the ocean floor. This may have led to extension of national sovereignties farther into the oceans and "claim staking" with concomitant political tensions. International treaties, modeled after the 1959 Antarctica Treaty, will probably have been used to permit more orderly exploitation of the oceans.

An essential feature of man's growing control over his environment will be the relative ease with which he can create ecological catastrophe. His intrusions into the oceans and the advent of weather control, for example, will be subjected not only to political scrutiny but to ecological judgment as well. This new conscience will lead finally to very strong pressure to control the most threatening of all ecological problems: population expansion in the presence of inadequate food. Legislation, tax incentives, propaganda, and sterilization, as well as abortions in certain cases, will be in intensive use. Many aspects of scientific and technological development will be directed toward coping with problems that stem from the world's increasing population levels. For example, waste disposal will have become even more of a problem by the year 2000, necessitating innovations in the use of self-destroying material. Equally important will be the institution of new types of legislation and incentives which encourage the avoidance of pollution and the creation of a favorable environment.

Several other breakthroughs in physical technologies will have occurred between 1985 and 2000. Complex programmable and self-adaptive robots capable of performing many chores will have found use in the households of advanced countries. With such devices available, discretionary time will also have increased and with it the demand for educational and recreational services. Computers will have been built that will comprehend standard IQ tests and score above 150. On-the-spot communication will be increasingly available to the citizens of most advanced countries; individual, portable two-way communication devices will be in use, much to the consternation of teenagers required to "call in" on dates and to regulatory authorities required to allocate and control frequencies.

A permanent base will have been established on the moon. Its life support systems will be capable of sustaining ten men indefinitely. This base will provide the earth's most important radio and astronomical observatory. A radio observatory designed primarily to search for extraterrestrial life will have been constructed. Planetary exploration, primarily unmanned, will be continuing.

The Technological World of 2025. The biological research begun in the last decades of the twentieth century will have continued into the twenty-first, yielding new techniques of control and understanding of human development and behavior. A range of new human reproductive techniques will exist, including extrauterine development (as a result of the successful simulation of the placenta) and parthenogenesis. Of course, the choice of sex of one's offspring and human cloning, both demonstrated earlier, will have come into wider use. All of these techniques will have raised serious threats to conventional family structuring and many other social institutions that we currently take for granted.

Of particular importance to biomedicine early in the next century will be the capability of modifying genes through molecular engineering to overcome some human hereditary defects. This development will have stemmed from better understanding of the processes of differentiation and development and will provide the ability to control certain human phenotypes. Furthermore, skill in genetic engineering and deeper understanding of the genetic processes may have provided the capability to repair the central nervous system through regeneration of individual neurons; perhaps it will have been possible also to stimulate the growth of new organs and limbs in human beings.

This development will probably lead to intense discussion about which diseases should or should not be controlled. The arguments may involve the possibility of producing specialized classes, such as menials and supermen, and will probably consider the danger that a division between socioeconomic classes and, perhaps, between developed and less-developed nations will grow, depending on who has the technological capability and required financing to construct molecular engineering centers. Of course, the application of these techniques to food production will have proven beneficial to the world. The spectacular genetic breakthroughs expected earlier will have been matched by our growing control over the aging process; life expectancy at birth may have been extended chemically by fifty years, with a commensurate increase in vigor. New drugs will also have been used for raising the intelligence of some human beings and for the purpose of producing specific changes in personal characteristics, such as alterations in attitudes and life styles. This new capability of determining the effects of drugs will have resulted from the development of a theoretical pharmacological discipline and, thus, the prior analytic prediction of the medical effects of drugs.

The impact of these kinds of changes on social structure will have been immense. Some of the developments might be used to reward special groups, such as high ranking officials. Scientists might organize to prevent these capabilities from being used adversely. Less-developed nations might demand being made part of the technological present.

In the first part of the twenty-first century, research into the means of directly stimulating the cortex may have led to demonstration of man-machine symbiosis in which certain men (perhaps with implanted electrodes or other, less repugnant devices) will extend their intelligence by being connected to a computer. This development might have the effect of multiplying human intelligence manyfold.

Significant amounts of electrical power will have been transmitted by wireless means; superconductors operating in the range of 20-30°K, or even room temperature, will have been demonstrated. Use of these new materials and processes will have resulted in the development of new families of vehicles and devices; room-temperature superconductors, for example, could be used to make cars that float over magnetic highways. These techniques will permit cheaper electricity to be produced and, with it, the development of new techniques for refrigeration, communication, and transportation, amounting to a new dimension of control by man over his world. It is possible that research into the composition of matter will lead to the ability to produce any element from subatomic particles. If such a capability should be attained, rare earth elements could be produced in whatever quantities needed, and alloys and materials virtually unknown today would come into wide use.

Can Technology Replace Social Engineering?

ALVIN M. WEINBERG

During World War II, and immediately afterward, our federal government mobilized its scientific and technical resources, such as the Oak Ridge National Laboratory, around great technological problems. Nuclear reactors, nuclear weapons, radar, and space are some of the miraculous new technologies that have been created by this mobilization of federal effort. In the past few years there has been a major change in focus of much of our federal research. Instead of being preoccupied with technology, our government is now mobilizing around problems that are largely social. We are beginning to ask what can we do about world population, about the deterioration of our environment, about our educational system, our decaying cities, race relations, poverty. Presidents Johnson [and Nixon have] dedicated the power of a scientifically oriented federal apparatus to finding solutions for these complex social problems.

Social problems are much more complex than are technological problems. It is much harder to identify a social problem than a technological problem: how do we know when our cities need renewing, or when our population is too big, or when our modes of transportation have broken down? The problems are, in a way, harder to identify just because their solutions are never clear-cut: how do we know when our cities are renewed, or our air clean enough, or our transportation convenient enough? By contrast, the availability of a crisp and beautiful technological *solution* often helps focus on the problem to which the new technology is the solution. I doubt that we would have been nearly as concerned with an eventual shortage of energy as we now are if we had not had a neat solution—nuclear energy—available to eliminate the shortage.

There is a more basic sense in which social problems are much more difficult than are technological problems. A social problem exists because many people behave, individually, in a socially unacceptable way. To solve a social problem one must induce social change—one must persuade many people to behave differently than they have behaved in the past. One must persuade many people to have fewer babies, or to drive more carefully, or to refrain from disliking Negroes. By contrast, resolution of a technological problem involves many fewer individual decisions. Once President Roosevelt decided to go after atomic energy, it was by comparison a relatively simple task to mobilize the Manhattan Project.

The resolution of social problems by the traditional methods—by motivating or forcing people to behave more rationally—is a frustrating business. People don't behave rationally; it is a long, hard business to persuade individuals to forego immediate personal gain or pleasure (as seen by the individual) in favor of longer term social gain. And indeed, the aim of social engineering is to invent the social devices—usually legal, but also moral and educational and organizational—that will change each person's motivation and redirect his activities along ways that are more acceptable to the society.

The technologist is appalled by the difficulties faced by the social engineer; to engineer even a small social change by inducing individuals to behave differently is always hard even when the change is rather neutral or even beneficial. For example, some rice eaters in India are reported to prefer starvation to eating wheat which we send to them. How much harder it is to change motivations where the individual is insecure and feels threatened if he acts differently, as illustrated by the poor white's reluctance to accept the Negro as an equal. By contrast, technological engineering is simple: the rocket, the reactor, and the desalination plants are devices that are expensive to develop, to be sure, but their feasibility is relatively easy to assess, and their success relatively easy to achieve once one understands the scientific principles that underlie them. It is, therefore, tempting to raise the following question: In view of the simplicity of technological engineering, and the complexity of social engineering, to what extent can social problems be circumvented by reducing them to technological problems? Can we identify Quick Technological Fixes for profound and almost infinitely complicated social problems, "fixes" that are within the grasp of modern technology, and which would either eliminate the original social problem without requiring a change in the individual's social attitudes, or would so alter the problem as to make its resolution more feasible? To paraphrase Ralph Nader, to what extent can technological *remedies* be found for social problems without first having to remove the *causes* of the problem? It is in this sense that I ask, "Can technology replace social engineering?"

THE MAJOR TECHNOLOGICAL FIXES OF THE PAST

To better explain what I have in mind, I shall describe how two of our profoundest social problems—poverty and war—have in some limited degree been solved by the Technological Fix, rather than by the methods of social engineering. Let me begin with poverty.

The traditional Marxian view of poverty regarded our economic ills as being primarily a question of maldistribution of goods. The Marxist recipe for elimination of poverty, therefore, was to eliminate profit, in the erroneous belief that it was the loss of this relatively small increment from the worker's paycheck that kept him poverty-stricken. The Marxist dogma is typical of the approach of the social engineer: one tries to convince or coerce many people to forego their short-term profits in what is presumed to be the long-term interest of the society as a whole.

The Marxian view seems archaic in this age of mass production and automation not only to us, but apparently to many Eastern bloc economists. For the brilliant advances in the technology of energy, of mass production, and of automation have created the affluent society. Technology has expanded our productive capacity so greatly that even though our distribution is still inefficient, and unfair by Marxian precepts, there is more than enough to go around. Technology has provided a "fix"—greatly expanded production of goods—which enables our capitalistic society to achieve many of the aims of the Marxist social engineer without going through the social revolution Marx viewed as inevitable. Technology has converted the seemingly intractable social problem of *widespread* poverty into a relatively tractable one.

My second example is war. The traditional Christian position views war as primarily a moral issue: if men become good, and model themselves after the Prince of Peace, they will live in peace. This doctrine is so deeply ingrained in the spirit of all civilized men that I suppose it is a blasphemy to point out that it has never worked very well—that men have not been good, and that they are not paragons of virtue or even of reasonableness.

Though I realize it is terribly presumptuous to claim, I believe that Edward Teller may have supplied the nearest thing to a Quick Technological Fix to the problem of war. The hydrogen bomb greatly increases the provocation that would precipitate large-scale war—and not because men's motivations have been changed, not because men have become more tolerant and understanding, but rather because the appeal to the primitive instinct of self-preservation has been intensified far beyond anything we could have imagined before the H-bomb was invented. To point out these things today, with the United States involved in a shooting war, may sound hollow and unconvincing; yet the desperate and partial peace we have now is much better than a full-fledged exchange of thermonuclear weapons. One cannot deny that the Soviet leaders now recognize the force of H-bombs, and that this has surely contributed to the less militant attitude of the USSR. One can only hope that the Chinese leadership, as it acquires familiarity with H-bombs, will also become less militant. If I were to be asked who has given the world a more effective means of achieving peace, our great religious leaders who urge men to love their neighbors and, thus, avoid fights, or our weapons technologists who simply present men with no rational alternative to peace, I would vote for the weapons technologist. That the peace we get is at best terribly fragile, I cannot deny; yet, as I shall explain, I think technology can help stabilize our imperfect and precarious peace.

THE TECHNOLOGICAL FIXES OF THE FUTURE

Are there other Technological Fixes on the horizon, other technologies that can reduce immensely complicated social questions to a matter of "engineering"? Are there new technologies that offer society ways of circumventing social problems and at the same time do *not* require individuals to renounce short-term advantage for long-term gain?

Probably the most important new Technological Fix is the Intra-Uterine Device for birth control. Before the IUD was invented, birth control demanded very strong motivation of countless individuals. Even with the pill, the individual's motivation had to be sustained day in and day out; should it flag even temporarily, the strong motivation of the previous month might go for naught. But the IUD, being a one-shot method, greatly reduces the individual motivation required to induce a social change. To be sure, the mother must be sufficiently motivated to accept the IUD in the first place, but, as experience in India already seems to show, it is much easier to persuade the Indian mother to accept the IUD once, than it is to persuade her to take a pill every day. The IUD does not completely replace social engineering by technology; and indeed, in some Spanish American cultures where the husband's manliness is measured by the number of children he has, the IUD attacks only part of the problem. Yet, in many other situations, as in India, the IUD so reduces the social component of the problem as to make an impossibly difficult social problem much less hopeless.

Let me turn now to problems which from the beginning have had both technical and social components—broadly, those concerned with conservation of our resources: our environment, our water, and our raw materials for production of the means of subsistence. The social issue here arises because many people by their individual acts cause shortages and, thus, create economic, and ultimately social, imbalance. For example, people use water wastefully, or they insist on moving to California because of its climate, and so we have water shortages; or too many people drive cars in Los Angeles with its curious meteorology, and so Los Angeles suffocates from smog.

The water resources problem is a particularly good example of a complicated problem with strong social and technological connotations. Our management of water resources in the past has been based largely on the ancient Roman device, the aqueduct: every water shortage was to be relieved by stealing water from someone else who at the moment didn't need the water or was too poor or too weak to prevent the steal. Southern California would steal from Northern California, New York City from upstate New York, the farmer who could afford a cloud-seeder from the farmer who could not afford a cloud-seeder. The social engineer insists that such shortsighted expedients have got us into serious trouble; we have no water resources policy, we waste water disgracefully, and, perhaps, in denying the ethic of thriftiness in using water, we have generally undermined our moral fiber. The social engineer, therefore, views such technological shenanigans as being shortsighted, if not downright immoral. Instead, he says, we should persuade or force people to use less water, or to stay in the cold Middle West where water is plentiful instead of migrating to California where water is scarce.

The water technologist, on the other hand, views the social engineer's approach as rather impractical. To persuade people to use less water, to get along with expensive water, is difficult, time-consuming, and uncertain in the extreme. Moreover, say the technologists, what right does the water resources expert have to insist that people use water less wastefully? Green lawns and clean cars and swimming pools are part of the good life, American style, . . . and what right do we have to deny this luxury if there is some alternative to cutting down the water we use?

Here we have a sharp confrontation of the two ways of dealing with a complex social issue: the social engineering way which asks people to behave more "reasonably," the technologists' way which tries to avoid changing people's habits or motivation. Even though I am a technologist, I have sympathy for the social engineer. I think we must use our water as efficiently as possible, that we ought to improve people's attitudes toward the use of water, and that everything that can be done to rationalize our water policy will be welcome. Yet as a technologist, I believe I see ways of providing more water more cheaply than the social engineers may concede is possible.

I refer to the possibility of nuclear desalination. The social engineer dismisses the technologist's simpleminded idea of solving a water shortage by transporting more water primarily because, in so doing, the water user steals water from someone else—possibly foreclosing the possibility of ultimately utilizing land now only sparsely settled. But surely water drawn from the sea deprives no one of his share of water. The whole issue is then a technological one; can fresh water be drawn from the sea cheaply enough to have a major impact on our chronically water-short areas like Southern California, Arizona, and the Eastern seaboard?

I believe the answer is yes, though much hard technical work remains to be done. A large program to develop cheap methods of nuclear desalting has been undertaken by the United States, and I have little doubt that within the next ten to twenty years we shall see huge dual-purpose desalting plants springing up on many parched seacoasts of the world. At first these plants will produce water at municipal prices. But I believe, on the basis of research now in progress at ORNL and elsewhere, water from the sea at a cost acceptable for agriculture—less than ten cents per 1,000 gallons—is eventually in the cards. In short, for areas close to the seacoasts, technology can provide water without requiring a great and difficult-to-accomplish change in people's attitudes toward the utilization of water.

The Technological Fix for water is based on the availability of extremely cheap energy from very large nuclear reactors. What other social consequences can one foresee flowing from really cheap energy eventually available to every country regardless of its endowment of conventional resources? Though we now see only vaguely the outlines of the possibilities, it does seem likely that from very cheap nuclear energy we shall get hydrogen by electrolysis of water, and, thence, the all important ammonia fertilizer necessary to help feed the hungry of the world; we shall reduce metals without requiring coking coal; we shall even power automobiles with electricity, via fuel cells or storage batteries, thus reducing our world's dependence on crude oil, as well as eliminating our air pollution insofar as it is caused by automobile exhaust or by the burning of fossil fuels. In short, the widespread availability of very cheap energy everywhere in the world ought to lead to an energy autarky in every country of the world; and eventually to an autarky in the many staples of life that should flow from really cheap energy.

WILL TECHNOLOGY REPLACE SOCIAL ENGINEERING?

I hope these examples suggest how social problems can be circumvented or at least reduced to less formidable proportions by the application of the Technological Fix. The examples I have given do not strike me as being fanciful, nor are they at all exhaustive. I have not touched, for example, upon the extent to which really cheap computers and improved technology of communication can help improve elementary teaching without having first to improve our elementary teachers. Nor have I mentioned Ralph Nader's brilliant observation that a safer car, and even its development and adoption by the auto company, is a quicker and probably surer way to reduce traffic deaths than is a campaign to teach people to drive more carefully. Nor have I invoked some really fanciful Technological Fixes: like providing air conditioners and free electricity to operate them for every Negro family in Watts on the assumption (suggested by Huntington) that race rioting is correlated with hot, humid weather; or the ultimate Technological Fix, Aldous Huxley's soma pills that eliminate human unhappiness without improving human relations in the usual sense.

My examples illustrate both the strength and the weakness of the Technological Fix for social problems. The Technological Fix accepts man's intrinsic shortcomings and circumvents them or capitalizes on them for socially useful ends. The Fix is, therefore, eminently practical and, in the short term, relatively effective. One does not wait around trying to change people's minds: if people want more water, one gets them more water rather than requiring them to reduce their use of water; if people insist on driving autos while they are drunk, one provides safer autos that prevent injuries even after a severe accident.

But the technological solutions to social problems tend to be incomplete and metastable, to replace one social problem with another. Perhaps the best example of this instability is the peace imposed upon us by the H-bomb. Evidently the pax hydrogenica is metastable in two senses: in the short term, because the aggressor still enjoys such an advantage; in the long term, because the discrepancy between have and have-not nations must eventually be resolved if we are to have permanent peace. Yet, for these particular shortcomings, technology has something to offer. To the imbalance between offense and defense, technology says let us devise passive defense which redresses the balance. A world with H-bombs and adequate civil defense is less likely to lapse into thermonuclear war than a world with H-bombs alone, at least if one concedes that the danger of the thermonuclear war mainly lies in the acts of irresponsible leaders. Anything that deters the irresponsible leader is a force for peace: a technologically sound civil defense therefore would help stabilize the balance of terror.

To the discrepancy between haves and have-nots, technology offers the nuclear energy revolution, with its possibility of autarky for haves and have-nots alike. How this might work to stabilize our metastable thermonuclear peace is suggested by the possible political effect of the recently proposed Israeli desalting plant. The Arab states I should think would be much less set upon destroying the Jordan River Project if the Israelis had a desalination plant in reserve that would nullify the effect of such action. In this connection, I think countries like ours can contribute very much. Our country will soon have to decide whether to continue to spend $5.5 x 10^9$ per year for space exploration after our lunar landing. Is it too outrageous to suggest that some of this money be devoted to building huge nuclear desalting complexes in the arid ocean rims of the troubled world? If the plants are powered with breeder reactors, the out-of-pocket costs, once the plants are built, should be low enough to make large-scale agriculture feasible in these areas. I estimate that for $4 x 10^9$ per year we could build enough desalting capacity to feed more than ten million new mouths per year (provided we use agricultural methods that husband water), and we would, thereby, help stabilize the metastable, bomb-imposed balance of terror.

Yet, I am afraid we technologists shall not satisfy our social engineers, who tell us that our Technological Fixes do not get to the heart of the problem; they are at best temporary expedients; they create new problems as they solve old ones; to put a Technological Fix into effect requires a positive social action. Eventually, social engineering, like the Supreme Court decision on desegregation, must be invoked to solve social problems. And, of course, our social engineers are right. Technology will never *replace* social engineering. But technology has provided and will continue to provide to the social engineer broader options, to make intractable social problems less intractable; perhaps, most of all, technology will buy time—that precious commodity that converts violent social revolution into acceptable social evolution.

Our country now recognizes and is mobilizing around the great social problems that corrupt and disfigure our human existence. It is natural that in this mobilization we should look first to the social engineer. But, unfortunately, the apparatus most readily available to the government, like the great federal laboratories, is technologically oriented, not socially oriented. I believe we have a great opportunity here; for, as I hope I have persuaded you, many of our seemingly social problems do admit of partial technological solutions. Our already deployed technological apparatus can contribute to the resolution of social questions. I plead, therefore, first for our government to deploy its laboratories, its hardware contractors, and its engineering universities around social problems. And I plead, secondly, for understanding and cooperation between technologist and social engineer. Even with all the help he can get from the technologist, the social engineer's problems are never really solved. It is only by cooperation between technologist and social engineer that we can hope to achieve what is the aim of all technologists and social engineers—a better society, and thereby, a better life, for all of us who are part of society.

Pure Technology

"DAEDALUS OF NEW SCIENTIST"

In a characteristic passage in Plato's *Republic* we find Glaucon and Socrates discussing the nature of the Good. Glaucon suggests that there are three kinds of good: the simple, inconsequential pleasures; then activities pleasurable both in themselves and their consequences; and finally those tasks and duties not inherently pleasant but undertaken for subsequent advantage. He then asks Socrates to locate "honesty" in one of these categories.

Socrates: I should say, in the best of the three, those which a man must like both for their own sake and for their consequences, if he's going to live the kind of life one wants to have.

Glaucon: Well, that's not what most people think; they reckon it belongs to the tedious kind of good, which has to be pursued in order to earn a wage, or, for appearance's sake, to be well thought of.

Glaucon's threefold subdivision remains relevant to this day, and the passage would retain its point if the philosophers had been discussing technology. The usual attitude taken toward technology—certainly by those who put up the money for it—is that its value lies only in its profitable consequences, and research and development in itself is an unavoidable interim expense. Yet to the engineer the chase may be as rewarding as the kill; he may well privately place his activities in the second or even in the first category of good, divorcing it partly or almost wholly from the sordid aftermath of profitable application.

This attitude of mind defines the *Pure Technologist.* Pure technology is the building of machines for their own sake and for the pride or pleasure of accomplishment. It is a creative art form somewhere between art and science. Some examples of pure technology are the record-breaking vehicle, built purely to see if it will behave as intended; the chess-playing computer program, devised for the sheer entertainment of seeing how well it makes out; and that masterpiece in miniature, *Scientific American's* Great International Paper Airplane Competition.

Most other technical projects have some degree of purity, though the assessment of such a subjective quality will rarely be clear-cut. What is the purity status of a cuckoo in a cuckoo clock, for example? Or on a grander scale, is a particle accelerator pure technology? To the physicist it is as applied as any other of his instruments; to the engineer constructing it, it has only to work as intended, and so is pure; an outsider will judge it as pure or as applied according as he judges nuclear physics itself. Yet despite its confusion with (and indeed, latterly, deliberate disguise as) the applied variety, pure technology is recognizable throughout history as one of the minor muses.

CLASSICAL PIONEERS

The first indubitable instances occur rather late in Classical times. The great Athenian achievements in art and science occurred without any comparable revolution in technology. Nowhere do Glaucon or Socrates express any appreciation of the aesthetically or intellectually stimulating qualities of technology—for them it was firmly in the third, humdrum class of good. Not until Alexandria took over from Athens as the intellectual center of the world did major progress in empirical techniques occur. The "Museum" at Alexandria, founded around 300 B.C. by one of Alexander the Great's generals to be the intellectual showpiece of his regime, was for many centuries a unique library, artistic center, and research institute, and shared so many of the features of modern research establishments that it may fairly be called the MIT of the ancient world.

The Alexandrian pure technologists were the mechanicians, chiefly Ctesibius, Philo, and Hero. That part of their research which directly served the interests of their employers was, as one might expect, military—improving the catapults and ballistas which launched the missiles of the time. But they also carried out much more fundamental and far-reaching research in pure physics.

We know little of Ctesibius except from contemporary references. The Roman engineer Vitruvius tells us that he invented the force-pump, a hydraulic organ, two different forms of catapult, the water-clock, and several types of automata. The stern, practical Roman describes only the pump, the organ, and the clock, and refers us to Ctesibius's own book (now lost) for details of other devices "which serve no useful purpose, but the pleasure of delight."

These delightful inventions are described in one of the surviving treatises of his follower, the famous Hero of Alexandria. Hero probably lived about 100 B.C. and wrote treatises on catapults and missiles, on automata, and on the studies in pneumatics for which he is best known. His books give the first description in recorded history of the works of men who, fascinated by a new science, set out to see what could be done with it for the sheer pleasure of creation. Pure technology was on the march!

Some of the *jeux d'esprit* of the Alexandrian mechanicians is shown in the [treatises'] diagrams. All five "classical machines" (lever, wedge, screw, pulley, and winch) are used in these little contrivances, as well as the float, syphon, water-whistle and other elements discovered or at least first understood at Alexandria. The elasticity of air and the incompressibility of water are recognized and ingeniously exploited; and despite the dry and Euclidean way Hero expounds their working, it is clear what fun he had putting them together.

Some commentators have ridiculed them as "mere scientific toys," but I think this misses the point. Toys they were indeed for the most part, but they were toys embodying new and important principles which the mechanicians used in more practical equipment, and attempted to explain by theory. Hero never quite explicitly expounds the concept of atmospheric pressure, but he is quite sure that air is a material substance, and gives directions for constructing apparatus to prove the existence of a vacuum. For 100 B.C. this is physics of a high order indeed!

The most famous of all Hero's "toys" is his steam reaction-turbine or Aeolipile, number 50 of the 78 inventions in his *Pneumatics*. This simple machine merely drove itself and illustrated a principle, and there is no reason to suppose that Hero ever envisaged scaling it up. Nowhere in the ancient world was there a more propitious place to make such a revolutionary invention than the Museum at Alexandria; yet nothing came of it. The technical and intellectual and social infrastructure was far too inadequate to handle the application of this piece of pure technology, and the Alexandrian achievement petered out with the general decline of the ancient world in the first few centuries A.D.

The technoscientific reactor did not go critical for over another thousand years, until the European Renaissance. The first really striking piece of pure technology to emerge from the intellectual ferment that followed was the balloon.

THE BALLOON GOES UP

The brothers Montgolfier were papermakers of Annonay in France, and were of an inventive and curious turn of mind. Etienne Montgolfier once tested Leonardo's concept of the parachute by jumping from the top of a building holding a large umbrella! The concept of lighter-than-air flight seems to have matured in their minds from 1767 onwards. They knew of Cavendish's preparation of hydrogen, but a small pilot balloon lost the gas so rapidly by diffusion through the (paper) envelope that they abandoned this notion.

The idea of the fire-balloon is said to have occurred to Etienne on a carriage ride. Immediately on reaching the inn of his destination he called for taffeta and fire, and, to the horror of the proprietor, the world's first lighter-than-air flying machine, made of badly singed taffeta, rose nobly to the ceiling of one of his bedrooms!

The Montgolfiers organized their first demonstration flight from Annonay market square on June 5, 1783. The craft was made of paper (the material they were most familiar with) and reached a height of 6,000 feet. Garbled reports by the mystified local authorities reached Paris, where Professor Cesar

Charles (of Charles' Law fame) deduced that the Montgolfiers must have been using hydrogen. Determined to emulate their feat, he set about the frightening task of filling a 1,000-cubic-foot rubberized silk balloon with hydrogen generated from iron and sulphuric acid.

Four days it took, during which time the Professor and his assistants were in constant fear of an explosion: at times the exothermic reaction became so violent that the whole assembly had to have water played over it. But all went well, and the first hydrogen balloon ascended triumphantly from Paris on August 26, 1783, travelled 15 miles, and was destroyed on landing by horrified peasants. Only when the Montgolfiers exhibited their invention in Paris did Charles realize that he had invented the hydrogen balloon by mistake.

Ballooning soon became a popular activity throughout the Continent. Brave men ascended in both hot-air and hydrogen balloons (Charles reached 10,000 feet on December 1, 1783, and returned safely). The new invention was soon subsidized by the military, who dreamt of balloon transport and aerial observation flights. Indeed, a ballooning corps was formed in the French army after the Revolution; but this near-farcical concept was never a serious threat. The House of Lords dissolved in laughter when Lord St. Vincent, in 1802, speaking of the defense of Britain against Napoleonic invasion, remarked "I do not say they cannot come. I only say they cannot come by sea." Again, a novel extension of human abilities had been developed and exercised for its own sake, and funded by authority on grounds that would not stand up to hostile cost-effectiveness analysis.

MODERN PURE TECHNOLOGY

The massive flowering of invention of the modern era poses for the connoisseur of pure technology the challenge of identifying unambiguous examples of the genre. This is surprisingly difficult. On the face of it, practically every invention made since about 1800 was immediately applied.

But this may not mean that pure technology ceased to exist—only that it was rapidly overtaken by applications. Many of Hero's inventions were never applied at all—the concept of research-based technology scarcely existed in his society. Leonardo da Vinci's beautiful mechanical concepts took centuries to reach fruition (I cannot claim him as a pure technologist because he was essentially a theoretician rather than a practical inventor); Montgolfier's remained pure long enough to recognize as such. But the genius of a technological age lies not in scientific advance or creative imagination, but in seeking applications, in consciously and persistently asking the question, "How can I exploit this?"

Just how automatic and comprehensive this technique of progress has become, with each new piece being fitted into the growing jigsaw puzzle as soon as the development of neighboring fields permits, may be judged by trying to think of inventions in the mainstream of technology which might have been made much before they actually were. (After some cogitation, I can list only seven: gas-phase chromatography, the hovercraft, the standardized goods-container, prestressed concrete, the disc brake, casein glue, and DDT-based insecticides. Perhaps readers can add to—or subtract from—the list?) The great majority of inventions appear just as soon as they become feasible.

The clue to discovering pure technology—things made for the sake of making them—in this relentless advance, is to identify developments which, although they occupy obvious and clearly fillable gaps in the jigsaw, are simply unnecessary: gaps which are not worth filling on any rational basis. This test works best on fairly new inventions, before the patina of age and seeming inevitability has settled on them.

A prime example is the SST, an indubitable masterpiece of thinly disguised pure technology. I need not detail here the ample demonstrations which have been given of the pointlessness and social drawbacks of this project. But given a journey of, say, seven hours at an average of 10 mi./h and another six at 600 mi./h (a fair profile of a typical translantic air excursion), the expenditure of millions of dollars to clip a few hours off the *high-speed* section seems misguided to say the least, even assuming it is worth shortening the time at all in view of the increased disruption of circadian rhythms. Balancing this insignificant gain and the tiny minority who gain it against the solid debit in expense and noise pollution inflicted on the majority, we can see how unexpectedly powerful is the drive to pure technology in our supposedly cost-conscious society—for the only really compelling reason for building the SST (and of course its rival the Concorde) is the sheer entertainment of overcoming all the technical problems and finally flying such a thrilling machine!

MORE EXAMPLES

The same motivation applies in a practically overt manner to the space rocket. The big rocket is the twentieth-century pure-technological achievement par excellence, but all its pioneers—Oberth, Goddard, von Braun—saw it not as an end in itself but as a means toward the larger pure-technological goal of space flight. Even when the first successful V-2 ballistic rocket was fired in 1942, officially part of German war research, von Braun exclaimed jubilantly that the only trouble was that it landed on the wrong planet! Again, no scientific or technical considerations can justify on economic grounds the billions of dollars invested in the space program. Even the solid military interest in rocketry and radar and long-distance communication would have been far better served at a fraction of the cost by normal research and development. Yet the splendor of setting foot on our satellite, the sheer poetry of sending our creations out to scan other worlds and report back what they see—these represent pure technology at its best. It seems almost carping and small-souled to query whether the money might not have been better spent on more urgent terrestrial matters.

A quite different instance of modern pure technology, this time not quite rapidly enough overtaken by events to obscure its real appeal, is the laser. The appearance of the first practical prototype in 1960 created such interest that, in the words of the *New York Times,* "almost every corporation and every self-respecting university in the nation obtained a laser of some sort." The appeal of the new device was so widespread, and yet actual commercial applications so elusive, that the laser rapidly acquired the reputation of a solution in search of a problem. In particular, the millions of dollars disbursed by the military to explore its potential as a destructive weapon had so little result that one cynic exclaimed in disgust that the most offensive use you could make of a laser was to hit someone over the head with it.

The laser is still (judging by the number used in research compared to that in solid commercial applications) a machine with few uses—yet there is no doubt of its powerful hold on the imagination of the technical community. The charm of being able to drill a hole in a razorblade with a beam of light, or bounce photons off the moon, is so great that the actual value of being able to do so is irrelevant.

THE MILITARY TRADITION

These instances of pure technology past and present give an insight into the nature of the discipline. Its central characteristic, like those of art and science, is acceptance of self-imposed challenge and the aggrandizement of the human spirit. It occurs alongside and within applied technology in dynamic and intellectually active societies. It is one of the dramatic arts, and since by and large the human sense of the dramatic is rather direct and unsophisticated, pure technology tends to address itself to naive and, in the fashionable term, charismatic challenges—making large objects go fast, discharging high concentrations of energy, "conquering" space. It is funded on misleading grounds. And behind it, more often than not, lurks the military, like a dim but suspicious creditor, paying up uneasily in the hope of ultimate advantage.

I believe the closeness of the association between militarism and pure technology to be significant. In the convoluted, multidimensional psychospace of all human mental constructs which it is the ultimate goal of psychology to map, the two are very close together. Both are manifestations of aggression, of dynamic material response to a felt challenge, posed in one case by a like-minded group of people and in the other by Nature herself. In both of them the emotive appeal loosely summed up by the word "glory" is as important as the overt goals. This thesis is implicit in the common claim that the space race with Russia is a valuable "sublimation" of political rivalries, but it also explains many other features of military history.

Historians have long debated the motives behind the replacement of the longbow by the musket in European armies around 1600, despite the former's clear superiority in cheapness, accuracy, range, reliability, and rate of fire—advantages it held until the invention of the rifle in the nineteenth century! It has been suggested that expertise in archery declined for some reason after the twelfth century, and that less trainable conscripts had to be used. But the overwhelming melodramatic appeal of the thunderous discharge of gunpowder weapons was probably the key factor.

The same lure of the grandiose is evident in the archmilitarist Prussian tradition. Big Bertha, the enormous gun that shelled Paris from 76 miles away during World War I, was hardly a cost-effective weapon. And the development of the German V-weapons during World War II is an even clearer instance. V-1, a pilotless aircraft, cost about $600 (then) to produce, whereas V-2, the ballistic rocket, cost $25,500; both delivered about the same warhead (around a ton of high explosive) with comparable range and accuracy. Clearly V-1 was by far the better weapon, comparing favorably in cost-effectiveness with manned bombers. Yet V-2, which replaced it, was far more flamboyant.

D. Irving[1] supports the conclusion of Dr. R. V. Jones, a British intelligence officer concerned with countermeasures to the V-weapons, that V-2 was supported for "romantic" reasons. He describes the overwhelming, Wagnerian

1. See Suggested Reading at the end of this article.

impact repeatedly produced on Nazi officials by the ". . . intoxicating sight of the 13-ton rocket blasting aloft atop a lengthening pillar of fire and condensation, and the roar of its motor echoing back over the sea"—and concludes that such military romanticism probably cost Germany the war. Certainly in the later stages of the struggle von Braun's expensive piece of pure technology, by its wholesale consumption of vital raw materials and labor, inflicted far more damage on Germany than it ever did on Britain. As an inhabitant of old London town at the time, it is clear that my attitude should be one of gratitude.

All approved weapons of war seem to have evolved to meet some minimum level of flashing, banging, shrieking romantic appeal. Subsequent developments have given us the doubly dramatic nuclear ICBM, and promise to deliver a still more expensive, problematically effective, but pure-technologically challenging toy, the ABM. In *Scientific American* (Vol. 221, No. 2, p. 17) H. F. York outlined the grave drawbacks of this strictly technological approach to security. But what fun to make a missile like Sprint, which goes so fast that its outside gets hotter than its inside! Indeed, one must suspect that the universal opprobrium directed at chemical and biological weapons stems not from any deviation from accepted standards of beastliness or efficacy, but simply from their deplorable lack of theatrical impact.

STATIC PURE TECHNOLOGY

But not all fields of pure technology are complicated by military appeal. Architectural pure technology, for example, is concerned with the grandeur of impressive monuments, rather than of wonderful machines. The most outstanding example may also be the very first—the Egyptian pyramids. Kurt Mendelssohn (*Science Journal*, Vol. 4, No. 3, p. 48) has argued persuasively from structural and historical evidence that these were not primarily built as tombs to ensure personal immortality for the Pharaohs (though presumably this suggestion was as attractive to the Pharaohs as any hinted prestigious or military implications in a modern grant application), but as gigantic exercises in pure technology, "built because man had reached the stage at which he was able to build them." Similarly one must acknowledge the considerable pure-technological component in the magnificent cathedrals created in Europe during the ages of faith. But the finest recent example is undoubtedly the Eiffel Tower in Paris. This completely purposeless structure, simply a fine piece of megastatuary, has become a proud symbol and a focal point of the city. One can hardly imagine Paris without it.

Yet, increasingly, modern architectural practice disdains such overt frivolity, and degrades pure-technological aspirations into commercially respectable but inhuman office blocks. The architect W. W. Frischmann believes that it is now technically possible to build a tower two miles high, so naturally he wants to do it (*Science Journal*, Vol. 1, No. 8, p. 62). But in justification he feels impelled to suggest it as a "vertical city" holding half a million people—thus creating about the most obscene human environment of all time.

WHAT TO DO ABOUT IT

It is clear that the malevolent aspect which pure technology is increasingly assuming stems not from its own proud nature but from our obsession with applications. It would take a brave man openly to deny the grey dogma of our time that all human activity must be economically justified, that nothing should ever be done unless it will return 8 percent on capital.

The worst consequences of accepting it can, however, be evaded. And it is here, I believe, that the more flexible and devious European mind has much to teach the innocent technologists of the USA. Consider the noble record of the British aerospace industry. A long series of pure-technological triumphs—among them the Princess Flying Boat, the Brabazon super-airliner, the Blue Streak ICBM and the TSR2 supersonic fighter-bomber—were developed just to the point where the prototype had successfully flown, and were then cancelled (though Blue Streak was kept on in a pure-technological capacity as a space-launcher).

All the satisfaction of dramatic pure technology was gained without inflicting the products on a helpless public or on an already unstable situation. (I like to think that in the case of Blue Streak and TSR2, the engaging British habit of "leaking" information on such machines to the Russians was designed to encourage them to invest heavily in countermeasures tailored to the weak points of weapons that were in fact purely hypothetical. But even the devious European mind rarely attains such an Oriental level of duplicity.)

There is every reason to hope that the pattern will be repeated with Concorde. Once the prototype has been exhaustively tested, the program will be cancelled to save money, and peace-loving citizens will be able to breathe freely again. But this civilized technique has only imperfectly crossed the Atlantic. The American counterpart of TSR2, the F-111, was, after prototype testing, procured for the armed forces, to everybody's sorrow. And if the American SST is once successfully flown, what considerations can hope to arrest it?

We are mishandling the forces of pure technology. We dare not suppress it: for the subjective motivation of every dedicated inventor is basically pure-technological—to rise to envisaged challenge and create objects of pride. The nineteenth-century inventors and engineers understood this: that is why their creations had a style and confidence almost unknown today. The economic prudery which forces the once proud art form to don the respectable mantle of application is now actively harmful, and does much to justify the growing and well-founded dislike of juggernautical technomania.

So pure technology must be recognized and fostered. Even in Britain, one of the world's leaders in pure technology, the stifling doctrine of social relevance and immediate profitability is beginning to clip the wings of the more imaginative and high-flying research projects. I would like to see official bodies set up to protect pure technological endeavor, equivalent in function to Britain's Arts Council. In the United States, this might take the form of a National Pure Technology Foundation. Given such a source of funds, it would be possible to devote one's efforts to seeing in the dark, or making machines that play with building-blocks, or constructing mechanical elephants, without having to waste time on the shaky sophistry of practical application at present required.

Allowing pure technology an honest existence will not only leave certain pure-technologically hag-ridden industries free to return to humane and reasonable techniques (I am particularly thinking of the adoption by the airlines of silent, safe, luxurious, city-center to city-center helium-filled airships) but may also restore confidence in technology among a suspicious populace, and introduce a welcome component of aesthetics into the technical scene at large. But most importantly, pure technology promises to be that "moral equivalent of war" advocated by the great American philosopher William James. Its close psychological affinity to military display may fit it to replace actual combat, just as in the animal kingdom the professional carnivores such as wolves have perfected aggression-rituals which resolve their disputes without bloodshed. Technology has given us the power to exterminate ourselves, and it is fitting that technology should also provide the safe outlet for our overamplified aggression. Let us hope that the space race, that triumph of pure technology, may be an archetype of triumphs yet to come!

Suggested Reading

Plato, *Republic,* Book 2, pp. 357a ff. K. J. Dover trans.

J. Mander, G. Dippel, and H. Gossage, *The Great International Paper Airplane Book,* Simon and Schuster, New York, 1967.

Hero of Alexandria, *A Treatise on Pneumatics,* section 15 ff. Bennett Woodcroft, ed., Lord, 1851.

K. Lorenz, *On Aggression,* Methuen, 1967.

D. Irving, *The Mare's Nest,* William Kimber, 1964.

Suggested Listening

T. Lehrer, "A Song of Wernher von Braun," *That Was the Year That Was,* Reprise LP Album No. 6179.

Reflections of a Working Scientist

STEVEN WEINBERG

I once heard the period from 1900 to the present described as "this slum of a century." Certainly the case could be made that the twentieth century fails to come up to the nineteenth in the grand arts—in music, in literature, or in painting. Yet the twentieth century does stand among the heroic periods of human civilization in one aspect of its cultural life—in science. We have radically revised our perceptions of space, time, and causation; we have learned the basic principles which govern the behavior of matter on all scales from the atomic to the galactic; we now understand pretty well how continents form and how the genetic mechanism works; we may be on the verge of finding out the over-all space-time geometry of the universe; and with any luck we will learn by the end of the century how the brain is able to think. It seems strange to me that of all the enterprises of our century, it should be science that has come under attack, and indeed from just those who seem most in tune with our times, with contemporary arts and ways of life.

[My intent here] is not so much to defend science—if science turns you off, then a scientist defending science must absolutely disconnect . . . you—but rather to serve as an exhibit of the "genuine article," the unreformed working scientist. I will therefore simply list three of what I take to be the common current challenges to science, and react to each in turn.

For help in the preparation of this article, I wish to thank M. Katz, E. Skolnikoff, L. Weinberg, and V. F. Weiskopf.

These reflections arise from my own experiences as a theoretical physicist specializing in the theory of elementary particles, and I am not really certain how far they would apply to other areas of science. I intend most of my remarks to apply to the whole range of natural nonbehavioral pure sciences, but some of them may have a more limited validity. On the other hand, I explicitly do not intend my remarks to apply to the social or psychological sciences, which seem to me to face challenges of a special and different sort.

THE SCIENTIST AS DR. FRANKENSTEIN

I suppose that public attitudes toward science, favorable or unfavorable, are shaped far more by the expectation of good or evil technological developments, than by approval or disapproval of the scientific enterprise itself. This is much too big a problem to cover here in any but the most fragmentary way, and it can be logically separated from a judgment of science *qua* science, but it is a matter of such overriding public concern that it cannot be altogether passed over. I will discuss it briefly under the headings of five criticisms of the part that "pure" scientists have played in the creation of new technology.

1. Scientists pursue their research, without taking due account of the harm that may be done by practical application of their work.

This is in some degree true. There are even some scientists, though I think not many, who argue that it is their business to pursue knowledge wherever it leads them, leaving the question of practical application to businessmen, statesmen, and generals whose responsibility it is to worry about such matters. For example, many critics point to the nuclear weapon as the ugliest product of "pure" research. But this charge overestimates the degree to which the scientist can look into the future. The nuclear physicists who discovered fission at the end of the 1930's were not so much indifferent to the danger of nuclear weapons as they were unaware of it. (Meitner, Strassmann, and Hahn, for example, published their work in the open literature in 1938-1939.[1]) Later, of course, nuclear weapons were developed in the United States and

1. L. Meitner, F. Strassmann, and O. Hahn, *Zeitschrift für Physik,* 109 (1938), p. 538; O. Hahn and F. Strassmann, *Naturwissenschaften,* 26 (1938), p. 756.

elsewhere by scientists who knew perfectly well what they were doing, but this was no longer for the sake of pure research, but in the hope of helping to win World War II.

I do not see how my present work on elementary particles and cosmology could possibly have any applications, good or evil, for at least twenty years. But how can I be sure? One can think of many dangers that might arise from present pure research, especially research on genetics and the human mind, and I hope that the researchers will be able to hold back the most dangerous lines of research, but they will not have an easy time of it. For a scientist unilaterally to cut off progress along certain lines because he calculates that more harm than good will come out of it requires a faith in the accuracy of his calculations more often found among businessmen, statesmen, and generals than among natural scientists. And do the critics of science really want the scientist and not the public to make these decisions?

2. In order to gain material support for their "pure" research or for themselves, scientists prostitute themselves to industry or government by working directly on harmful technological developments.

Again, scientists being human, this charge is, in some measure, true. One has only to think of Leonardo's letter to the Duke of Milan offering his services in the construction of ingenious instruments of war. It seems strange to me, however, to single out scientists to bear the burden of this charge. Returning to the unavoidable example of nuclear weapons, Oppenheimer, Fermi, and the others who developed the nuclear fission bomb in World War II did so because it seemed to them that otherwise Germany would develop the bomb first and would use it to enslave the world. Since World War II a large fraction of the physicists whom I know personally have washed their hands of any involvement, part-time or full-time, in military research and development. I know of no other group, certainly not workers or businessmen, who have shown a similar moral discrimination. And what of those scientists who have not washed their hands? Admittedly, there are some who work on defense problems for money, power, or fun. There are a few others who are convinced on political grounds that any weapon that adds to military strength should be developed. However, most of the "pure" scientists in the U. S. who have been involved in military work have tried to draw a line at one point or another, and to work only on a limited class of problems where, rightly or wrongly, they felt that more good than harm could be done. My own experience has been mostly through work in the JASON group of the Institute for Defense Analyses, and more recently for the U.S. Arms Control and Disarmament Agency. Many of the members of JASON, myself among them, simply declined to do work in support of the U. S. effort in Vietnam. Others worked on the so-called "electronic battlefield," because they believed (as it happened, wrongly) that by laying an impassible barrier between North and South Vietnam, they would induce the U. S. to stop bombing North Vietnam. In recent years many of us have tried to switch our work over entirely to problems of strategic arms control, but it is not easy; the Nixon administration . . . fired or canceled the consultant contracts of many of those in the Arms Control Agency (including me) who had worked on SALT.

I would like to be able to argue that academic scientists have had a humane and restraining influence on military policy, but looking back, it is hard to find evidence that I, or even those much more active and influential than myself, have had any influence at all. However, I am convinced at least that the world would not be better off if we had kept our hands out.

3. *Scientific research of all types is oppressive, because it increases the power of the developed nations relative to the underdeveloped, and increases the power of the ruling classes relative to the ruled.*

This charge rests on such far-ranging political and historical assumptions that I cannot begin to do it justice. I am not convinced that new technology tends to support old power structures more than it tends to shake them up and put power in new hands. I am also not convinced that one should always support underdeveloped nations in conflict with more modern ones; for instance, it is the Arab states that threaten the existence of Israel, not the other way around. Furthermore, this argument for stopping scientific research logically requires a permanent general strike by everyone whose work helps to keep modern industrialized society going, not just by scientists. Perhaps some do reach this conclusion, but they must have more faith in their ability to look into the future than I have in mine. I would agree, however, that certain special kinds of technology are particularly liable to be used in an oppressive way, especially the modern computer with its capacity for keeping track of enormous quantities of detailed information. I would be in favor of cutting off specific kinds of research where specific dangers clearly present themselves, but decisions in this realm are always very hard to make. Usually, as in the case of computer technology, it is not possible, by closing off lines of research, to ward off the dangers of technology without at the same time giving up its opportunities.

4. *Scientific research tends to produce technological changes which destroy human culture and the natural order of life.*

I am more sympathetic to this charge than to most of the others. Even apart from what has been done with new weapons of war, a terrible ugliness seems to have been brought into the world since the industrial revolution through the practical applications of science. As an American, I naturally think of what I see from my car window: the great super-highways cutting cross the countryside, the suburban strips with their motels and gas stations, and the glittering lifelessness of Park Avenue.

I am not sure why this should have happened. Earlier new technology, such as the pointed arch and the windmill, created more beauty than ugliness. Perhaps it is a question of scale; so many people now have cars and electric appliances that the impact of highways, factories, and power stations is too great to be absorbed into the natural background—unlike an occasional windmill or cathedral.

If this diagnosis is correct, then a cure will be extraordinarily difficult. When industrialization offered cars and electric appliances to the general public, it offered a mobility and ease previously enjoyed only by the few who could keep carriages and servants, and people accepted with alacrity. Are we now going to ask them to go back to the status quo ante? I suppose that the only answer here, as before, is to make judgments as well as we can in favor of the civilizing technology and against the brutalizing. And there *are* examples of civilizing technology, like the bicycle, the LP record, and the railroad. As W. G. Hoskins, himself a bitter enemy of the superhighway and the jet airport, says in his wonderful book, *The Making of the English Landscape:*[2]

Indeed, the railways created as much beauty as they inadvertently destroyed, but of a totally different kind. The great gashes they inflicted on the landscape in their cuttings and embankments healed over, and wild flowers grew abundantly once

2. W. G. Hoskins, *The Making of the English Landscape* (London: Hodder and Stoughton, 1955).

more. Going down to the south-west in spring, the cuttings through Somerset and Devon sparkle with primroses. Even in Clare's own country, the railway has been absorbed into the landscape, and one can enjoy the consequent pleasure of trundling through Rutland in a stopping-train on a fine summer morning; the barley fields shaking in the wind, the slow sedgy streams with their willows shading meditative cattle, the early Victorian stations built of the sheep-grey Ketton stone and still unaltered. . . .

The problem of identifying the civilizing technology and of regulating society so as to suppress the rest is far too complicated to go into here. In any case, it is not a problem on which scientists' opinions are worth more than anyone else's.

5. *While serious human needs go unfulfilled, scientists spend large sums on accelerators, telescopes, etc., which serve no purpose other than the gratification of their own curiosity.*

There is no doubt that a great deal of scientific work is carried out without any expectation of practical benefit, and indeed would be carried out even if it were certain that no practical benefit would result. It is also true that some of this work is very expensive, for the simple reason that in any given field the experiments that can be done with string and sealing wax tend to have been done already.

I suppose that if one takes the strictly utilitarian view that the only standard of value is integrated public happiness, then scientists ought to be blamed for doing any research not motivated by calculations of how much it would contribute to public welfare. By the same reasoning, no one ought to support the ballet, write honest history, or protect the blue whale, unless it can be shown that this will maximize public happiness. However, anyone who believes that knowledge of the universe is, like beauty or honesty, a good thing in itself, will not condemn the scientist for seeking the support he needs to carry out his work.

This does not mean that the support must be granted; the public has to weigh the practical benefits that will be "spun off"—the teaching that most pure scientists do to earn their salaries and the general strengthening of technological capabilities that seems to accompany pure research. These are hard to calculate. As Julian Schwinger points out,[3]

---

3. J. Schwinger, in *Nature of Matter—Purposes of High Energy Physics,* ed. L. C. L. Yuan (Upton, N.Y.: Brookhaven National Laboratory, 1965), p. 23.

And one should not overlook how fateful a decision to curtail the continued development of an essential element of the society may be. By the Fifteenth Century, the Chinese had developed a mastery of ocean voyaging far beyond anything existing in Europe. Then, in an abrupt change of intellectual climate, the insular party at court took control. The great ships were burnt and the crews disbanded. It was in those years that small Portuguese ships rounded the Cape of Good Hope.

I do not want to argue here about whether the public gets its money's worth. My point is that, in seeking support for scientific research, scientists need not agree with the public as to why the work should be done.

THE SCIENTIST AS MANDARIN

There is a widespread suspicion that science operates as a closed shop, closed to unorthodox ideas or uncomfortable data, especially if these originate outside a small circle of established leaders. One recalls countless movies in which elderly scientists in white coats wag their grey goatees at the young hero and expostulate, "But what you propose is quite impossible, because . . . " If the public is receptive to Sunday supplement stories about unidentified flying objects or quack cures for arthritis, it is in part because they do not believe the scientific establishment gives the possibility of such things a fair hearing. In short, not everyone is convinced that the scientists are as open-minded as they ought to be.

This is not one of the most important or profound challenges to science; nevertheless, I want to present some answers to it here, because this will give me a chance to explain some of my enthusiasm for the *process* of scientific research. Also, this is an easy challenge to meet, because it arises not so much from political or philosophical differences, as from simple misapprehensions of fact. For convenience I will discuss separately the questions of the receptivity of scientists to ideas from young or unestablished scientists; to ideas from outside the scientific profession; to unorthodox ideas from whatever source; and to uncomfortable data.

1. *How open is science to new ideas from the young, unestablished scientist?*

Of course, there is a scientific *cursus honorum*, and those who are just starting are less influential than their seniors. The fact is, however, the system of communication in science, probably more than that in any other area of our society, allows the newcomer a chance at influencing his field.[4]

In physics, my own field, the preëminent journal is the *Physical Review*. Almost all physicists at least scan the abstracts of the articles in their own specialties in each issue. The *Physical Review* has a panel of over a thousand reviewers who referee submitted papers, but in fact about 80 percent of all papers are accepted, and of the others a good proportion are rejected only because they are unoriginal. The *Physical Review* is an expensive operation, supported by subscriptions and page charges paid by the authors' institutions, but if an author cannot arrange to have the page charge paid, the paper is published anyway (though admittedly with a few months' delay).

There is also a more exclusive journal, *Physical Review Letters*, which publishes only short papers judged to contain material of special importance. As might be expected, there is a crush of authors trying to get their papers published in *Physical Review Letters*, and every year sees several editorials in which the editor wrings his hands over the difficulty of making selections. Nevertheless, *Physical Review Letters* does a good job of judging the paper rather than the author. (In 1959, when I was an unknown research associate, I had several papers accepted by *Physical Review Letters*; in 1971, as a reasonably well-known professor at M.I.T., I had one rejected.)

In addition to the *Physical Review* and *Physical Review Letters*, there are a great number of other physics journals in which it is even easier to publish. So well does this system work that it has become quite common for a physics department chairman who needs advice on the work of a young physicist in his own department to solicit comments from senior physicists in other universities who have never even met the young physicist, on the assumption that they will of course be familiar with his or her published work.

Of course, the humanities and social sciences also have widely

---

4. The following remarks are based on my own observations, but the general conclusion, that the scientific communication system operates in a fair and open manner, is supported by detailed statistical studies. See H. Zuckerman and R. K. Merton, *Minerva*, 9 (1971), p. 66 and *Physics Today* (July 1971), p. 28. For comments on the reward system in science, see S. Cole and J. R. Cole, *American Sociological Review*, 32 (1967), p. 377.

circulated journals, but I have the impression that they do not provide anywhere near so effective a channel of communication for the young or unestablished scholar as do the natural science journals. The reason is that the natural sciences have more objective (though not necessarily more reliable) standards for judging the value of a piece of work. A young physicist who succeeds in calculating the fine-structure constant from first principles, or in solving any one of dozens of other outstanding problems, is sure of a hearing. For instance, my own subfield of theoretical physics was shaken up in 1971 by work of a previously unknown graduate student at Utrecht,[5] and then again in 1973 by a previously unknown graduate student at Harvard.[6] I suspect that a graduate student in history who has revolutionary ideas about the fall of the Roman Empre might have a harder time getting a hearing.

The less academic professions such as law, medicine, business, the military, and the church, are even less open. In these, a young person's work is, I believe, directed to a small circle of superiors rather than to an international community, and it is natural for their judgment of his ideas to be colored by subjective factors, such as the degree to which he accommodates himself to their preconceptions. Only a few, after getting over these hurdles, reach a level from which they can communicate to their whole profession.

None of this reflects any moral superiority in the scientists themselves. It is a natural outgrowth of the fact that they work in specialties small enough that a beginner has a chance to communicate with the whole international community of specialists, and with standards objective enough that they all can recognize the value of a piece of important research. However, it does seem peculiarly inappropriate to charge the sciences with being closed to new ideas from the young and unestablished.

For the sake of fairness, I should add here that these observations are strongly colored by my own experience as a theoretical physicist who works alone at his desk or at a blackboard with one or two colleagues. I concede that the scientific enterprise may look very different to experimental scientists, and most especially to those experimentalists in high energy nuclear physics who work in large research teams. For instance, a recent paper[7] reporting the discovery of an important new class

5. G. 't Hooft, *Nuclear Physics*, B33 (1971), p. 173.
6. H. D. Politzer, *Physical Review Letters*, 30 (1973), p. 1346.
7. F. J. Hasert *et al.*, *Physical Review Letters*, 46B (1973), p. 121.

of neutrino interaction had no less than fifty-five authors from seven different institutions. I do not know to what extent a junior member of such a team can really get a hearing for an idea of his own.

2. *How open is science to new ideas from outside?*

My remarks so far only indicate the openness of the scientific community to ideas which are at least expressed in a language that is familiar to established scientists and deal with problems that they recognize as important. Otherwise, the work is unlikely to be published in a scientific journal or, if published, to be read. Then what about the prophet in the wilderness, the truly original genius outside the scientific community whose ideas cannot be understood by the pedants in university science departments?

I submit that there is no such person. I do not know of any piece of work in physics in this century which was originally generally regarded as crack-pot—as opposed to merely wrong—which subsequently turned out to be of value. It is true that Einstein was only a patent clerk when he invented special relativity, but his work was on a recognized problem, was duly published in the *Annalen der Physik,* and was received with respect, though not with instant acceptance by the physics community.

In reaching a judgment on the closed-mindedness of scientists to ideas from outside their ranks, it should be kept in mind that the system of scientific communication has evolved, not merely to transmit ideas and data, but to do so in a way that leaves the scientist time to get some of his own work done. If we had to struggle through every paper, even when the author did not accept the conventions of scientific language, we would literally have no time to do anything else. It may be that we miss a pearl of wisdom every century or so, but the price has to be paid.

3. *How open is science to truly revolutionary ideas?*

Even granting that the scientific communication system works as well as it ought to, are not scientists' minds closed to ideas, from whatever source, which challenge orthodox scientific dogma? (As Gershwin tells us, "They all laughed at Wilbur and his brother, when they said that man could fly.") Many laymen and some scientists seem to believe that any number of scientific revolutions would immediately become possible if only scientists would give up some of their preconceptions.

I believe that this is a mistake, and arises from a misconception as to the nature of scientific advance. The scientific principles which at any given moment are accepted as fundamental are like structural timbers which support a great superstructure of successful predictions. It is easy to imagine knocking down any of these timbers, but very hard to imagine what would then keep the roof from falling on our heads.

For a major scientific advance to occur, it must become clear not only that fundamental changes are necessary, but also how the successes of the previous theory can be saved. For example in 1957 T. D. Lee and C. N. Yang brought about a revolution in physics through their proposal that parity is not conserved—that is, that there is an absolute distinction in nature between left and right.[8] (It can be shown mathematically that if right and left are equivalent, then every physical state can be classified as having odd or even parity, according to how it seems to change when viewed in a mirror. It can also be shown that the parity is conserved—that is, it does not change with time.) It was quite easy to imagine that parity is not conserved; what was hard to see was that parity conservation had to be violated, and that it could be violated without losing the spectroscopic selection rules and other consequences which had given rise in the first place to the idea of parity conservation. As it happened, Lee and Yang were led to their proposal by a puzzle in meson physics. Two different kinds of meson were identified as having positive and negative parity respectively, through their decay into states of positive and negative parity, and yet the masses and lifetimes of the two mesons were observed to be identical. Many solutions were tried, including fundamental changes in the principles of quantum mechanics. Finally, rejecting any such radical solution, Lee and Yang proposed that the two different mesons were really only one, that the meson had seemed like two because it could decay both into states of the same and of different parity. This proposal would have gotten nowhere if they had not pointed out at the same time that parity could be changed in these decays because they were "weak" (that is, they have rates only of order 10^{10}/sec per particle), thereby leaving unchallenged the successful predictions of parity conservation in the much faster (say, 10^{20} to 10^{24}/sec) "strong" and electromagnetic processes.

Even the greatest scientific revolutions show a similar conservatism. Einstein changed our understanding of space and time, but he did so in

8. The original papers on this subject are conveniently assembled in *The Development of Weak Interaction Theory*, ed. P. K. Kabir (New York: Gordon and Breach, 1963).

a way which was specifically designed to leave our understanding of electricity and magnetism intact. What the scientist needs is not a wide open mind, but a mind that is open just enough, and in just the right direction.

4. *How open is science to uncomfortable new data?*

One often reads in popular histories of science that "So and so's data showed clearly that this and that were false, but no one at the time was willing to believe him." Again, this impression that scientists wantonly reject uncomfortable data is based on a misapprehension as to the way scientific research is carried on.

The fact is that a scientist in any active field of research is continually bombarded with new data, much of which eventually turns out to be either misleading or just plain wrong. (I speak here on the basis of my experience in elementary particle physics and astrophysics, but I presume that the same is true in other fields as well.) When a new datum appears which contradicts our expectations, the likelihood of its being correct and relevant must be measured against the total mass of previously successful theory which might have to be abandoned if it were accepted.

During the latter half of the nineteenth century, for instance, there were known anomalies in the motions of the moon, Encke's comet, Halley's comet, and the planet Mercury, all of which seemed to contradict Newton's theory of gravitation. These anomalies might have caused a tremendous amount of effort to be wasted looking for alternative theories of gravitation, but most physicists either ignored the data or assumed that some less radical explanation would turn up.[9] As it happened, they were 75 percent correct; simple explanations (such as an improvement in the treatment of tidal forces) were later found for the anomalies in the motions of the moon and the comets. The anomaly in the motion of Mercury did, in 1916, turn out to be of fundamental importance when Einstein showed how it arose from relativisitic corrections to Newtonian mechanics. But even this is an exception that proves the rule. If physicists had taken the anomaly in the motion of Mercury seriously from the beginning, presumably they would also have taken the anomalies in lunar

9. The history of these problems is reviewed by S. Weinberg, *Gravitation and Cosmology* (New York: John Wiley, 1972), Sec. I.2. Also see E. Whittaker, *A History of the Theories of Aether and Electricity* (Edinburgh: Thomas Nelson, 1953), 2, Ch. 5.

and cometary motions seriously, and would thereby have been led away from rather than toward the discovery of general relativity.

Here is a simpler and more recent example. At a high energy physics conference in 1962, data were reported to the effect that neutral K mesons and their antiparticles can both decay into a positive pi-meson, an electron, and a neutrino. If true, this would have overturned a theory of weak interactions, the "current-current model," which had served as the basis of a great number of successes in other contexts. I remember Murray Gell-Mann rising and suggesting to the meeting that since the experiments didn't agree with the theory, the experiments were probably wrong. The next generation of experiments showed that this was indeed the case.

I realize that it may seem to the reader that the theorists in these examples were merely closed-minded and lucky. However, no scientist is clever enough to follow up hundreds of clues that lead in hundreds of different directions away from existing theories. (This is especially true of data of dubious provenance which would revolutionize scientific knowledge, such as evidence on unidentified flying objects, psychokinesis, and copper health bracelets.) What a scientist must do is to be open to just that piece of new data which can be integrated into a comprehensive new theory, and to file the rest.

Above all, in judging the openness of science, one should remember its unique capacity for discovering its own mistakes. Most natural scientists have the experience several times in their lives of being forced by new data or mathematical demonstrations to recognize that they have been seriously wrong about some important issue. (For instance, I was sure that Lee and Yang were wrong when they first proposed that parity is not conserved, and became convinced only by subsequent experiments.) On a larger scale, the physics community has many times been forced by new data to scrap large bodies of existing theory. If this takes away from our reputation for infallibility, it should also take away the impression that our minds are closed.

THE SCIENTIST AS ADDING MACHINE

The most profound challenge to science is presented by those, such as Laing and Roszak, who reject its coldness, its objectivity, its nonhumanity, in favor of other modes of knowledge that are more human, more direct,

more rapturous.[10] I have tried to understand these critics by looking
through some of their writings, and have found a good deal that is
pertinent, and even moving. I especially share their distrust of those, from
David Ricardo to the Club of Rome, who too confidently apply the
methods of the natural sciences to human affairs. But in the end I am
puzzled. What is it that they want *me* to do? Do they merely want the
natural scientist to respect and participate in other modes of knowledge
as well as the scientific? Or do they want science to change in some
fundamental way to incorporate these other modes? Or do they want
science simply to be abandoned? These three possible demands run
together confusingly in the writings of the critics of science, with
arguments for one demand often being made for another, or for all three.
In accordance with my role here as a specimen of the unregenerate working
scientist, I will try in what follows to keep the issues raised by these three
demands logically distinct, and to analyze each in turn.

1. *We should recognize the validity of other modes of knowledge, more
human and direct than scientific knowledge.*

Roszak expresses this view in terms of a metaphor he attributes to
Stephen Toulmin:[11]

When we insist on making scientific expertise the arbiter of all knowledge, it is
exactly like believing that cartographers know more about the terrain than the
natives who live there, or the artists who have come to paint its beauties, or the
priests who tend its holy places.

This does not seem to me to be an issue which raises any problems for
science. Scientists, like other folk, are perfectly willing to respect and
participate in various kinds of mental activity—aesthetic, moral, even
religious. Perhaps the hang-up is with the word "know." For my part,
since I view all epistemological arguments with perplexity anyway, I am
willing to describe the perceptions of the Lake of Nemi experienced by
Turner or the priests of Diana as "knowledge." For certain practical
decisions, such as where to have a picnic, I would even be guided by this
"knowledge" rather than by a contour map of the lake. Continuing

10. For a bibliography and useful comments, see C. Frankel, *Science*, 180 (1973),
p. 927.
11. T. Roszak, *Where the Wasteland Ends* (Garden City, N.Y.: Doubleday Anchor
Books, 1973), p. 375.

Toulmin's metaphor, the real problem is whether maps should all be redesigned to incorporate aesthetic and moral information, or, if this is impossible, whether maps have any value at all? This is the problem I address below.

2. *Science should change so as to incorporate other modes of knowledge.*

To quote Roszak again,[12]

What should come of this ideally is not some form of separate-but-equal coexistence, but a new cultural synthesis.

And again,[13]

It is a matter of changing the fundamental sensibility of scientific thought—and doing so even if we must drastically revise the professional character of science and its place in our culture. There is no doubt in my mind that such a revision would follow. Rhapsodic intellect would slacken the pace and scale of research to a degree that would be intolerable by current professional standards. It would subordinate much research to those contemplative encounters with nature that deepen, but do not increase knowledge. And it would surely end some lines of research entirely out of repugnance for their reductionism, insensitivity, and risk.

My answer is that science cannot change in this way without destroying itself, because however much human values are involved in the scientific process or are affected by the results of scientific research, there is an essential element in science that is cold, objective, and nonhuman.

At the center of the scientific method is a free commitment to a standard of truth. The scientist may let his imagination range freely over all conceivable world systems, orderly or chaotic, cold or rhapsodic, moral or value-free. However, he commits himself to work out the consequences of his system and to test them against experiment, and he agrees in advance to discard whatever does not agree with observation. In return for accepting this discipline, he enters into a relationship with nature, as a pupil with a teacher, and gradually learns its underlying laws. At the same time, he learns the boundaries of science, marking the class of phenomena which must be approached scientifically, not morally, aesthetically, or religiously.

One of the lessons we have been taught in this way is that the laws of

12. T. Roszak, unpublished comment on an earlier version of the present article.
13. Roszak, *Where the Wasteland Ends*, pp. 374–375.

nature are as impersonal and free of human values as the rules of arithmetic. We didn't want it to come out this way, but it did. When we look at the night sky we see a pattern of stars to which the poetic imagination gives meaning as beasts, fishes, heroes, and virgins. Occasionally there is drama—a meteor moves briefly across the sky. If a correlation were discovered between the positions of constellations and human personalities, or between the fall of a meteor and the death of kings, we would not have turned our backs on this discovery, we would have gone on to a view of nature which integrated all knowledge—moral, aesthetic, and scientific.

But there are no such correlations. Instead, when we turn our telescopes on the stars and carefully measure their parallaxes and proper motions, we learn that they are at different distances, and that their grouping into constellations is illusory, only a few constellations like the Hyades and Pleiades representing true associations of stars. With more powerful instruments, the whole system of visible stars stands revealed as only a small part of the spiral arm of one of a huge number of galaxies, extending away from us in all directions. Nowhere do we see human value or human meaning.

But there are compensations. Precisely at the most abstract level, furthest removed from human experience, we find harmony and order. The enormous firmament of galaxies is in a state of uniform expansion. Calculations reveal that the rate of this expansion is not very different from the "escape velocity" which would just barely allow the expansion to continue forever. Furthermore, there seems to be a frame of reference in which the expansion is spherically symmetric, and we find that this cosmic frame is rotating at less than one second of arc per century.

The order we find in astronomy on the largest scale is only a small part of a much grander intellectual picture, in which all the systematic features of nature revealed by experiment flow deductively from a few simple general laws. The search for these laws forces us to turn away from the ordinary world of human perception, and this may seem to the outsider to be a needless specialization and dehumanization of experience, but it is nature that dictates the direction of our search.

When Galileo measured the frequencies of pendulums of varying lengths, Simplicio might have objected that this was a purely artifical phenomenon invented by Galileo himself, less worthy of attention than the natural bodies falling freely through the open air that had been discussed by Aristotle. However, Galileo perceived the existence of laws of motion which could easily be approached through the nearly frictionless motion of a pendulum than through the study of bodies subject to the resistance of the air. Indeed, Galileo's great contribution to mechanics was precisely this perception, rather than the discovery of any particular law of motion.

In the same way, when we spend millions today to study the behavior of particles that exist nowhere in the universe except in our accelerators, we do so not out of a perverse desire to escape ordinary life, but because this is the best way we know right now to approach the underlying laws of nature. It is fashionable these days to emphasize the social and political influences upon scientific research, but my reading of history and my own experience in physics convince me that society provides only the *opportunity* for scientific research, and that the *direction* of this research is what it is to an overwhelming degree because the universe is the way it is.

We have, of course, a long way to go in understanding the laws of nature.[14] However, as far as we can now see, these laws are utterly cold, impersonal, and value free. By this, I don't at all mean that they are without beauty, or that there are no consolations in science. What I mean is that there does not seem to be anything in the laws of nature which expresses any concern for human affairs, of the sort which we, in our warm-blooded furry mammalian way, have happily learned to feel for one another.

Having committed ourselves to the scientific standard of truth, we have thus been forced, not by our own choosing, away from the rhapsodic sensibility. We can follow Roszak's lead only by abandoning our commitment. To do so would be to lose all of science, and break off our search for its ultimate laws.

3. *If science cannot be reformed, it should be abandoned.*

One must doubt that the world would be happier if we could forget all about the laws of nature. The prescientific mind peopled the world not only with nymphs and dryads, but also with monsters and devils; at least

14. I have attempted to describe how far along we are now in coming to an understanding of this deductive order, in *Science*, 180 (1973), p. 276.

in one historian's view, it was only the triumph of science that put an end to the burning of witches.[15] But suppose for the sake of argument that the case could be made that we would be happier if science were driven into some obscure utilitarian corner of our consciousness. Should we let this happen?

In the end, the choice is a moral, or even a religious, one. Having once committed ourselves to look at nature on its own terms, it is something like a point of honor not to flinch at what we see. For me, and perhaps for others, the helplessness of man in the face of pain and death also gives a certain bitter satisfaction to the attempt to master the objective world, if only in the mind. Roszak and Laing point out what they see as the moral dangers of objectivity, fearing that it is likely to leave the scientist himself as cold and value free as an adding machine. I do not see this happening to my colleagues in science. But, in gurus and flower-children, I do see the danger of subjectivity, that the rejection of an external standard of truth can leave a person as solipsistic and self-satisfied as a baby.

Finally, I must emphasize again that the "coldness" I have referred to above only characterizes the discovered *content* of science, and has nothing to do with wonderfully satisfying *process* of scientific research. In the last section I tried to show how scientists are joined together in a world society, fairer and more open than most. On an individual level, although we accept a discipline in testing our ideas against experiment, the generation of scientific premises is left to the scientist's imagination, guided but not governed by his previous experience. As Gerald Holton recently reminded us in citing Einstein's letter to Solovine, the method of scientific discovery often involves a logically discontinuous leap upward from the plane of experience to premises.[16] For some scientists, in our time notably Einstein and Dirac, the aesthetic appeal of the mathematical formalism itself often suggested the direction for this leap. And even though scientific research may not fill us with the rapture suggested by a van Gogh, the mood of science has its own beauty—clear, austere, and reflective, like the art of Vermeer. Or to use a different simile: if you accept the cliché that hearing a Bach fugue is like working out a

15. H. R. Trevor-Roper, *The European Witch-Crazes of the Sixteenth and Seventeenth Centuries* (Hammondsworth, England: Penguin Books, 1969), Ch. 5.

16. G. Holton, address at the Copernicus Celebration, National Academy of Sciences, Smithsonian Institution, April, 1973.

mathematical theorem, then you ought also to realize that working out a mathematical theorem is like hearing a Bach fugue.

In the Science Museum in Kensington there is an old picture of the Octagon Room of the Greenwich Observatory, which seems to me beautifully to express the mood of science at its best: the room laid out in a cool, uncluttered, early eighteenth-century style, the few scientific instruments standing ready for use, clocks of various sorts ticking on the walls, and, from the many windows, filling the room, the clear light of day.

Technology and the Limits to Growth

DONELLA H. MEADOWS et al.

INTRODUCTION

Our world model was built specifically to investigate five major trends of global concern—accelerating industrialization, rapid population growth, widespread malnutrition, depletion of nonrenewable resources, and a deteriorating environment. These trends are all interconnected in many ways, and their development is measured in decades or centuries, rather than in months or years. With the model we are seeking to understand the causes of these trends, their interrelationships, and their implications as much as one hundred years in the future.

The model we have constructed is, like every other model, imperfect, oversimplified, and unfinished. We are well aware of its shortcomings, but we believe that it is the most useful model now available for dealing with problems far out on the space-time graph. To our knowledge it is the only formal model in existence that is truly global in scope, that has a time horizon longer than thirty years, and that includes important variables such as population, food production, and pollution, not as independent entities, but as dynamically interacting elements, as they are in the real world.

Since ours is a formal, or mathematical, model it also has two important advantages over mental models. First, every assumption we make is written in a precise form so that it is open to inspection and criticism by all. Second, after the assumptions have been scrutinized, discussed, and revised to agree with our best current knowledge, their implications for the future behavior of the world system can be traced without error by a computer, no matter how complicated they become.

We feel that the advantages listed above make this model unique among all mathematical and mental world models available to us today. But there is no reason to be satisfied with it in its present form. We intend to alter, expand, and improve it as our own knowledge and the world data base gradually improve.

In spite of the preliminary state of our work, we believe it is important to publish the model and our findings now. Decisions are being made every day, in every part of the world, that will affect the physical, economic, and social conditions of the world system for decades to come. These decisions cannot wait for perfect models and total understanding. They will be made on the basis of some model, mental or written, in any case. We feel that the model described here is already sufficiently developed to be of some use to decision-makers. Furthermore, the basic behavior modes we have already observed in this model appear to be so fundamental and general that we do not expect our broad conclusions to be substantially altered by further revisions.

It is not the purpose ... [here] to give a complete, scientific description of all the data and mathematical equations included in the world model. Such a description can be found in the final technical report of our project. Rather, in *The Limits to Growth* we summarize the main features of the model and our findings in a brief, nontechnical way. The emphasis is meant to be not on the equations or the intricacies of the model, but on what it tells us about the world. We have used a computer as a tool to aid our own understanding of the causes and consequences of the accelerating trends that characterize the modern world, but familiarity with computers is by no means necessary to comprehend or to discuss our conclusions. The implications of those accelerating trends raise issues that go far beyond the proper domain of a purely scientific document. They must be debated by a wider community than that of scientists alone. Our purpose here is to open that debate.

The following conclusions have emerged from our work so far. We are by no means the first group to have stated them. For the past several decades, people who have looked at the world with a global, long-term perspective have reached similar conclusions. Nevertheless, the vast majority of policymakers seems to be actively pursuing goals that are inconsistent with these results.

Our conclusions are:

1. If the present growth trends in world population, industrialization, pollution, food production, and resource depletion continue unchanged, the limits to growth on this planet will be reached sometime within the next one hundred years. The most probable result will be a rather sudden and uncontrollable decline in both population and industrial capacity.

2. It is possible to alter these growth trends and to establish a condition of ecological and economic stability that is sustainable far into the future. The state of global equilibrium could be designed so that the basic material needs of each person on earth are satisfied and each person has an equal opportunity to realize his individual human potential.

3. If the world's people decide to strive for this second outcome rather than the first, the sooner they begin working to attain it, the greater will be their chances of success.

These conclusions are so far-reaching and raise so many questions for further study that we are quite frankly overwhelmed by the enormity of the job that must be done. We hope that this [study] will serve to interest other people, in many fields of study and in many countries of the world, to raise the space and time horizons of their concerns and to join us in understanding and preparing for a period of great transition—the transition from growth to global equilibrium.

. . .

PUSHING BACK LIMITS

Although the history of human effort contains numerous incidents of mankind's failure to live within physical limits, it is success in overcoming limits that forms the cultural tradition of many dominant people in today's world. Over the past three hundred years, mankind has compiled an impressive record of pushing back the apparent limits to population and economic growth by a series of spectacular technological advances. Since the recent history of a large part of human society has been so continuously successful, it is quite natural that many people expect technological breakthroughs to go on raising physical ceilings indefinitely. These people speak about the future with resounding technological optimism.

There are no substantial limits in sight either in raw materials or in energy that alterations in the price structure, product substitution, anticipated gains in technology and pollution control cannot be expected to solve.[1]

Given the present capacity of the earth for food production, and the potential for additional food production if modern technology were more fully employed, the human race clearly has within its grasp the capacity to chase hunger from the earth—within a matter of a decade or two.[2]

Humanity's mastery of vast, inanimate, inexhaustible energy sources and the accelerated doing more with less of sea, air, and space technology has proven Malthus to be wrong. Comprehensive physical and economic success for humanity may now be accomplished in one-fourth of a century.[3]

Can statements like these be reconciled with the evidence for the limits to growth we have discussed here? Will new technologies alter the tendency of the world system to grow and collapse? Before accepting or rejecting these optimistic views of a future based on technological solutions to mankind's problems, one would like to know more about the global impact of new technologies, in the short term and the long term, and in all five interlocking sectors of the population-capital system.

TECHNOLOGY IN THE WORLD MODEL

There is no single variable called "technology" in the world model. We have not found it possible to aggregate and generalize the dynamic implications of technological development because different technologies arise from and influence quite different sectors of the model. Birth control

1. Frank W. Notestein, "Zero Population Growth: What Is It?" *Family Planning Perspectives* 2 (June 1970): 20.
2. Donald J. Bogue, *Principles of Demography* (New York: John Wiley and Sons, 1969), p. 828.
3. R. Buckminster Fuller, *Comprehensive Design Strategy,* World Resources Inventory, Phase II (Carbondale, Ill.: University of Illinois, 1967), p. 48.

pills, high-yield grains, television, and off-shore oil-drilling rigs can all be considered technological developments, but each plays a distinct role in altering the behavior of the world system. Therefore we must represent each proposed technology separately in the model, considering carefully how it might affect each of the assumptions we have made about the model elements. In this section we shall present some examples of this approach to global, long-term "technology assessment."

Energy and Resources. The technology of controlled nuclear fission has already lifted the impending limit of fossil fuel resources. It is also possible that the advent of fast breeder reactors and perhaps even fusion nuclear reactors will considerably extend the lifetime of fissionable fuels, such as uranium. Does this mean that man has mastered "vast, inanimate, inexhaustible energy sources" that will release unlimited raw materials for his industrial plants? What will be the effect of increasing use of nuclear power on resource availability in the world system?

Some experts believe that abundant energy resources will enable mankind to discover and utilize otherwise inaccessible materials (in the sea bed, for example); to process poorer ores, even down to common rock; and to recycle solid waste and reclaim the metals it contains. Although this is a common belief, it is by no means a universal one, as the following quotation by geologist Thomas Lovering indicates.

Cheaper energy, in fact, would little reduce the total costs (chiefly capital and labor) required for mining and processing rock. The enormous quantities of unusable waste produced for each unit of metal in ordinary granite (in a ratio of at least 2,000 to 1) are more easily disposed of on a blueprint than in the field. . . . To recover minerals sought, the rock must be shattered by explosives, drilled for input and recovery wells, and flooded with solutions containing special extractive chemicals. Provision must then be made to avoid the loss of solutions and the consequent contamination of groundwater and surface water. These operations will not be obviated by nuclear power.[4]

Let us assume, however, that the technological optimists are correct and that nuclear energy will solve the resource problems of the world. The result of including that assumption in the world model is shown in Fig. 1. To express the possibility of utilizing lower grade ore or mining the seabed, we have doubled the total amount of resources available, . . . We

4. Thomas S. Lovering, "Mineral Resources from the Land," in Committee on Resources and Man, *Resources and Man* (San Francisco, Calif.: W. H. Freeman and Company, 1969), p. 122–23.

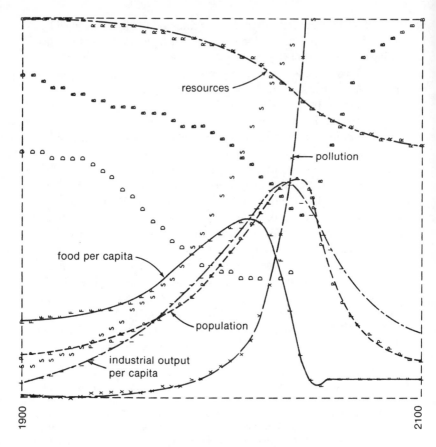

1900   2100

Fig. 1 WORLD MODEL WITH "UNLIMITED" RESOURCES
*The problem of resource depletion in the world model system is eliminated
by two assumptions: first, that "unlimited" nuclear power will double the
resource reserves that can be exploited and, second, that nuclear energy will
make extensive programs of recycling and substitution possible. If these
changes are the only ones introduced in the system, growth is stopped by
rising pollution . . .*

have also assumed that, starting in 1975, programs of reclamation and
recycling will reduce the input of virgin resources needed per unit of
industrial output to only one-fourth of the amount used today. Both
of these assumptions are, admittedly, more optimistic than realistic.

In Fig. 1 resource shortages indeed do not occur. Growth is stopped by rising pollution . . . The absence of any constraint from resources allows industrial output, food, and services to rise slightly higher than in. . .[a previous run with world resource reserves doubled] before they fall. Population reaches about the same peak level as it did in . . .[the previous run] , but it falls more suddenly and to a lower final value.

"Unlimited" resources thus do not appear to be the key to sustaining growth in the world system. Apparently the economic impetus such resource availability provides must be accompanied by curbs on pollution if a collapse of the world system is to be avoided.

Pollution Control. We assumed in Fig. 1 that the advent of nuclear power neither increased nor decreased the average amount of pollution generated per unit of industrial output. The ecological impact of nuclear power is not yet clear. While some by-products of fossil fuel consumption, such as CO_2 and sulfur dioxide, will be decreased, radioactive by-products will be increased. Resource recycling will certainly decrease pollution from solid waste and from some toxic metals. However, a changeover to nuclear power will probably have little effect on most other kinds of pollution, including by-products of most manufacturing processes, thermal pollution, and pollution arising from agricultural practices.

It is likely, however, that a world society with readily available nuclear power would be able to control industrial pollution generation by technological means. Pollution control devices are already being developed and installed on a large scale in industrialized areas. How would the model behavior be changed if a policy of strict pollution control were instituted in, say, 1975?

Strict pollution control does not necessarily mean *total* pollution control. It is impossible to eliminate all pollution because of both technological and economic constraints. Economically, the cost of pollution control soars as emission standards become more severe. Fig. 2 shows the cost of reducing water pollution from a sugar-processing plant as a function of organic wastes removed. If *no* organic wastes were allowed to leave the plant, the cost would be 100 times greater than if only 30 percent of the wastes were removed from the effluent. Table 1 below shows a similar trend in the projected costs of reducing air pollution in a US city.[5]

In Fig. 3 the world model output is plotted assuming *both* the

5. *Second Annual Report of the Council on Environmental Quality,* p. 118.

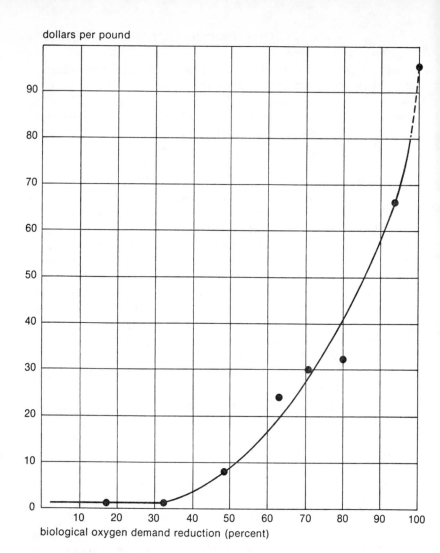

Fig. 2 COST OF POLLUTION REDUCTION
Incremental cost of reducing organic wastes from a 2,700-ton-per-day beet sugar plant rises steeply as emission standards approach complete purity. Reduction of biological oxygen demand (a measure of the oxygen required to decompose wastes) costs less than $1 a pound up to 30 percent reduction. Reduction beyond 65 percent requires more than $20 for each additional pound removed, and at 95 percent reduction, each pound removed costs $60.

SOURCE: Second Annual Report of the Council on Environmental Quality (Washington, DC: Government Printing Office, 1971).

reduction in resource depletion of Fig. 1 *and* a reduction in pollution
generation from all sources by a factor of four, starting in 1975

Table 1 COST OF REDUCING AIR POLLUTION IN A U.S. CITY

Percent reduction in SO_2	*Percent reduction in particulates*	*Projected cost*
5	22	$ 50,000
42	66	7,500,000
48	69	26,000,000

Reduction to less than one-fourth of the present rate of pollution
generation is probably unrealistic because of cost, and because of the
difficulty of eliminating some kinds of pollution, such as thermal pollution
and radioisotopes from nuclear power generation, fertilizer runoff, and
asbestos particles from brake linings. We assume that such a sharp
reduction in pollution generation could occur globally and quickly for
purposes of experimentation with the model, not because we believe it
is politically feasible, given our present institutions.

As Fig. 3 shows, the pollution control policy is indeed successful in
averting the pollution crisis of the previous run. Both population and
industrial output per person rise well beyond their peak values in Fig. 1
and yet resource depletion and pollution never become problems. The
overshoot mode is still operative, however, and the collapse comes about
this time from food shortage.

As long as industrial output is rising in Fig. 3, the yield from each
hectare of land continues to rise (up to a maximum of seven times the
average yield in 1900) and new land is developed. At the same time,
however, some arable land is taken for urban-industrial use, and some land
is eroded, especially by highly capitalized agricultural practices. Eventually
the limit of arable land is reached. After that point, as population
continues to rise, food per capita decreases. As the food shortage becomes
apparent, industrial output is diverted into agricultural capital to increase
land yields. Less capital is available for investment, and finally the
industrial output per capita begins to fall. When food per capita sinks to
the subsistence level, the death rate begins to increase, bringing an end to
population growth.

Increased Food Yield and Birth Control. The problem in Fig. 3 could be viewed either as too little food or as too many people. The technological response to the first situation would be to produce more

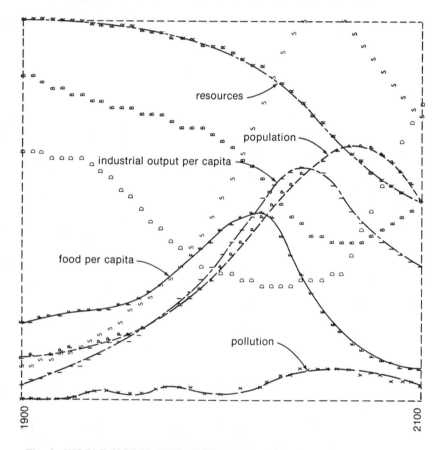

Fig. 3   WORLD MODEL WITH "UNLIMITED" RESOURCES AND POLLUTION CONTROLS

A further technological improvement is added to the world model in 1975 to avoid the resource depletion and pollution problems of previous model runs. Here we assume that pollution generation per unit of industrial and agricultural output can be reduced to one-fourth of its 1970 value. Resource policies are the same as those in Fig. 1. These changes allow population and industry to grow until the limit of arable land is reached. Food per capita declines, and industrial growth is also slowed as capital is diverted to food production.

food, perhaps by some further extension of the principles of the Green Revolution. (The development of the new, high-yield grain varieties which constitutes the Green Revolution has been included in the original model equations.) The technological solution to the second problem

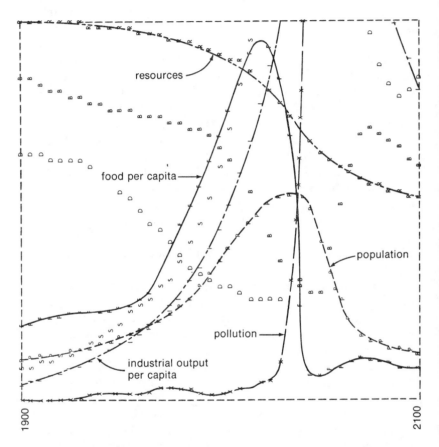

1900   2100

Fig. 4 WORLD MODEL WITH "UNLIMITED" RESOURCES, POLLUTION CONTROLS, AND INCREASED AGRICULTURAL PRODUCTIVITY

To avoid the food crisis of the previous model run, average land yield is doubled in 1975 in addition to the pollution and resource policies of previous figures. The combination of these three policies removes so many constraints to growth that population and industry reach very high levels. Although each unit of industrial production generates much less pollution, total production rises enough to create a pollution crisis that brings an end to growth.

would be to provide better methods of birth control. The results of these two changes, instituted in 1975 along with the changes in resource use and pollution generation we have already discussed, are shown both separately and simultaneously in Figs. 4, 5, and 6.

In Fig. 4 we assume that the normal yield per hectare of all the world's land can be further increased by a factor of two. The result is an enormous increase in food, industrial output, and services per capita. Average industrial output per person for all the world's people becomes nearly equal to the 1970 US level, but only briefly. Although a strict pollution control policy is still in effect, so that pollution per unit of output is reduced by a factor of four, industry grows so quickly that soon it is producing four times as much output. Thus the level of pollution rises in spite of the pollution control policy, and a pollution crisis stops further growth, as it did in Fig. 1.

Fig. 5 shows the alternate technological policy—perfect birth control, practiced voluntarily, starting in 1975. The result is not to stop population growth entirely because such a policy prevents only the births of *unwanted* children. The birth rate does decrease markedly, however, and the population grows more slowly than it did in Figs. 3 and 4. In this run growth is stopped by a food crisis occurring about 20 years later than in Fig. 3.

In Fig. 6 we apply increased land yield and perfect birth control simultaneously. Here we are utilizing a technological policy in every sector of the world model to circumvent in some way the various limits to growth. The model system is producing nuclear power, recycling resources, and mining the most remote reserves; withholding as many pollutants as possible; pushing yields from the land to undreamed-of heights; and producing only children who are actively wanted by their parents. The result is still an end to growth before the year 2100. In this case growth is stopped by three simultaneous crises. Overuse of land leads to erosion, and food production drops. Resources are severely depleted by a prosperous world population (but not as prosperous as the present US population). Pollution rises, drops, and then rises again dramatically, causing a further decrease in food production and a sudden rise in the death rate. The application of technological solutions alone has prolonged the period of population and industrial growth, but it has not removed the ultimate limits to that growth.

The Overshoot Mode. Given the many approximations and limitations of the world model, there is no point in dwelling glumly on the series of

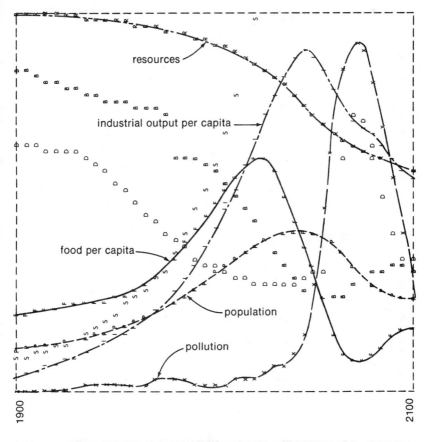

1900   2100

Fig. 5 WORLD MODEL WITH "UNLIMITED" RESOURCES, POLLUTION CONTROLS, AND "PERFECT" BIRTH CONTROL

Instead of an increase in food production, an increase in birth control effectiveness is tested as a policy to avert the food problem. Since the birth control is voluntary and does not involve any value changes, population continues to grow, but more slowly than it did in Fig. 3. Nevertheless, the food crisis is postponed for only a decade or two.

catastrophes it tends to generate. We shall emphasize just one more time that none of these computer outputs is a prediction. We would not expect the real world to behave like the world model in any of the graphs we have shown, especially in the collapse modes. The model contains dynamic statements about only the physical aspects of man's activities. It assumes

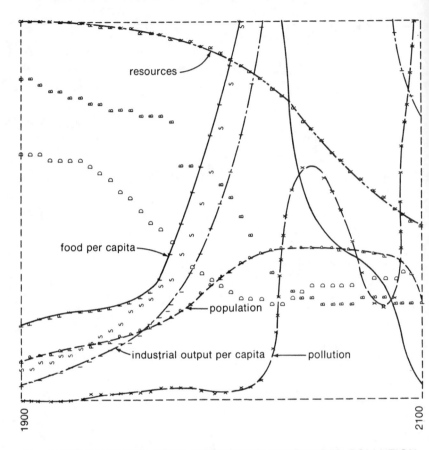

Fig. 6   WORLD MODEL WITH "UNLIMITED" RESOURCES, POLLUTION CONTROLS, INCREASED AGRICULTURAL PRODUCTIVITY, AND "PERFECT" BIRTH CONTROL

Four simultaneous technological policies are introduced in the world model in an attempt to avoid the growth-and-collapse behavior of previous runs. Resources are fully exploited, and 75 percent of those used are recycled. Pollution generation is reduced to one-fourth of its 1970 value. Land yields are doubled, and effective methods of birth control are made available to the world population. The result is a temporary achievement of a constant population with a world average income per capita that reaches nearly the present US level. Finally, though, industrial growth is halted, and the death rate rises as resources are depleted, pollution accumulates, and food production declines.

that social variables—income distribution, attitudes about family size, choices among goods, services, and food—will continue to follow the same patterns they have followed throughout the world in recent history. These patterns, and the human values they represent, were all established in the growth phase of our civilization. They would certainly be greatly revised as population and income began to decrease. Since we find it difficult to imagine what new forms of human societal behavior might emerge and how quickly they would emerge under collapse conditions, we have not attempted to model such social changes. What validity our model has holds up only to the point in each output graph at which growth comes to an end and collapse begins.

Although we have many reservations about the approximations and simplifications in the present world model, it has led us to one conclusion that appears to be justified under all the assumptions we have tested so far. *The basic behavior mode of the world system is exponential growth of population and capital, followed by collapse.* As we have shown in the model runs presented here, this behavior mode occurs if we assume no change in the present system or if we assume any number of technological changes in the system.

The unspoken assumption behind all of the model runs we have presented in this chapter is that population and capital growth should be allowed to continue until they reach some "natural" limit. This assumption also appears to be a basic part of the human value system currently operational in the real world. Whenever we incorporate this value into the model, the result is that the growing system rises above its ultimate limit and then collapses. When we introduce technological developments that successfully lift some restraint to growth or avoid some collapse, the system simply grows to another limit, temporarily surpasses it, and falls back. Given that first assumption, that population and capital growth should not be deliberately limited but should be left to "seek their own levels," we have not been able to find a set of policies that avoids the collapse mode of behavior.

It is not really difficult to understand how the collapse mode comes about. Everywhere in the web of interlocking feedback loops that constitutes the world system we have found it necessary to represent the real-world situation by introducing time delays between causes and their ultimate effects. These are natural delays that cannot be controlled by technological means. They include, for example, the delay of about fifteen years between the birth of a baby and the time that baby can first reproduce itself. The time delay inherent in the aging of a population introduces a certain unavoidable lag in the ability of the population to respond through the birth rate to changing conditions. Another delay occurs between the time a pollutant is released into the environment and the time it has a measurable influence on human health. This delay includes the passage of the pollutant through air or rivers or soil and into the food chain, and also the time from human ingestion or absorption of the pollutant until clinical symptoms appear. This second delay may be as long as 20 years in the case of some carcinogens. Other delays occur because capital cannot be transferred instantly from one sector to another to meet changing demands, because new capital and land can only be produced or developed gradually, and because pollution can only slowly be dispersed or metabolized into harmless forms.

Delays in a dynamic system have serious effects only if the system itself is undergoing rapid changes. Perhaps a simple example will clarify that statement. When you drive a car there is a very short, unavoidable delay between your perception of the road in front of you and your reaction to it. There is a longer delay between your action on the accelerator or brakes and the car's response to that action. You have learned to deal with those delays. You know that, because of the delays, it is unsafe to drive too fast. If you do, you will certainly experience the overshoot and collapse mode, sooner or later. If you were blindfolded and had to drive on the instructions of a front-seat passenger, the delay between perception and action would be considerably lengthened. The only safe way to handle the extended delay would be to slow down. If you tried to drive your normal speed, or if you tried to accelerate continuously (as in exponential growth), the result would be disastrous.

In exactly the same way, the delays in the feedback loops of the world system would be no problem if the system were growing very slowly or not at all. Under those conditions any new action or policy could be instituted gradually, and the changes could work their way through the delays to feed back on every part of the system before some other action or policy would have to be introduced. Under conditions of rapid growth, however, the system is forced into new policies and actions long before the results of old policies and actions can be properly assessed. The situation is even worse when the growth is exponential and the system is changing ever more rapidly.

Thus population and capital, driven by exponential growth, not only reach their limits, but temporarily shoot beyond them before the rest of the system, with its inherent delays, reacts to stop growth. Pollution generated in exponentially increasing amounts can rise past the danger point, because the danger point is first perceived years after the offending pollution was released. A rapidly growing industrial system can build up a capital base dependent on a given resource and then discover that the exponentially shrinking resource reserves cannot support it. Because of delays in the age structure, a population will continue to grow for as long as 70 years, even after average fertility has dropped below the replacement level (an average of two children for each married couple).

TECHNOLOGY IN THE REAL WORLD

The hopes of the technological optimists center on the ability of technology to remove or extend the limits to growth of population and capital. We have shown that in the world model the application of technology to apparent problems of resource depletion or pollution or food shortage has no impact on the *essential* problem, which is exponential growth in a finite and complex system. Our attempts to use even the most optimistic estimates of the benefits of technology in the model did not prevent the ultimate decline of population and industry, and in fact did not in any case postpone the collapse beyond the year 2100. Before we go on. . .to test other policies, which are not technological, let us extend our discussion of technological solutions to some aspects of technology that could not be included in the world model.

Technological Side-Effects. Dr. Garrett Hardin has defined side-effects as "effects which I hadn't foreseen or don't want to think about."[6] He has suggested that, since such effects are actually inseparable from the principal effect, they should not be labeled *side*-effects at all. Every new technology has side-effects, of course, and one of the main purposes of model-building is to anticipate those effects. The model runs in this chapter have shown some of the side-effects of various technologies on the world's physical and economic systems. Unfortunately the model does not indicate, at this stage, the *social* side-effects of new technologies.

6. Garrett Hardin, "The Cybernetics of Competition: A Biologist's View of Society," *Perspectives in Biology and Medicine* 7 (Autumn 1963): 58, reprinted in Paul Shepard and Daniel McKinley, eds., *The Subversive Science* (Boston: Houghton Mifflin, 1969), p. 275.

These effects are often the most important in terms of the influence of a technology on people's lives.

A recent example of social side-effects from a successful new technology appeared as the Green Revolution was introduced to the agrarian societies of the world. The Green Revolution—the utilization of new seed varieties, combined with fertilizers and pesticides—was designed to be a technological solution to the world's food problems. The planners of this new agricultural technology foresaw some of the social problems it might raise in traditional cultures. The Green Revolution was intended not only to produce more food but to be labor-intensive—to provide jobs and not to require large amounts of capital. In some areas of the world, such as the Indian Punjab, the Green Revolution has indeed increased the number of agricultural jobs faster than the rate of growth of the total population. In the East Punjab there was a real wage increase of 16 percent from 1963 to 1968.[7]

The principal, or intended, effect of the Green Revolution—increased food production—seems to have been achieved. Unfortunately the social side-effects have not been entirely beneficial in most regions where the new seed varieties have been introduced. The Indian Punjab had, before the Green Revolution, a remarkably equitable system of land distribution. The more common pattern in the nonindustrialized world is a wide range in land ownership, with most people working very small farms and a few people in possession of the vast majority of the land.

Where these conditions of economic inequality already exist, the Green Revolution tends to cause widening inequality. Large farmers generally adopt the new methods first. They have the capital to do so and can afford to take the risk. Although the new seed varieties do not require tractor mechanization, they provide much economic incentive for mechanization, especially where multiple cropping requires a quick harvest and replanting. On large farms, simple economic considerations lead almost inevitably to the use of labor-displacing machinery and to the purchase of still more land.[8] The utlimate effects of this socio-economic positive feedback loop are agricultural unemployment, increased migration

7. S. R. Sen, *Modernizing Indian Agriculture* vol. 1, Expert Committee on Assessment and Evaluation (New Delhi: Ministry of Food, Agriculture, Community Development, and Cooperatives, 1969).

8. For an excellent summary of this problem see Robert d'A. Shaw, *Jobs and Agricultural Development,* (Washington, DC: Overseas Development Council, 1970).

to the city, and perhaps even increased malnutrition, since the poor and unemployed do not have the means to buy the newly produced food.

A specific example of the social side-effects of the Green Revolution in an area where land is unequally distributed is described below.

A landless laborer's income in West Pakistan today is still just about what it was five years ago, less than $100 a year. In contrast, one landlord with a 1,500-acre wheat farm told me when I was in Pakistan this winter that he had cleared a net profit of more than $100,000 on his last harvest.[9]

Statistics from Mexico, where the Green Revolution began in the 1940's, provide another example. From 1940 to 1960 the average growth rate of agricultural production in Mexico was 5 percent per year. From 1950 to 1960, however, the average number of days worked by a landless laborer fell from 194 to 100, and his real income decreased from $68 to $56. Eighty percent of the increased agricultural production came from only 3 percent of the farms.[10]

These unexpected social side-effects do not imply that the technology of the Green Revolution was unsuccessful. They do imply that social side-effects must be anticipated and forestalled *before* the large-scale introduction of a new technology.

As agriculture emerges from its traditional subsistence state to modern commercial farming . . . it becomes progressively more important to ensure that adequate rewards accrue directly to the man who tills the soil. Indeed, it is hard to see how there can be any meaningful modernization of food production in Latin America and Africa south of the Sahara unless land is registered, deeded, and distributed more equitably.[11]

Such preparation for technological change requires, at the very least, a great deal of time. Every change in the normal way of doing things requires an adjustment time, while the population, consciously or unconsciously, restructures its social system to accommodate the change. While technology can change rapidly, political and social institutions generally change very slowly. Furthermore, they almost never change *in anticipation* of a social need, but only in response to one.

9. Richard Critchfield, "It's a Revolution All Right," Alicia Patterson Fund paper (New York: Alicia Patterson Fund, 1971).

10. Robert d'A. Shaw, *Jobs and Agricultural Development*, p. 44.

11. Lester R. Brown, *Seeds of Change*, (New York: Praeger, 1970), p. 112.

We have already mentioned the dynamic effect of physical delays in the world model. We must also keep in mind the presence of social delays—the delays necessary to allow society to absorb or to prepare for a change. Most delays, physical or social, reduce the stability of the world system and increase the likelihood of the overshoot mode. The social delays, like the physical ones, are becoming increasingly more critical because the processes of exponential growth are creating additional pressures at a faster and faster rate. The world population grew from 1 billion to 2 billion over a period of more than one hundred years. The third billion was added in 30 years and the world's population has had less than 20 years to prepare for its fourth billion. The fifth, sixth, and perhaps even seventh billions may arrive before the year 2000, less than 30 years from now. Although the rate of technological change has so far managed to keep up with this accelerated pace, mankind has made virtually no new discoveries to increase the rate of social (political, ethical, and cultural) change.

Problems with No Technical Solutions.   When the cities of America were new, they grew rapidly. Land was abundant and cheap, new buildings rose continuously, and the population and economic output of urban regions increased. Eventually, however, all the land in the city center was filled. A physical limit had been reached, threatening to stop population and economic growth in that section of the city. The technological answer was the development of skyscrapers and elevators, which essentially removed the constraint of land area as a factor in suppressing growth. The central city added more people and more businesses. Then a new constraint appeared. Goods and workers could not move in and out of the dense center city quickly enough. Again the solution was technological. A network of expressways, mass transit systems, and helicopter ports on the tops of the tallest buildings was constructed. The transportation limit was overcome, the buildings grew taller, the population increased.

Now most of the larger US cities have stopped growing. (Of the ten largest, five—New York, Chicago, Philadelphia, Detroit, and Baltimore— decreased in population from 1960 to 1970. Washington, D.C., showed no change. Los Angeles, Houston, Dallas, and Indianapolis continued to grow, at least in part by annexing additional land.)[12] The wealthier people, who have an economic choice, are moving to the ever-expanding ring of suburbs

12.   U.S. Bureau of the Census, *1970 Census of Population and Housing, General Demographic Trends of Metropolitan Areas, 1960–70* (Washington, D.C.: Government Printing Office, 1971).

around the cities. The central areas are characterized by noise, pollution, crime, drug addiction, poverty, labor strikes, and breakdown of social services. The quality of life in the city core has declined. Growth has been stopped in part by problems with no technical solutions.

A technical solution may be defined as "one that requires a change only in the techniques of the natural sciences, demanding little or nothing in the way of change in human values or ideas of morality."[13] Numerous problems today have no technical solutions. Examples are the nuclear arms race, racial tensions, and unemployment. Even if society's technological progress fulfills all expectations, it may very well be a problem with no technical solution, or the interaction of several such problems, that finally brings an end to population and capital growth.

A Choice of Limits. Applying technology to the natural pressures that the environment exerts against any growth process has been so successful in the past that a whole culture has evolved around the principle of fighting against limits rather than learning to live with them. This culture has been reinforced by the apparent immensity of the earth and its resources and by the relative smallness of man and his activities.

But the relationship between the earth's limits and man's activities is changing. The exponential growth curves are adding millions of people and billions of tons of pollutants to the ecosystem each year. Even the ocean, which once appeared virtually inexhaustible, is losing species after species of its commercially useful animals. Recent FAO statistics indicate that the total catch of the world's fisheries decreased in 1969 for the first time since 1950, in spite of more mechanized and intensive fishing practices. (Among commercial species becoming increasingly scarce are Scandinavian herring, menhaden, and Atlantic cod.)[14]

Yet man does not seem to learn by running into the earth's obvious limits. The story of the whaling industry demonstrates, for one small system, the ultimate result of the attempt to grow forever in a limited environment. Whalers have systematically reached one limit after another and have attempted to overcome each one by increases in power and technology. As a result, they have wiped out one species after another. The outcome of this particular grow-forever policy can only be the final extinction of both whales and whalers. The alternative policy is the

13. Garrett Hardin, "The Tragedy of the Commons," *Science* 162 (1968): 1243.
14. UN Food and Agriculture Organization, *The State of Food and Agriculture* (Rome: UN Food and Agriculture Organization, 1970), p. 6.

imposition of a *man-determined limit* on the number of whales taken each year, set so that the whale population is maintained at a steady-state level. The self-imposed limit on whaling would be an unpleasant pressure that would prevent the growth of the industry. But perhaps it would be preferable to the gradual disappearance of both whales and whaling industry.

The basic choice that faces the whaling industry is the same one that faces any society trying to overcome a natural limit with a new technology. *Is it better to try to live within that limit by accepting a self-imposed restriction on growth? Or is it preferable to go on growing until some other natural limit arises, in the hope that at that time another technological leap will allow growth to continue still longer?* For the last several hundred years human society has followed the second course so consistently and successfully that the first choice has been all but forgotten.

There may be much disagreement with the statement that population and capital growth must stop *soon.* But virtually no one will argue that material growth on this planet can go on forever. At this point in man's history, the choice posed above is still available in almost every sphere of human activity. Man can still choose his limits and stop when he pleases by weakening some of the strong pressures that cause capital and population growth, or by instituting counterpressures, or both. Such counterpressures will probably not be entirely pleasant. They will certainly involve profound changes in the social and economic structures that have been deeply impressed into human culture by centuries of growth. The alternative is to wait until the price of technology becomes more than society can pay, or until the side-effects of technology suppress growth themselves, or until problems arise that have no technical solutions. At any of those points the choice of limits will be gone. Growth will be stopped by pressures that are not of human choosing, and that, as the world model suggests, may be very much worse than those which society might choose for itself.

We have felt it necessary to dwell so long on an analysis of technology here because we have found that technological optimism is the most common and the most dangerous reaction to our findings from the world model. Technology can relieve the symptoms of a problem without affecting the underlying causes. Faith in technology as the ultimate solution to all problems can thus divert our attention from the most fundamental problem—the problem of growth in a finite system—and prevent us from taking effective action to solve it.

On the other hand, our intent is certainly not to brand technology as evil or futile or unnecessary. We are technologists ourselves, working in a technological institution. We strongly believe, . . . that many of the technological developments mentioned here—recycling, pollution control devices, contraceptives—will be absolutely vital to the future of human society *if they are combined with deliberate checks on growth.* We would deplore an unreasoned rejection of the benefits of technology as strongly as we argue here against an unreasoned acceptance of them. Perhaps the best summary of our position is the motto of the Sierra Club: "Not blind opposition to progress, but opposition to blind progress."

We would hope that society will receive each new technological advance by establishing the answers to three questions *before* the technology is widely adopted. The questions are:

1. What will be the side-effects, both physical and social, if this development is introduced on a large scale?

2. What social changes will be necessary before this development can be implemented properly, and how long will it take to achieve them?

3. If the development is fully successful and removes some natural limit to growth, what limit will the growing system meet next? Will society prefer its pressures to the ones this development is designed to remove?

Malthus with a Computer

CHRISTOPHER FREEMAN

Take for instance Malthus' book on Population. In its first edition it was nothing but a sensational pamphlet and plagiarism from beginning to end into the bargain. And yet what a stimulus was produced by this libel on the human race!–(Karl Marx, in The Poverty of Philosophy).

The MIT *World Dynamics* and *The Limits to Growth* models* represent the most ambitious attempt so far to bring together forecasts of population growth, resource depletion, food supply, capital investment and pollution into one general model of the future of the world. In view of the wide interest this MIT work has attracted and the importance of the issues it raises, it deserves thorough and constructive criticism. That is the purpose of this publication. Since the criticism is extensive, and

* *World Dynamics*, by Jay W. Forrester, was published in 1971 (Cambridge, Massachussetts, Wright-Allen Press). It contains the first description of the world model, called World 2, as well as commentaries on the various runs of the model. *The Limits to Growth*, by Donella H. Meadows, Dennis L. Meadows, Jorgen Randers and William W. Behrens III, was published in 1972 (New York, Universe Books, and London, Earth Island). It outlines a more elaborate world model, called World 3, built under the direction of Dennis Meadows and based on Forrester's original. The detailed description of this model is contained in a separate Technical Report. This Technical Report has gone through several (mimeographed) editions. The final revised version. . .[was] published in. . .1973 under the title, *The Dynamics of Growth in a Finite World* (Wright-Allen Press). The paper published here [is] concerned with *World Dynamics*, *The Limits to Growth* and the early versions of the Technical Report, which are the most relevant in considering the arguments advanced in *The Limits to Growth* and the computer runs presented in that book.

When the comments and criticisms pertain to all of them, the publications are referred to either as the MIT model (or models), or as the work of Forrester and Meadows. Otherwise, reference is made to the specific publications and/or their authors. The use of MIT as an adjective is purely a matter of convenience, to indicate the geographical origin of the research team. It does not of course imply any institutional responsibility for the models. We are well aware that many members of that institution do not share the views expressed in these publications.

sometimes severe, it is essential to make several points quite clear at the outset.

First, although. . . [we] disagree strongly with much of the MIT analysis and also disagree with each other about some of the issues raised, we are in complete agreement with the MIT authors and their sponsors, the Club of Rome, about the urgency of many of the social problems with which they are concerned.

Our critique must not be taken in any way as justifying complacency about such issues as population growth rates in some areas of the world, the development of satisfactory national and international mechanisms for the monitoring and prevention of pollution hazards, or conservation of amenity. We *do* believe that these issues are extremely important for the future of the world and that they are urgent and of global concern.

Secondly. . .our critique should not be taken as an attack on the use of mathematical model-building in the social sciences. On the contrary, we agree with Gabor[1] that the social sciences can benefit from the use of computer model-building techniques and specifically from system dynamics. As will be explained, however, we also believe that such models have serious limitations and dangers of misuse.

Thirdly, we do not underestimate the positive importance of the MIT work as a courageous and pioneering attempt to make a computer model of the future of the world. As a result of reading *The Limits to Growth* many people are now thinking anew about long-term problems and discussing them much more seriously. In particular, they are discussing once again whether or not the world is likely to run up against physical limits. This is a very important achievement.

Moreover, we do not accept the precious and self-centred view that systems analysts and natural scientists have no business to trespass in the exclusive realm of the social sciences. On the contrary, we think that the MIT work has done a great deal of good in compelling social scientists to re-examine some of their assumptions and in exposing the limitations both of data and of satisfactory explanatory theories for some of the most important social mechanisms.

Since the days of Malthus and Ricardo, economists have tended to neglect problems of resource depletion; they have been slow to develop

1. D. Gabor, "The new responsibilities of science," *Science Policy*, Vol. 1, no. 3 (May–June 1972).

the economics of pollution; and it is good for them to be reminded that their explanations of long-term growth and technical progress are still in an unsatisfactory state. Neither economists, nor sociologists, nor political scientists have satisfactory theories of social change and it is unlikely that they will develop them unless they overcome their fragmentation into separate jealously guarded kingdoms and learn to cooperate with each other and with natural scientists, looking at the kind of fundamental long-term problems which are at the heart of the MIT work.

Consequently, we do not reproach the MIT group with being over-ambitious in attempting to bring together expertise from many different disciplines, although we are critical in many respects of the way in which they have done it. If anything, we might reproach them for not being inter-disciplinary enough. Our own essays** were prepared by an equally mixed team: Cole is a mathematical physicist, Sinclair a health physicist and nuclear engineer, Pavitt an engineer and an economist, Page a social psychologist, Surrey and Bromley are economists specialising in energy, Curnow is a statistician, Julien and Cooper are economists, Marstrand an applied biologist, and Simmons a political scientist. The whole team was co-ordinated by Marie Jahoda, Professor of Social Psychology at Sussex, and Chairman of the forecasting research group. In addition we had the benefit of valuable comments on our drafts from demographers, geologists, sociologists, geographers, ecologists, agricultural economists, control engineers and systems analysts. . . .

The question which we ask in relation to each sub-system and the model as a whole is: how far do the assumptions made correspond to what is known about the real world before 1970, and to what might be plausibly assumed about the world's probable future development from then onwards? Admittedly this is a severe test for any model to satisfy since the real world is extremely complex and diverse and it is very difficult to make simplifying assumptions which are realistic and mutually consistent. Some may doubt whether it is feasible to satisfy this requirement for world model-building at all. However, this is the test which is actually prescribed by the MIT team for their own work.[2]

They rightly believe that ideally each relationship in the model should be an accurate representation of a real world phenomenon and that model

---

** Contained in H. S. D. Cole et al. eds., *Models of Doom: A Critique of the Limits to Growth* (New York: Universe Books, 1973).

2. Technical Report and *The Limits to Growth*.

behaviour must be in reasonable agreement with real world behaviour. This implies the need to assemble time series data on the variables in the real world from 1900 to 1970.

Our examination suggests that the MIT models do not on the whole satisfy these requirements. This is partly a problem of data and partly a question of assumptions about relationships. The MIT team cannot be blamed for the lack of data, although they may be criticised for trying to erect such an elaborate theoretical structure and such sweeping conclusions on so precarious a data base. The MIT team are, however, responsible for the choice of assumptions and for the relative neglect of economics and sociology.

The nature of their assumptions is not a purely technical problem. It is essential to look at the political bias and the values implicitly or explicitly present in any study of social systems. The apparent detached neutrality of a computer model is as illusory as it is persuasive. Any model of any social system necessarily involves assumptions about the workings of that system, and these assumptions are necessarily coloured by the attitudes and values of the individual or groups concerned. For this reason too Cole and Curnow conclude that computer models should be regarded as an integral part of political debate, just because they may hide possible sources of bias. The model is the message.

This is particularly important in relation to forecasting models. Subjective values and attitudes do influence forecasts, however much the individual may strive for objectivity. It does matter in considering forecasts of the future patterns of world energy demand and their implications for pollution whether the forecasters are working in the oil industry, the nuclear power industry or the coal industry. This does not mean that all forecasters are paid hacks or manipulate their data in a dishonest way but only that the environment in which a forecaster works influences his theoretical assumptions. His sources of data necessarily influence (often unconsciously) the form and presentation of a complex argument in which values are inevitably and inextricably involved.

The MIT system dynamics group is no exception to this rule. As we shall see, they place great emphasis on "computer models" versus "mental models". They argue that in understanding the behaviour of complex systems, computer models have great advantages. This view is unex - ceptionable if we are considering the number of variables, complex interactions and speed of calculation. But it can easily and dangerously be exaggerated into what is best described as computer fetishism. The computer fetishist endows the computer model with a validity and an independent power which altogether transcends the mental models which are its essential basis. Because of the prevalence of this computer fetishism it cannot be repeated too often that the validity of any computer calculation depends entirely on the quality of the data and the assumptions (mental models) which are fed into it. Computer models cannot replace theory.

The healthy reaction to computer fetishism is exemplified by the terse aphorism "Garbage in, garbage out." What has gone into the *The Limits to Growth* model is not garbage. On the contrary a great deal of effort has been made to find data, to develop reasonable assumptions about the real world and to test the model. But Meadows has himself emphasised that only about 0.1% of the data on the variables required to construct a satisfactory world model is now available. Moreover, . . . little is known about the forces which determined past relationships between some of the variables; still less about their future relationships.

This inevitably means that the modellers are required to make assumptions about relationships and to make estimates about data. There are many possible assumptions about such a complex system as the future of the human race. Consequently, the MIT team has had to choose between alternative assumptions. Moreover, since the world is so complex they (or anyone else attempting a world model) had to omit what they consider to be irrelevant. These decisions are matters of judgement, not of fact or mathematics. (Meadows calls them "Hazards of Omission".) For example, the MIT team tried to concentrate on physical limits to growth and omit changes in values, yet these changes may be the most important dynamic element in the whole system.

The assumptions and judgements made by the computer modellers depend no less than those of other social scientists on their mental models—on their information, their bias, their experience, their capacity and their values. Consequently, although it would be quite wrong to talk of "garbage" in the MIT model, there is a real point in the description: "Malthus in, Malthus out". In fact, as we shall see, the MIT model is not strictly Malthusian. Many assumptions are made which have little to do with that country parson. But the expression: "Malthus in, Malthus out" does bring out the essential point that what is on the computer print-out depends on the assumptions which are made about real-world relationships, and these assumptions in turn are heavily influenced by those contemporary social theories and values to which the computer modellers are exposed.

Therefore, the critique of a computer model is not just a question of looking at the structure, or conducting mathematical tests. Far more important is the examination of the underlying assumptions. That is the reason for this chapter's title. It is also the reason for devoting the second part of the critique to a discussion of the ideological background to the distinctive MIT approach to world forecasting. This may reasonably and precisely be described as a neo-Malthusian approach.

The MIT work is the most numerate, influential and clearly formulated statement of this position. Because of the prestige of the computer and of MIT, it is also frequently cited in other doomsday literature as an authoritative source for views which otherwise might be rather difficult to justify. Thus, for example, the *Ecologist* "Blueprint for Survival" cites Forrester's work as justification for the view that economic growth in Britain must cease and the population decline to 30 million.[3]

This resurgence of Malthusian ideas is combined in the MIT approach with a strong, almost Messianic faith in the more modern system dynamics, and a strong pre-occupation with environmental issues characteristic of contemporary American thought. It is the convergence of these various strands which gives the MIT work its peculiar flavour, conveyed in the title to this chapter. . . .

We. . .believe that discussion of the ideological background of the MIT work is just as important as the technical aspects and indeed, for reasons which have already been discussed, the two are intimately related. We would, nevertheless, certainly accept that the views advanced in these essays reflect our own political biases and subjective limitations. Our value judgements and intellectual assumptions are as much a part of the debate as those of MIT. As we shall see, there are obviously some big differences in the approach of Forrester on the one hand and Meadows on the other, and no doubt there were many other differences of opinion between the various members of the MIT team, as there certainly were in ours. It is similarly difficult to generalize about the bias of our group. It included people of very diverse political views ranging across the whole spectrum from Conservative to Marxist, and some of no identifiable political complexion. It included members from many different disciplines, and we

3. E. Goldsmith, ed, "Blueprint for survival", *Ecologist,* Vol. 2, No. 1, January, 1972.

were not united, as were the MIT group, by a common faith in system dynamics. But we were, and are, agreed on the urgency of many of the social and political problems raised by *The Limits to Growth,* and the belief that satisfactory solutions can only emerge as a result of a continuing process of research, political debate, and social experiment.

It is for this reason that I personally believe that the open public debate surrounding the MIT work is their most important achievement. To remove any possible misconception, I am not suggesting through my choice of quotation at the beginning of this introduction that the MIT work is a piece of plagiarism. On the contrary, it is one of the most original and ambitious constructions in the history of the social sciences. The parallel which is implied between the work of Malthus and that of MIT lies purely in the stimulus which they have both given to an extremely important debate. Because our team at Sussex is agreed that science and social policy can only advance by continuous critical debate and discussion, we see our own contribution as only one stage in this continuing process. Therefore it may be useful in this [article] to focus on three of the essential differences between our views and those of MIT.

First, we put much greater emphasis on the political and social limits to growth than on the purely physical limits. Our reasons for scepticism and disagreement about many of the MIT physical estimates are explained in detail [in *Models of Doom*]. Since we believe that brute poverty is still a major problem for most people in the world, and since in general we do not believe that the physical constraints are quite so pressing as the MIT team suggest, we do not accept their enthusiastic endorsement of zero growth as the ideal for the world. We do agree with them, however, on the need to develop new technologies which do not damage the environment and which contribute to the conservation of finite resources. In our view the Growth versus No Growth debate has become a rather sterile one of the Tweedledum/Tweedledee variety, because it tends to ignore the really important issues of the *composition* of growth in output, and the *distribution* of the fruits of growth. Some types of growth are quite consistent not merely with conservation of the environment, but with its enhancement. The problem, in our view, is a socio-political one of stimulating this type of growth and of more equitable distribution, both between countries and within them.

Secondly, technical change is at the heart of our differences. We believe that, like Malthus, the MIT group is underestimating the possibilities of continuous technical progress. "Progress" is used here in the economic sense of greater output from the same inputs or reduced inputs, or the introduction of new products and processes. It does not necessarily imply a value judgement on the desirability of a particular set of technical changes. As Cole and Curnow demonstrate. . .(and as other critics have also shown), the inclusion of technical progress in the MIT model in sectors from which it is omitted has the effect of indefinitely postponing the catastrophes which the model otherwise predicts.

When we are making forecasts for 130 years ahead, as in the MIT models, it is extremely important to make realistic judgements about technical progress. As Surrey and Bromley point out. . .a forecast made in 1870 would have omitted the principal source of energy in 1970 (oil) and the fastest growing new source (nuclear power). It would probably have excluded not only all the synthetic materials, fibres and rubbers, but probably aluminium and sundry other metals. As Page points out . . . the concept of "reserves" in most resource forecasting is techno-economic rather than geo-physical and the world reserves of most known materials would probably have been underestimated by orders of magnitude. The technologies of resource exploration, extraction and recycling have changed the picture out of all recognition. We should not fall into the error of some of the more pessimistic ecologists: failure to consider the tremendous potential of changing technology in relation to human social systems.

This does not mean, of course, that continuous technical progress will inevitably occur. The fact that it has occurred between 1870 and 1970 does not necessarily mean that it will continue to 2070. There are two perfectly respectable grounds for pessimism. It could be maintained on purely technical grounds that the world has now encountered or is about to encounter technical problems of such difficulty and magnitude that discontinuities may reasonably be expected. Or, it could be maintained that, although technically feasible, progress cannot be sustained for institutional reasons. It is apparently for some combination of these reasons that Meadows is particularly harsh in his attack on "technological optimism". While we do not believe that the model itself validates these arguments, they may nevertheless be true and certainly deserve serious consideration and debate.

The resources now devoted to organized research and development are many times greater than they were in 1870. At that time the social invention of the industrial research laboratory had only just been made.

Today these laboratories are characteristic institutions in industry as well as in government and universities. In addition the resources now devoted to dissemination of knowledge are huge and still growing. On these grounds it might reasonably be supposed that the rate of technical change could be expected to accelerate rather than to diminish, and this is indeed the supposition of many environmentalists as well as economists. But there are several grounds for doubt. First, there is some evidence of diminishing returns to investment in research and development and education. This might be expected as scientists and engineers approach extreme limits of temperature, pressure and size as well as for other reasons. The very high cost of some types of research equipment is one reflection of these problems although there is the counter argument of the revolutionary breakthrough, such as the transistor in communications equipment.

Secondly, there is much stronger evidence of serious mal-distribution of the large resources which are now devoted to R and D. These problems are at the heart of our own interest in Sussex as a Research Unit concerned with policy for science and technology. As members of our team have shown in detail elsewhere,[4] there are very disquieting features in the pattern of deployment of the world's scientific and technical resources. About half the total is devoted to military and prestige objectives and less than 2% of the world's R and D effort is devoted to the urgent agricultural, environmental and industrial problems of the developing countries. Although there has been a welcome impetus to the development of new techniques from recent environmental legislation in the richer countries, the scale of effort remains very small. Unless this imbalance is rectified, there must be continuing cause for concern about the possibility of sustained technical progress in food supply, energy and environmental improvement. This is at the heart of the political and social changes we believe to be necessary.

The MIT work rightly points to the importance of the delays in response mechanisms, which may make remedial or avoiding action too little and too late. Nowhere is this more true than in relation to investment in R and D. The quality of life for future generations depends in large measure on a wise deployment of scientific resources today. From this standpoint, a high priority for much long-term R and D can be justified,

4. C. Freeman *et al.*, "The goals of R & D in the 1970s", *Science Studies,* Vol. 1, pages 357–406, 1971.

including for example, both research on solar energy and on fusion power. World R and D is in the nature of a global insurance policy.

Moreover, we agree with the MIT group that the problem of unwelcome secondary effects of technical change is a very serious one. In retrospect, the decision of the United States Congress to set up an Office of Technology Assessment may appear as a political turning point, since it marks the recognition that a policy of "laissez-innover" is as undesirable as "laissez-faire" in relation to social and economic policy. We would agree with the MIT group that social institutions for anticipating and coping with the manifold problems of technical change are embryonic and still inadequate. But we have perhaps greater faith than they have in the adaptive response of human beings to these problems. This in turn is related to our differing views of social change . . .

Finally, we are not wholly convinced that world models based on system dynamics can develop into satisfactory tools of forecasting and policy-making. We regard this as still a question for experiment and discussion, whereas the MIT team are prepared to base a prescription for the world on the results of their model. Although we believe that mathematical modelling and system dynamics can make an important contribution to the social sciences, we also believe that there are serious dangers in the way that these models are often used or misused. One of our colleagues in the University, Dr. R. Golub, a physicist, has argued strongly that the MIT approach is inherently dangerous, since it encourages self-delusion in five ways:

- By giving the spurious appearance of precise knowledge of quantities and relationships which are unknown and in many cases unknowable.
- By encouraging the neglect of factors which are difficult to quantify such as policy changes or value changes.
- By stimulating gross over-simplification, because of the problem of aggregation and the comparative simplicity of our computers and mathematical techniques.
- By encouraging the tendency to treat some features of the model as rigid and immutable.
- By making it extremely difficult for the non-numerate or those who do not have access to computers to rebut what are essentially tendentious and rather naive political assumptions.

In short, Golub believes that the method is an attempt to substitute mathematics for knowledge and computation for understanding. We agree with him that these dangers are present in the world models, and often in other models too. Some members of our team would agree with Golub that these arguments constitute reason for rejecting altogether the system dynamics approach to the world. Harvey Simmons too argues. . .that there are strong simplistic technocratic tendencies inherent in Forrester's approach. Ida Hoos has given a similar warning about the uncritical application of systems research techniques to social problems.[5] Moreover, the experience of systems model-building in ecology and meteorology lends considerable weight to the view that our attempts to model complex systems are still at a very primitive level.

However, most members of our team, among them myself, while agreeing with Golub and Simmons about all the dangers which they point to, nevertheless believe that the attempt to develop satisfactory mathematical models is worthwhile and can be a valuable aid to systematic thought. . . It may prove difficult for a long time to overcome the justifiable objections which can be raised and we would certainly all approach social systems models with great scepticism. Any attempt to represent future tendencies in the world, whether in words or in numbers, is attended by great difficulties. We nevertheless believe such attempts to be of great importance, whether in the arts or the sciences. Even if our judgement on this particular MIT model is largely negative, we may nevertheless see some point in the quotation with which this chapter begins, in the sense of its being a stimulus for an extremely fundamental debate.

2

Technology and Philosophy

The scientists and technologists whose views make up part one are not all of one mind with respect to the impact of technology on society. Part two contains a collection of articles by writers whose views of technology may be a bit more detached from the concrete substance of technology, but are not less diverse. Most of these articles are by humanist philosophers and social critics. Their analyses are often complex, abstract, and difficult to comprehend. For anyone seeking to develop an understanding of the full range of perspectives on technology and society, however, the effort required is a worthwhile investment.

Several of the authors represented here explore a dimension of interaction between technology and society that goes beyond a linear cause and effect relationship. In their view, technology affects not only social and political structures but also the human psyche—the way people see, think about, and relate to their world. In developing technology and incorporating it into their social institutions, human beings therefore are not only changing these institutions but are changing *themselves* in ways they can neither foresee nor necessarily desire.

Marshall McLuhan is one of these writers, and the first article in part two is excerpted from his famous book *Understanding Media.* Although McLuhan builds on the ideas of a number of earlier scholars of communications without really acknowledging his debt to them, *Understanding Media* is still a remarkable work. Rejecting the form of a structured argument, McLuhan presents a cafeteria of ideas that immerses the reader in his thought process, in much the same way he says technology immerses the human psyche. In the now classic phrase "the medium is the message" lies the central theme of McLuhan's vision. The content of a technology is really irrelevant, as is any argument over its moral neutrality. It is the changes produced in ourselves that are important. "The effects of technology do not occur at the level of opinions or concepts, but alter sense ratios or patterns of perception steadily and without any resistance." McLuhan sees technology as the prime mover behind all social change; yet in his view it operates not through the social structure, but through the individual. Despite this, the essence of *Understanding Media* is not a cry of alarm about where technology is leading us. It is rather a paean to the wonders of the new technology, especially the technology of communications, and an attempt to deal with technology on its own terms.

The writings of Herbert Marcuse, although similar to those of McLuhan in certain ways, are strikingly different in their pessimistic evaluation of technology's role in social change. *One-Dimensional Man*, from which the present selection is taken, is a major work of contemporary philosophy. A full understanding of the ideas Marcuse presents here requires that the reader have a substantial background in philosophy, particularly in Hegel and Marx. Nevertheless, Marcuse's influence as a philosopher of the technological society has been at least as great among those who lack such a background as among those who possess it, and it is in this light that it is treated here. Like McLuhan, Marcuse believes that technology manifests its most profound effects through changes in human character. The technological system creates "false" needs in individuals that serve to sustain the system while repressing true human needs. The technological state is basically totalitarian. From the inside, it appears completely rational, but from the outside, one can see that it is totally irrational, since it excludes qualitative social change. Marcuse is pessimistic about the prospects for humanity in the face of the technological system. Nevertheless, in the final analysis, he does not seek to do away with technology. Rather, he sees technology as potentially capable of ending humanity's constant "struggle for existence." Thus, if we can find the means to reassert our control over the system, technology offers the one real chance for us to attain true freedom and fulfillment.

Even this slim ray of hope appears beyond our reach in the view of the contemporary French philosopher and social critic Jacques Ellul. In his long, complex, often obscure, and enormously influential work, *The Technological Society*, from which several excerpts are included, Ellul analyzes technology as the central factor in modern society. Like Marcuse, Ellul sees technology as a self-enclosed, totalitarian system. In this totalitarian system, true human values are lost and technology becomes an autonomous force guided by internal values that bear no necessary relation to the needs of humanity. Means become ends, and every aspect of society—the individual, the family, the state—becomes subservient to the system. If Ellul sees a way out of this dilemma, he does not share it with us. In his view, the domination of technology is complete and inevitable.

If Marcuse and Ellul are, as one observer has characterized them, among the "soothsayers of doom and gloom," then Buckminster Fuller is their antithesis. This is not to say that Fuller believes all is well in our technological society. But Fuller—philosopher, architect, designer, social critic and inventor perhaps best known for his invention of the geodesic dome—contends that humankind has the capacity to solve its present dilemmas and create a technology that would truly serve its needs. His designs, he believes, can lead the way. In Fuller's words:

My task as inventor is to employ the earth's resources and energy income in such a way as to support all humanity while also enabling all people to enjoy the whole earth, all its historical artifacts and its beautiful places without one man interfering with the other, and without any man enjoying life around earth at the cost of another. Always the cost must be prepaid by design-science competence in modifying the environment.

Technology per se is not the problem. Rather, it is the kind of outmoded technology with which we are living today.

What can one make of such a diverse set of perspectives? Can we examine the impact of technology on society in a more empirical fashion and begin to get a sense of who is closer to the truth, McLuhan or Marcuse, Fuller or Ellul? In 1964 the IBM Corporation, a firm whose name is practically synonymous with modern technology, awarded a $5 million grant to Harvard University to conduct such a comprehensive program of study. Under the grant, a program was established to "undertake an inquiry in depth into the effects of technological change on the economy, on public policies, and on the character of society, as well as into the reciprocal effects of social progress on the nature, dimension, and directions of scientific and technological developments." Although the program eventually became enmeshed in institutional politics at Harvard and was terminated prematurely, during its several years of existence it did manage to produce a number of extremely interesting studies. Included in this part is an essay by the former director of the Harvard Program on Technology and Society, Emmanuel Mesthene. In his essay, which is taken from the program's fourth annual report, Mesthene attempts to present a general statement of what the program learned about the implications of technological change for society.

Mesthene sees two mechanisms through which technology appears to induce social change. Simply stated, technology creates new opportunities and also generates new problems for individuals and for societies. "It has both positive and negative effects, and it usually has the two *at the same time and in virtue of each other.*" The relationship of technology to social change cannot be fully understood without exploring technology's effect upon social and individual values. By enlarging the realm of goal choice, or by altering the relative costs associated with the implementation of different values, technology can induce value change. Mesthene's essay deals briefly with the value implications of economic change, the impact of technology on religion, and the impact of technology on individuals. In all these areas, technology is seen to have two faces, one positive and one negative.

Ultimately, through changes in social structure and values, technology creates problems that must be considered political. Of central importance, according to Mesthene, is the fact that "technological change has the effect of enhancing the importance of public decision-making in society. . . ." Not only must more decisions be made in a public manner, but because of technological change, any decision once made is likely to require reevaluation sooner than was previously the case. Given that framework, Mesthene explores problems raised for the economic market system by technological change and the shift in demand toward public goods and services. He also examines the implications of new information-handling devices and scientific decision-making techniques for the political process, in light of the program's research. Finally, he deals with the "need to develop new institutional forms and new mechanisms to replace established ones that can no longer deal effectively with the new kinds of problems with which we are increasingly faced." Institutional innovation, says Mesthene, is one area where the program's work may produce direct inputs into the solution of current problems.

Several months after the report containing Mesthene's essay was released, a sharply critical essay-review by John McDermott appeared in the *New York Review of Books.* McDermott's review, entitled "Technology: The Opiate of the Intellectuals," is not a point-by-point analysis or rebuttal of the Mesthene work. Rather, it is an attempt to critique the entire point of view that McDermott sees as epitomized by Mesthene—"a not new but . . . newly aggressive right wing ideology in this country." In dissecting Mesthene's belief structure, McDermott focuses upon the notion of *"laissez innover,"* a modern equivalent of the old *laissez faire* principle in economics.

Laissez innover holds that technology is a "self-correcting system" and that we mortals should not attempt to restrict its free play. Mesthene is said to find this principle acceptable because he defines technology in an abstract sense as "organized knowledge for practical purposes." McDermott rejects *laissez innover* because he claims to see certain very specific trends and characteristics in contemporary technology that overshadow the importance of technology as an abstraction. Concentrating upon the application of technology to the war in Vietnam—"the very frontier of American technology"—McDermott performs an "empirical" examination of the nature of technology, from which he concludes that "technology, in its concrete, empirical meaning, refers fundamentally to systems of rationalized control over large groups of men, events and machines by small groups of technically skilled men operating through organizational hierarchy."

This definition is the crux of McDermott's analysis, and basing his essay upon it, he proceeds to discuss the social effect of modern technology in America. Technological society is governed by "altruistic bureaucrats," a select class which possesses the skills needed to run society. The equality of opportunity that exists in this kind of skill-oriented system does not necessarily imply an egalitarian society, since society's rewards are still distributed inequitably. In fact, what equality of opportunity does assure, through the elevation of "trained talent" into "key decision making slots," is the preservation of the present social system and its inequities. The ideology of *laissez innover* is attractive to those in power since they are in a position to reap technology's benefits while avoiding its costs.

McDermott concludes by citing a set of hypotheses that he feels should be better guides to empirical investigation of technology than Mesthene's abstractions: (1) Technology should be viewed as an institutional system; (2) The most important dimension of advanced technological institutions is social—these institutions are instruments of centralized and intensive social control; (3) Profound social antagonisms exist in technological society; and (4) "Technology is creating the basis for new and sharp class conflict in our society," and *laissez innover* is the ideology of the right wing of this conflict.

The final article of this part is in one sense a response to McDermott. In a footnote within his essay, McDermott expresses his pessimism about the possibility of creating a humane technology out of our present system: "Any discussion of the reorganization of technology to serve human needs seems, at this point, so Utopian that it robs one of the conviction necessary to shape a believable vision." Rejecting the seeming hopelessness of this position, Paul Goodman asks in the title of his article, "Can Technology Be Humane?" In developing his response to this question, Goodman admits that there is no certainty that technology *will* become humane. Yet, in the classic style of a prophet—partly predictive and partly prescriptive—he asserts that our society is "on the eve of a new protestant Reformation, and no institution or status will go unaffected." At the same time, he offers a number of suggestions for channeling the energies of this Reformation into directions which he sees as critical to its success.

The types of changes Goodman envisions fall into three general categories. First, he speaks of the need for "prudence"—caution, foresight, and modesty —in the application of technology. The pace of innovation must be slowed and its trend must be turned away from increasing complexity and toward simplification. Second, the ecological viewpoint, with its emphases on balances and interdependence of a system's parts, must come to dominate technological affairs. Third, the institutions of technological society, particularly the research and development enterprise, ought to be widely decentralized. All of these notions are seen as constituting a return to the "pure faith," the basic tradition of science and technology. Goodman develops his Reformation analogy in some detail, but concludes, finally, that he does not know if it will actually occur. Everywhere, he says, there are contradictory signs and dilemmas.

from Understanding Media

MARSHALL MCLUHAN

In a culture like ours, long accustomed to splitting and dividing all things as a means of control, it is sometimes a bit of a shock to be reminded that, in operational and practical fact, the medium is the message. This is merely to say that the personal and social consequences of any medium—that is, of any extension of ourselves—result from the new scale that is introduced into our affairs by each extension of ourselves, or by any new technology. Thus, with automation, for example, the new patterns of human association tend to eliminate jobs, it is true. That is the negative result. Positively, automation creates roles for people, which is to say depth of involvement in their work and human association that our preceding mechanical technology had destroyed. Many people would be disposed to say that it was not the machine, but what one did with the machine, that was its meaning or message. In terms of the ways in which the machine altered our relations to one another and to ourselves, it mattered not in the least whether it turned out cornflakes or Cadillacs. The restructuring of human work and association was shaped by the technique of fragmentation that is the essence of machine technology. The essence of automation technology is the opposite. It is integral and decentralist in depth, just as the machine was fragmentary, centralist, and superficial in its patterning of human relationships.

The instance of the electric light may prove illuminating in this connection. The electric light is pure information. It is a medium without a message, as it were, unless it is used to spell out some verbal ad or name. This fact, characteristic of all media, means that the "content" of any medium is always another medium. The content of writing is speech, just as the written word is the content of print, and print is the content of the telegraph. If it is asked, "What is the content of speech?," it is necessary to say, "It is an actual process of thought, which is in itself nonverbal." An abstract painting represents direct manifestation of creative thought processes as they might appear in computer designs. What we are considering here, however, are the psychic and social consequences of the designs or patterns as they amplify or accelerate existing processes. For the "message" of any medium or technology is the change of scale or pace or pattern that it introduces into human affairs. The railway did not introduce movement or transportation or wheel or road into human society, but it accelerated and enlarged the scale of previous human functions, creating totally new kinds of cities and new kinds of work and leisure. This happened whether the railway functioned in a tropical or a northern environment, and is quite independent of the freight or content of the railway medium. The airplane, on the other hand, by accelerating the rate of transportation, tends to dissolve the railway form of city, politics, and association, quite independently of what the airplane is used for.

Let us return to the electric light. Whether the light is being used for brain surgery or night baseball is a matter of indifference. It could be argued that these activities are in some way the "content" of the electric light, since they could not exist without the electric light. This fact merely underlines the point that "the medium is the message" because it is the medium that shapes and controls the scale and form of human association and action. The content or uses of such media are as diverse as they are ineffectual in shaping the form of human association. Indeed, it is only too typical that the "content" of any medium blinds us to the character of the medium. It is only today that industries have become aware of the various kinds of business in which they are engaged. When IBM discovered that it was not in the business of making office equipment or business machines, but that it was in the business of processing information, then it began to navigate with clear vision. The General Electric Company makes a considerable portion of its profits from electric light bulbs and lighting systems. It has not yet discovered that, quite as much as A.T.&T., it is in the business of moving information.

The electric light escapes attention as a communication medium just because it has no "content." And this makes it an invaluable instance of how people fail to study media at all. For it is not till the electric light is used to spell out some brand name that it is noticed as a medium. Then it is not the light but the "content" (or what is really another medium) that is noticed. The message of the electric light is like the message of electric power in industry, totally radical, pervasive, and decentralized. For electric light and power are separate from their uses, yet they eliminate time and space factors in human association exactly as do radio, telegraph, telephone, and TV, creating involvement in depth.

*   *   *   *   *

In accepting an honorary degree from the University of Notre Dame a few years ago, General David Sarnoff made this statement: "We are too prone to make technological instruments the scapegoats for the sins of those who wield them. The products of modern science are not in themselves good or bad; it is the way they are used that determines their value." That is the voice of the current somnambulism. Suppose we were to say, "Apple pie is in itself neither good nor bad; it is the way it is used that determines its value." Or, "The smallpox virus is in itself neither good nor bad; it is the way it is used that determines its value." Again, "Firearms are in themselves neither good nor bad; it is the way they are used that determines their value." That is, if the slugs reach the right people firearms are good. If the TV tube fires the right ammunition at the right people it is good. ! am not being perverse. There is simply nothing in the Sarnoff statement that will bear scrutiny, for it ignores the nature of the medium, of any and all media, in the true Narcissus style of one hypnotized by the amputation and extension of his own being in a new technical form. General Sarnoff went on to explain his attitude to the technology of print, saying that it was true that print caused much trash to circulate, but it had also disseminated the Bible and the thoughts of seers and philosophers. It has never occurred to General Sarnoff that any technology could do anything but *add* itself on to what we already are.

*　　*　　*　　*　　*

Our conventional response to all media, namely, that it is how they are used that counts, is the numb stance of the technological idiot. For the "content" of a medium is like the juicy piece of meat carried by the burglar to distract the watchdog of the mind. The effect of the medium is made strong and intense just because it is given another medium as "content." The content of a movie is a novel or a play or an opera. The effect of the movie form is not related to its program content. The "content" of writing or print is speech, but the reader is almost entirely unaware either of print or of speech.

Arnold Toynbee is innocent of any understanding of media as they have shaped history, but he is full of examples that the student of media can use. At one moment he can seriously suggest that adult education, such as the Workers Educational Association in Britain, is a useful counterforce to the popular press. Toynbee considers that although all of the oriental societies have in our time accepted the industrial technology and its political consequences: "On the cultural plane, however, there is no uniform corresponding tendency." (Somervell, 1:267) This is like the voice of the literate man, floundering in a milieu of ads, who boasts, "Personally, I pay no attention to ads." The spiritual and cultural reservations that the oriental peoples may have toward our technology will avail them not at all. The effects of technology do not occur at the level of opinions or concepts, but alter sense ratios or patterns of perception steadily and without any resistance. The serious artist is the only person able to encounter technology with impunity, just because he is an expert aware of the changes in sense perception.

The operation of the money medium in seventeenth-century Japan had effects not unlike the operation of typography in the West. The penetration of the money economy, wrote G. B. Sansom (in *Japan,* Cresset Press, London, 1931) "caused a slow but irresistible revolution, culminating in the breakdown of feudal government and the resumption of intercourse with foreign countries after more than two hundred years of seclusion." Money has reorganized the sense life of peoples just because it is an *extension* of our sense lives. This change does not depend upon approval or disapproval of those living in the society.

Arnold Toynbee made one approach to the transforming power of media in his concept of "etherialization," which he holds to be the principle of progressive simplification and efficiency in any organization or technology. Typically, he is ignoring the *effect* of the challenge of these forms upon the response of our senses. He imagines that it is the response of our opinions that is relevant to the effect of media and technology in society, a "point of view" that is plainly the result of the typographic spell. For the man in a literate and homogenized society ceases to be sensitive to the diverse and discontinuous life of forms. He acquires the illusion of the third dimension and the "private point of view" as part of his Narcissus fixation, and is quite shut off from Blake's awareness or that of the Psalmist, that we become what we behold.

Today when we want to get our bearings in our own culture, and have need to stand aside from the bias and pressure exerted by any technical form of human expression, we have only to visit a society where that particular form has not been felt, or a historical period in which it was unknown. Professor Wilbur Schramm made such a tactical move in studying *Television in the Lives of Our Children.* He found areas where TV had not penetrated at all and ran some tests. Since he had made no study of the peculiar nature of the TV image, his tests were of "content" preferences, viewing time, and vocabulary counts. In a word, his approach to the problem was a literary one, albeit unconsciously so. Consequently, he had nothing to report. Had his methods been employed in 1500 A.D. to discover the effects of the printed book in the lives of children or adults, he could have found out nothing of the changes in human and social psychology resulting from typography. Print created individualism and nationalism in the sixteenth century. Program and "content" analysis offer no clues to the magic of these media or to their subliminal charge.

Leonard Doob, in his report *Communication in Africa,* tells of one African who took great pains to listen each evening to the BBC news, even though he could understand nothing of it. Just to be in the presence of those sounds at 7 P.M. each day was important for him. His attitude to speech was like ours to melody—the resonant intonation was meaning enough. In the seventeenth century our ancestors still shared this native's attitude to the forms of media, as is plain in the following sentiment of the Frenchman Bernard Lam expressed in *The Art of Speaking* (London, 1696):

'Tis an effect of the Wisdom of God, who created Man to be happy, that whatever is useful to his conversation (way of life) is agreeable to him . . . because all victual that conduces to nourishment is relishable, whereas other things that cannot be assimulated and be turned into our substance are insipid. A Discourse cannot be pleasant to the Hearer that is not easie to the Speaker; nor can it be easily pronounced unless it be heard with delight.

Here is an equilibrium theory of human diet and expression such as even now we are only striving to work out again for media after centuries of fragmentation and specialism.

Pope Pius XII was deeply concerned that there be serious study of the media today. On February 17, 1950, he said:

It is not an exaggeration to say that the future of modern society and the stability of its inner life depend in large part on the maintenance of an equilibrium between the strength of the techniques of communication and the capacity of the individual's own reaction.

Failure in this respect has for centuries been typical and total for mankind. Subliminal and docile acceptance of media impact has made them prisons without walls for their human users. As A. J. Liebling remarked in his book *The Press,* a man is not free if he cannot see where he is going, even if he has a gun to help him get there. For each of the media is also a powerful weapon with which to clobber other media and other groups. The result is that the present age has been one of multiple civil wars that are not limited to the world of art and entertainment. In *War and Human Progress,* Professor J. U. Nef declared: "The total wars of our time have been the result of a series of intellectual mistakes . . ."

If the formative powers in the media are the media themselves, that raises a host of large matters that can only be mentioned here, although they deserve volumes. Namely, that technological media are staples or natural resources, exactly as are coal and cotton and oil. Anybody will concede that society whose economy is dependent upon one or two major staples like cotton, or grain, or lumber, or fish, or cattle is going to have some obvious social patterns of organization as a result. Stress on a few major staples creates extreme instability in the economy but great endurance in the population. The pathos and humor of the American South are embedded in such an economy of limited staples. For a society configured by reliance on a few commodities accepts them as a social bond quite as much as the metropolis does the press. Cotton and oil, like radio and TV, become "fixed charges" on the entire psychic life of the community. And this pervasive fact creates the unique cultural flavor of any society. It pays through the nose and all its other senses for each staple that shapes its life.

That our human senses, of which all media are extensions, are also fixed charges on our personal energies, and that they also configure the awareness and experience of each one of us, may be perceived in another connection mentioned by the psychologist C. G. Jung:

Every Roman was surrounded by slaves. The slave and his psychology flooded ancient Italy, and every Roman became inwardly, and of course unwittingly, a slave. Because living constantly in the atmosphere of slaves, he became infected through the unconscious with their psychology. No one can shield himself from such an influence (*Contributions to Analytical Psychology,* London, 1928).

*   *   *   *   *

Any invention or technology is an extension or self-amputation of our physical bodies, and such extension also demands new ratios or new equilibriums among the other organs and extensions of the body. There is, for example, no way of refusing to comply with the new sense ratios or sense "closure" evoked by the TV image. But the effect of the entry of the TV image will vary from culture to culture in accordance with the existing sense ratios in each culture. In audile-tactile Europe TV has intensified the visual sense, spurring them toward American styles of packaging and dressing. In America, the intensely visual culture, TV has opened the doors of audile-tactile perception to the nonvisual world of spoken languages and food and the plastic arts. As an extension and expediter of the sense life, any medium at once affects the entire field of the senses, as the Psalmist explained long ago in the 113th Psalm:

Their idols are silver and gold,
The work of men's hands.
They have mouths, but they speak not;

> Eyes they have, but they see not;
> They have ears, but they hear not;
> Noses they have, but they smell not;
> They have hands, but they handle not;
> Feet have they, but they walk not;
> Neither speak they through their throat.
> They that make them shall be like unto them;
> Yea, every one that trusteth in them.

The concept of "idol" for the Hebrew Psalmist is much like that of Narcissus for the Greek mythmaker. And the Psalmist insists that the *beholding* of idols, or the use of technology, conforms men to them. "They that make them shall be like unto them." This is a simple fact of sense "closure." The poet Blake developed the Psalmist's ideas into an entire theory of communication and social change. It is in his long poem of *Jerusalem* that he explains why men have become what they have beheld. What they have, says Blake, is "the spectre of the Reasoning Power in Man" that has become fragmented and "separated from Imagination and enclosing itself as in steel." Blake, in a word, sees man as fragmented by his technologies. But he insists that these technologies are self-amputations of our own organs. When so amputated, each organ becomes a closed system of great new intensity that hurls man into "martyrdoms and wars." Moreover, Blake announces as his theme in *Jerusalem* the organs of perception:

> If Perceptive Organs vary, Objects of Perception seem to vary:
> If Perceptive Organs close, their Objects seem to close also.

To behold, use or perceive any extension of ourselves in technological form is necessarily to embrace it. To listen to radio or to read the printed page is to accept these extensions of ourselves into our personal system and to undergo the "closure" or displacement of perception that follows automatically. It is this continuous embrace of our own technology in daily use that puts us in the Narcissus role of subliminal awareness and numbness in relation to these images of ourselves. By continuously embracing technologies, we relate ourselves to them as servomechanisms. That is why we must, to use them at all, serve these objects, these extensions of ourselves, as gods or minor religions. An Indian is the servo-mechanism of his canoe, as the cowboy of his horse or the executive of his clock.

Physiologically, man in the normal use of technology (or his variously extended body) is perpetually modified by it and in turn finds ever new ways of modifying his technology. Man becomes, as it were, the sex organs of the machine world, as the bee of the plant world, enabling it to fecundate and to evolve ever new forms. The machine world reciprocates man's love by expediting his wishes and desires, namely, in providing him with wealth. One of the merits of motivation research has been the revelation of man's sex relation to the motorcar.

Socially, it is the accumulation of group pressures and irritations that prompt invention and innovation as counterirritants. War and the fear of war have always been considered the main incentives to technological extension of our bodies. Indeed, Lewis Mumford, in his *The City in History,* considers the walled city itself an extension of our skins, as much as housing and clothing. More even than the preparation for war, the aftermath of invasion is a rich technological period; because the subject culture has to adjust all its sense ratios to accommodate the impact of the invading culture. It is from such intensive hybrid exchange and strife of ideas and forms that the greatest social energies are released, and from which arise the greatest technologies. Buckminster Fuller estimates that since 1910 the governments of the world have spent 3½ trillion dollars on airplanes. That is 62 times the existing gold supply of the world.

The principle of numbness comes into play with electric technology, as with any other. We have to numb our central nervous system when it is extended and exposed, or we will die. Thus the age of anxiety and of electric media is also the age of the unconscious and of apathy. But it is strikingly the age of consciousness of the unconscious, in addition. With our central nervous system strategically numbed, the tasks of conscious awareness and order are transferred to the physical life of man, so that for the first time he has become aware of technology as an extension of his physical body. Apparently this could not have happened before the electric age gave us the means of instant, total field-awareness. With such awareness, the subliminal life, private and social, has been hoisted up into full view, with the result that we have "social consciousness" presented to us as a cause of guilt-feelings. Existentialism offers a philosophy of structures, rather than categories, and of total social involvement instead of the bourgeois spirit of individual separateness or points of view. In the electric age we wear all mankind as our skin.

The New Forms of Control

HERBERT MARCUSE

A comfortable, smooth, reasonable, democratic unfreedom prevails in advanced industrial civilization, a token of technical progress. Indeed, what could be more rational than the suppression of individuality in the mechanization of socially necessary but painful performances; the concentration of individual enterprises in more effective, more productive corporations; the regulation of free competition among unequally equipped economic subjects; the curtailment of prerogatives and national sovereignties which impede the international organization of resources. That this technological order also involves a political and intellectual coordination may be a regrettable and yet promising development.

The rights and liberties which were such vital factors in the origins and earlier stages of industrial society yield to a higher stage of this society: they are losing their traditional rationale and content. Freedom of thought, speech, and conscience were—just as free enterprise, which they served to promote and protect—essentially *critical* ideas, designed to replace an obsolescent material and intellectual culture by a more productive and rational one. Once institutionalized, these rights and liberties shared the fate of the society of which they had become an integral part. The achievement cancels the premises.

To the degree to which freedom from want, the concrete substance of all freedom, is becoming a real possibility, the liberties which pertain to a state of lower productivity are losing their former content. Independence of thought, autonomy, and the right to political opposition are being deprived of their basic critical function in a society which seems increasingly capable of satisfying the needs of the individuals through the way in which it is organized. Such a society may justly demand acceptance of its principles and institutions, and reduce the opposition to the discussion and promotion of alternative policies *within* the status quo. In this respect, it seems to make little difference whether the increasing satisfaction of needs is accomplished by an authoritarian or a nonauthoritarian system. Under the conditions of a rising standard of living, nonconformity with the system itself appears to be socially useless, and the more so when it entails tangible economic and political disadvantages and threatens the smooth operation of the whole. Indeed, at least in so far as the necessities of life are involved, there seems to be no reason why the production and distribution of goods and services should proceed through the competitive concurrence of individual liberties.

Freedom of enterprise was from the beginning not altogether a blessing. As the liberty to work or to starve, it spelled toil, insecurity, and fear for the vast majority of the population. If the individual were no longer compelled to prove himself on the market, as a free economic subject, the disappearance of this kind of freedom would be one of the greatest achievements of civilization. The technological processes of mechanization and standardization might release individual energy into a yet uncharted realm of freedom beyond necessity. The very structure of human existence would be altered; the individual would be liberated from the work world's imposing upon him alien needs and alien possibilities. The individual would be free to exert autonomy over a life that would be his own. If the productive apparatus could be organized and directed toward the satisfaction of the vital needs, its control might well be centralized; such control would not prevent individual autonomy, but render it possible.

This is a goal within the capabilities of advanced industrial civilization, the "end" of technological rationality. In actual fact, however, the contrary trend operates: the apparatus imposes its economic and political requirements for defense and expansion on labor time and free time, on the material and intellectual culture. By virtue of the way it has organized its technological base, contemporary industrial society tends to be totalitarian. For "totalitarian" is not only a terroristic political coordination of society, but also a nonterroristic economic-technical coordination which operates through the manipulation of needs by vested interests. It thus precludes the emergence of an effective opposition against the whole. Not only a specific form of government or party rule makes for totalitarianism, but also a specific system of production and distribution which may well be compatible with a "pluralism" of parties, newspapers, "countervailing powers," etc.

Today political power asserts itself through its power over the machine process and over the technical organization of the apparatus. The government of advanced and advancing industrial societies can maintain and secure itself only when it succeeds in mobilizing, organizing, and exploiting the technical, scientific, and mechanical productivity available to industrial civilization. And this productivity mobilizes society as a whole, above and beyond any particular individual or group interests. The brute fact that the machine's physical (only physical?) power surpasses that of the individual, and of any particular group of individuals, makes the machine the most effective political instrument in any society whose basic organization is that of the machine process. But the political trend may be reversed; essentially the power of the machine is only the stored-up and projected power of man. To the extent to which the work world is conceived of as a machine and mechanized accordingly, it becomes the *potential* basis of a new freedom for man.

Contemporary industrial civilization demonstrates that it has reached the stage at which "the free society" can no longer be adequately defined in the traditional terms of economic, political, and intellectual liberties, not because these liberties have become insignificant, but because they are too significant to be confined within the traditional forms. New modes of realization are needed, corresponding to the new capabilities of society.

Such new modes can be indicated only in negative terms because they would amount to the negation of the prevailing modes. Thus economic freedom would mean freedom *from* the economy—from being controlled by economic forces and relationships; freedom from the daily struggle for existence, from earning a living. Political freedom would mean liberation of the individuals *from* politics over which they have no effective control. Similarly, intellectual freedom would mean the restoration of individual thought now absorbed by mass communication and indoctrination, abolition of "public opinion" together with its makers. The unrealistic sound of these propositions is indicative, not of their utopian character, but of the strength of the forces which prevent their realization. The most effective and enduring form of warfare against liberation is the implanting of material and intellectual needs that perpetuate obsolete forms of the struggle for existence.

The intensity, the satisfaction and even the character of human needs, beyond the biological level, have always been preconditioned. Whether or not the possibility of doing or leaving, enjoying or destroying, possessing or rejecting something is seized as a *need* depends on whether or not it can be seen as desirable and necessary for the prevailing societal institutions and interests. In this sense, human needs are historical needs and, to the extent to which the society demands the repressive development of the individual, his needs themselves and their claim for satisfaction are subject to overriding critical standards.

We may distinguish both true and false needs. "False" are those which are superimposed upon the individual by particular social interests in his repression: the needs which perpetuate toil, aggressiveness, misery, and injustice. Their satisfaction might be most gratifying to the individual, but this happiness is not a condition which has to be maintained and protected if it serves to arrest the development of the ability (his own and others) to recognize the disease of the whole and grasp the chances of curing the disease. The result then is euphoria in unhappiness. Most of the prevailing needs to relax, to have fun, to behave and consume in accordance with the advertisements, to love and hate what others love and hate, belong to this category of false needs.

Such needs have a societal content and function which are determined by external powers over which the individual has no control; the development and satisfaction of these needs is heteronomous. No matter how much such needs may have become the individual's own, reproduced and fortified by the conditions of his existence; no matter how much he identifies himself with them and finds himself in their satisfaction, they continue to be what they were from the beginning—products of a society whose dominant interest demands repression.

The prevalence of repressive needs is an accomplished fact, accepted in ignorance and defeat, but a fact that must be undone in the interest of the happy individual as well as all those whose misery is the price of his satisfaction. The only needs that have an unqualified claim for satisfaction are the vital ones—nourishment, clothing, lodging at the attainable level of culture. The satisfaction of these needs is the prerequisite for the realization of *all* needs, of the unsublimated as well as the sublimated ones.

For any consciousness and conscience, for any experience which does not accept the prevailing societal interest as the supreme law of thought and behavior, the established universe of needs and satisfactions is a fact to be questioned—questioned in terms of truth and falsehood. These terms are historical throughout, and their objectivity is historical. The judgment of needs and their satisfaction, under the given conditions, involves standards of *priority*— standards which refer to the optimal development of the individual, of all individuals, under the optimal utilization of the material and intellectual resources available to man. The resources are calculable. "Truth" and "falsehood" of needs designate objective conditions to the extent to which the universal satisfaction of vital needs and, beyond it, the progressive alleviation of toil and poverty, are universally valid standards. But as historical standards, they do not only vary according to area and stage of development, they also can be defined only in (greater or lesser) *contradiction* to the prevailing ones. What tribunal can possibly claim the authority of decision?

In the last analysis, the question of what are true and false needs must be answered by the individuals themselves, but only in the last analysis; that is, if and when they are free to give their own answer. As long as they are kept incapable of being autonomous, as long as they are indoctrinated and manipulated (down to their very instincts), their answer to this question cannot be taken as their own. By the same token, however, no tribunal can justly arrogate to itself the right to decide which needs should be developed and satisfied. Any such tribunal is reprehensible, although our revulsion does not do away with the question: how can the people who have been the object of effective and productive domination by themselves create the conditions of freedom?

The more rational, productive, technical, and total the repressive administration of society becomes, the more unimaginable the means and ways by which the administered individuals might break their servitude and seize their own liberation. To be sure, to impose Reason upon an entire society is a paradoxical and scandalous idea—although one might dispute the righteousness of a society which ridicules this idea while making its own population into objects of total administration. All liberation depends on the consciousness of servitude, and the emergence of this consciousness is always hampered by the predominance of needs and satisfactions which, to a great extent, have become the individual's own. The process always replaces one system of preconditioning by another; the optimal goal is the replacement of false needs by true ones, the abandonment of repressive satisfaction.

The distinguishing feature of advanced industrial society is its effective suffocation of those needs which demand liberation—liberation also from that which is tolerable and rewarding and comfortable—while it sustains and absolves the destructive power and repressive function of the affluent society. Here, the social controls exact the overwhelming need for the production and consumption of waste; the need for stupefying work where it is no longer a real necessity; the need for modes of relaxation which soothe and prolong this stupefication; the need for maintaining such deceptive liberties as free competition at administered prices, a free press which censors itself, free choice between brands and gadgets.

Under the rule of a repressive whole, liberty can be made into a powerful instrument of domination. The range of choice open to the individual is not the decisive factor in determining the degree of human freedom, but *what* can be chosen and what *is* chosen by the individual. The criterion for free choice can never be an absolute one, but neither is it entirely relative. Free election of masters does not abolish the masters or the slaves. Free choice among a wide variety of goods and services does not signify freedom if these goods and services sustain social controls over a life of toil and fear—that is, if they sustain alienation. And the spontaneous reproduction of superimposed needs by the individual does not establish autonomy; it only testifies to the efficacy of the controls.

Our insistence on the depth and efficacy of these controls is open to the objection that we overrate greatly the indoctrinating power of the "media," and that by themselves the people would feel and satisfy the needs which are now imposed upon them. The objection misses the point. The preconditioning does not start with the mass production of radio and television and with the centralization of their control. The people enter this stage as preconditioned receptacles of long standing; the decisive difference is in the flattening out of the contrast (or conflict) between the given and the possible, between the satisfied and the unsatisfied needs. Here, the so-called equalization of class distinctions reveals its ideological function. If the worker and his boss enjoy the same television program and visit the same resort places, if the typist is as attractively made up as the daughter of her employer, if the Negro owns a Cadillac, if they all read the same newspaper, then this assimilation indicates not the disappearance of classes, but the extent to which the needs and satisfactions that serve the preservation of the Establishment are shared by the underlying population.

Indeed, in the most highly developed areas of contemporary society, the transplantation of social into individual needs is so effective that the difference between them seems to be purely theoretical. Can one really distinguish between the mass media as instruments of information and entertainment, and as agents of manipulation and indoctrination? Between the automobile as nuisance and as convenience? Between the horrors and the comforts of functional architecture? Between the work for national defense and the work for corporate gain? Between the private pleasure and the commercial and political utility involved in increasing the birth rate?

We are again confronted with one of the most vexing aspects of advanced industrial civilization: the rational character of its irrationality. Its productivity and efficiency, its capacity to increase and spread comforts, to turn waste into need, and destruction into construction, the extent to which this civilization transforms the object world into an extension of man's mind and body makes the very notion of alienation questionable. The people recognize themselves in their commodities; they find their soul in their automobile, hi-fi set, split-level home, kitchen equipment. The very mechanism which ties the individual to his society has changed, and social control is anchored in the new needs which it has produced.

The prevailing forms of social control are technological in a new sense. To be sure, the technical structure and efficacy of the productive and destructive apparatus has been a major instrumentality for subjecting the population to the established social division of labor throughout the modern period. Moreover, such integration has always been accompanied by more obvious forms of compulsion: loss of livelihood, the administration of justice, the police, the armed forces. It still is. But in the contemporary period, the technological controls appear to be the very embodiment of Reason for the benefit of all social groups and interests—to such an extent that all contradiction seems irrational and all counteraction impossible.

No wonder then that, in the most advanced areas of this civilization, the social controls have been introjected to the point where even individual protest is affected at its roots. The intellectual and emotional refusal "to go along" appears neurotic and impotent. This is the sociopsychological aspect of the political event that marks the contemporary period: the passing of the historical forces which, at the preceding stage of industrial society, seemed to represent the possibility of new forms of existence.

But the term "introjection" perhaps no longer describes the way in which the individual by himself reproduces and perpetuates the external controls exercised by his society. Introjection suggests a variety of relatively spontaneous processes by which a Self (Ego) transposes the "outer" into the "inner." Thus introjection implies the existence of an inner dimension distinguished from and even antagonistic to the external exigencies—an individual consciousness and an individual unconscious *apart from* public opinion and behavior.[1] The idea of "inner freedom" here has its reality: it designates the private space in which man may become and remain "himself."

Today this private space has been invaded and whittled down by technological reality. Mass production and mass distribution claim the *entire* individual, and industrial psychology has long since ceased to be confined to the factory. The manifold processes of introjection seem to be ossified in almost mechanical reactions. The result is, not adjustment but *mimesis:* an immediate identification of the individual with *his* society and, through it, with the society as a whole.

This immediate, automatic identification (which may have been characteristic of primitive forms of association) reappears in high industrial civilization; its new "immediacy," however, is the product of a sophisticated, scien-

1. The change in the function of the family here plays a decisive role: its "socializing" functions are increasingly taken over by outside groups and media. See my *Eros and Civilization* (Boston: Beacon Press, 1955), p. 96 ff.

tific management and organization. In this process, the "inner" dimension of the mind in which opposition to the status quo can take root is whittled down. The loss of this dimension, in which the power of negative thinking—the critical power of Reason—is at home, is the ideological counterpart to the very material process in which advanced industrial society silences and reconciles the opposition. The impact of progress turns Reason into submission to the facts of life, and to the dynamic capability of producing more and bigger facts of the same sort of life. The efficiency of the system blunts the individuals' recognition that it contains no facts which do not communicate the repressive power of the whole. If the individuals find themselves in the things which shape their life, they do so, not by giving, but by accepting the law of things—not the law of physics but the law of their society.

I have just suggested that the concept of alienation seems to become questionable when the individuals identify themselves with the existence which is imposed upon them and have in it their own development and satisfaction. This identification is not illusion but reality. However, the reality constitutes a more progressive stage of alienation. The latter has become entirely objective; the subject which is alienated is swallowed up by its alienated existence. There is only one dimension, and it is everywhere and in all forms. The achievements of progress defy ideological indictment as well as justification; before their tribunal, the "false consciousness" of their rationality becomes the true consciousness.

This absorption of ideology into reality does not, however, signify the "end of ideology." On the contrary, in a specific sense advanced industrial culture is *more* ideological than its predecessor, inasmuch as today the ideology is in the process of production itself. In a provocative form, this proposition reveals the political aspects of the prevailing technological rationality. The productive apparatus and the goods and services which it produces "sell" or impose the social system as a whole. The means of mass transportation and communication, the commodities of lodging, food, and clothing, the irresistible output of the entertainment and information industry carry with them prescribed attitudes and habits, certain intellectual and emotional reactions which bind the consumers more or less pleasantly to the producers and, through the latter, to the whole. The products indoctrinate and manipulate; they promote a false consciousness which is immune against its falsehood. And as these beneficial products become available to more individuals in more social classes, the indoctrination they carry ceases to be publicity; it becomes a way of life. It is a good way of life—much better than before—and as a good way of life, it militates against qualitative change. Thus emerges a pattern of *one-*

dimensional thought and behavior in which ideas, aspirations and objectives that, by their content, transcend the established universe of discourse and action are either repelled or reduced to terms of this universe. They are redefined by the rationality of the given system and of its quantitative extension.

The trend may be related to a development in scientific method: operationalism in the physical, behaviorism in the social sciences. The common feature is a total empiricism in the treatment of concepts; their meaning is restricted to the representation of particular operations and behavior. The operational point of view is well illustrated by P. W. Bridgman's analysis of the concept of length:[2]

> We evidently know what we mean by length if we can tell what the length of any and every object is, and for the physicist nothing more is required. To find the length of an object, we have to perform certain physical operations. The concept of length is therefore fixed when the operations by which length is measured are fixed: that is, the concept of length involves as much and nothing more than the set of operations by which length is determined. In general, we mean by any concept nothing more than a set of operations; *the concept is synonymous with the corresponding set of operations.*

Bridgman has seen the wide implications of this mode of thought for the society at large:

> To adopt the operational point of view involves much more than a mere restriction of the sense in which we understand "concept," but means a far-reaching change in all our habits of thought, in that we shall no longer permit ourselves to use as tools in our thinking concepts of which we cannot give an adequate account in terms of operations.

Bridgman's prediction has come true. The new mode of thought is today the predominant tendency in philosophy, psychology, sociology, and other fields. Many of the most seriously troublesome concepts are being "eliminated" by showing that no adequate account of them in terms of operations or behavior can be given. The radical empiricist onslaught . . . thus provides the methodological justification for the debunking of the mind by the intellectuals—a positivism which, in its denial of the transcending elements of Reason, forms the academic counterpart of the socially required behavior.

---

2. P. W. Bridgman, *The Logic of Modern Physics* (New York: Macmillan, 1928), p. 5 ff. The operational doctrine has since been refined and qualified. Bridgman himself has extended the concept of "operation" to include the "paper-and-pencil" operations of the theorist (in Philipp J. Frank, *The Validation of Scientific Theories* [Boston: Beacon Press, 1954], Chap. 2). The main impetus remains the same: it is "desirable" that the paper-and-pencil operations "be capable of eventual contact, although perhaps indirectly, with instrumental operations."

Outside the academic establishment, the "far-reaching change in all our habits of thought" is more serious. It serves to coordinate ideas and goals with those exacted by the prevailing system, to enclose them in the system, and to repel those which are irreconcilable with the system. The reign of such a one-dimensional reality does not mean that materialism rules, and that the spiritual, metaphysical, and bohemian occupations are petering out. On the contrary, there is a great deal of "Worship together this week," "Why not try God," Zen, existentialism, and beat ways of life, etc. But such modes of protest and transcendence are no longer contradictory to the status quo and no longer negative. They are rather the ceremonial part of practical behaviorism, its harmless negation, and are quickly digested by the status quo as part of its healthy diet.

One-dimensional thought is systematically promoted by the makers of politics and their purveyors of mass information. Their universe of discourse is populated by self-validating hypotheses which, incessantly and monopolistically repeated, become hypnotic definitions or dictations. For example, "free" are the institutions which operate (and are operated on) in the countries of the Free World; other transcending modes of freedom are by definition either anarchism, communism, or propaganda. "Socialistic" are all encroachments on private enterprises not undertaken by private enterprise itself (or by government contracts), such as universal and comprehensive health insurance, or the protection of nature from all too sweeping commercialization, or the establishment of public services which may hurt private profit. This totalitarian logic of accomplished facts has its Eastern counterpart. There, freedom is the way of life instituted by a communist regime, and all other transcending modes of freedom are either capitalistic, or revisionist, or leftist sectarianism. In both camps, nonoperational ideas are nonbehavioral and subversive. The movement of thought is stopped at barriers which appear as the limits of Reason itself.

Such limitation of thought is certainly not new. Ascending modern rationalism, in its speculative as well as empirical form, shows a striking contrast between extreme critical radicalism in scientific and philosophic method on the one hand, and an uncritical quietism in the attitude toward established and functioning social institutions. Thus Descartes' *ego cogitans* was to leave the "great public bodies" untouched, and Hobbes held that "the present ought always to be preferred, maintained, and accounted best." Kant agreed with Locke in justifying revolution *if and when* it has succeeded in organizing the whole and in preventing subversion.

However, these accommodating concepts of Reason were always contradicted by the evident misery and injustice of the "great public bodies" and the effective, more or less conscious rebellion against them. Societal conditions existed which provoked and permitted real dissociation from the established state of affairs; a private as well as political dimension was present in which dissociation could develop into effective opposition, testing its strength and the validity of its objectives.

With the gradual closing of this dimension by the society, the self-limitation of thought assumes a larger significance. The interrelation between scientific-philosophical and societal processes, between theoretical and practical Reason, asserts itself "behind the back" of the scientists and philosophers. The society bars a whole type of oppositional operations and behavior; consequently, the concepts pertaining to them are rendered illusory or meaningless. Historical transcendence appears as metaphysical transcendence, not acceptable to science and scientific thought. The operational and behavioral point of view, practiced as a "habit of thought" at large, becomes the view of the established universe of discourse and action, needs and aspirations. The "cunning of Reason" works, as it so often did, in the interest of the powers that be. The insistence on operational and behavioral concepts turns against the efforts to free thought and behavior *from* the given reality and *for* the suppressed alternatives. Theoretical and practical Reason, academic and social behaviorism meet on common ground: that of an advanced society which makes scientific and technical progress into an instrument of domination.

"Progress" is not a neutral term; it moves toward specific ends, and these ends are defined by the possibilities of ameliorating the human condition. Advanced industrial society is approaching the stage where continued progress would demand the radical subversion of the prevailing direction and organization of progress. This stage would be reached when material production (including the necessary services) becomes automated to the extent that all vital needs can be satisfied while necessary labor time is reduced to marginal time. From this point on, technical progress would transcend the realm of necessity, where it served as the instrument of domination and exploitation which thereby limited its rationality; technology would become subject to the free play of faculties in the struggle for the pacification of nature and of society.

Such a state is envisioned in Marx's notion of the "abolition of labor." The term "pacification of existence" seems better suited to designate the historical alternative of a world which—through the contradictions within the established societies—advances on the brink of a global war. "Pacification of existence" means the development of man's struggle with man and with nature, under conditions where the competing needs, desires, and aspirations are no longer organized by vested interests in domination and scarcity—an organization which perpetuates the destructive forms of this struggle.

Today's fight against this historical alternative finds a firm mass basis in the underlying population, and finds its ideology in the rigid orientation of thought and behavior to the given universe of facts. Validated by the accomplishments of science and technology, justified by its growing productivity, the status quo defies all transcendence. Faced with the possibility of pacification on the grounds of its technical and intellectual achievements, the mature industrial society closes itself against this alternative. Operationalism, in theory and practice, becomes the theory and practice of *containment*. Underneath its obvious dynamics, this society is a thoroughly static system of life: self-propelling in its oppressive productivity and in its beneficial coordination. Containment of technical progress goes hand-in-hand with its growth in the established direction. In spite of the political fetters imposed by the status quo, the more technology appears capable of creating the conditions for pacification, the more are the minds and bodies of man organized against this alternative.

The most advanced areas of industrial society exhibit throughout these two features: a trend toward consummation of technological rationality, and intensive efforts to contain this trend within the established institutions. Here is the internal contradiction of this civilization: the irrational element in its rationality. It is the token of its achievements. The industrial society which makes technology and science its own is organized for the ever-more-effective domination of man and nature, for the ever-more-effective utilization of its resources. It becomes irrational when the success of these efforts opens new dimensions of human realization. Organization for peace is different from organization for war; the institutions which served the struggle for existence cannot serve the pacification of existence. Life as an end is qualitatively different from life as a means.

Such a qualitatively new mode of existence can never be envisaged as the mere by-product of economic and political changes, as the more or less spontaneous effect of the new institutions which constitute the necessary prerequisite. Qualitative change also involves a change in the *technical* basis on which this society rests—one which sustains the economic and political institutions through which the "second nature" of man as an aggressive object of administration is stabilized. The techniques of industrialization are political techniques; as such, they prejudge the possibilities of Reason and Freedom.

To be sure, labor must precede the reduction of labor, and industrialization must precede the development of human needs and satisfactions. But as all freedom depends on the conquest of alien necessity, the realization of freedom depends on the *techniques* of this conquest. The highest productivity of labor can be used for the perpetuation of labor, and the most efficient industrialization can serve the restriction and manipulation of needs.

When this point is reached, domination—in the guise of affluence and liberty—extends to all spheres of private and public existence, integrates all authentic opposition, absorbs all alternatives. Technological rationality reveals its political character as it becomes the great vehicle of better domination, creating a truly totalitarian universe in which society and nature, mind and body are kept in a state of permanent mobilization for the defense of this universe.

from The Technological Society

JACQUES ELLUL

No social, human, or spiritual fact is so important as the fact of technique in the modern world. And yet no subject is so little understood. Let us try to set up some guideposts to situate the technical phenomenon.

SITUATING THE TECHNICAL PHENOMENON

Machines and Technique. Whenever we see the word *technology* or *technique,* we automatically think of machines. Indeed, we commonly think of our world as a world of machines. This notion—which is in fact an error—is found, for example, in the works of Oldham and Pierre Ducassé. It arises from the fact that the machine is the most obvious, massive, and impressive example of technique, and historically the first. What is called the history of technique usually amounts to no more than a history of the machine; this very formulation is an example of the habit of intellectuals of regarding forms of the present as identical with those of the past.

Technique certainly began with the machine. It is quite true that all the rest developed out of mechanics; it is quite true also that without the machine the world of technique would not exist. But to explain the situation in this way does not at all legitimatize it. It is a mistake to continue with this confusion of terms, the more so because it leads to the idea that, because the machine is at the origin and center of the technical problem, one is dealing with the whole problem when one deals with the machine. And that is a greater mistake still. Technique has now become almost completely independent of the machine, which has lagged far behind its offspring.

It must be emphasized that, at present, technique is applied outside industrial life. The growth of its power today has no relation to the growing use of the machine. The balance seems rather to have shifted to the other side. It is the machine which is now entirely dependent upon technique, and the machine represents only a small part of technique. If we were to characterize the relations between technique and the machine today, we could say not only that the machine is the result of a certain technique, but also that its social and economic applications are made possible by other technical advances. The machine is now not even the most important aspect of technique (though it is perhaps the most spectacular); technique has taken over all of man's activities, not just his productive activity.

From another point of view, however, the machine is deeply symptomatic: it represents the ideal toward which technique strives. The machine is solely, exclusively, technique; it is pure technique, one might say. For, wherever a technical factor exists, it results, almost inevitably, in mechanization: technique transforms everything it touches into a machine.

Another relationship exists between technique and the machine, and this relationship penetrates to the very core of the problem of our civilization. It is said (and everyone agrees) that the machine has created an inhuman atmosphere. The machine, so characteristic of the nineteenth century, made an abrupt entrance into a society which, from the political, institutional, and human points of view, was not made to receive it; and man has had to put up with it as best he can. Men now live in conditions that are less than human. Consider the concentration of our great cities, the slums, the lack of space, of air, of time, the gloomy streets and the sallow lights that confuse night and day. Think of our dehumanized factories, our unsatisfied senses, our working women, our estrangement from nature. Life in such an environment has no meaning. Consider our public transportation, in which man is less important than a parcel; our hospitals, in which he is only a number. Yet we call this progress. . . . And the noise, that monster boring into us at every hour of the night without respite.

It is useless to rail against capitalism. Capitalism did not create our world;

the machine did. Painstaking studies designed to prove the contrary have buried the obvious beneath tons of print. And, if we do not wish to play the demagogue, we must point out the guilty party. "The machine is antisocial," says Lewis Mumford. "It tends, by reason of its progressive character, to the most acute forms of human exploitation." The machine took its place in a social milieu that was not made for it, and for that reason created the inhuman society in which we live. Capitalism was therefore only one aspect of the deep disorder of the nineteenth century. To restore order, it was necessary to question all the bases of that society—its social and political structures, its art and its way of life, its commercial system.

But let the machine have its head, and it topples everything that cannot support its enormous weight. Thus everything had to be reconsidered in terms of the machine. And that is precisely the role technique plays. In all fields it made an inventory of what it could use, of everything that could be brought into line with the machine. The machine could not integrate itself into nineteenth-century society; technique integrated it. Old houses that were not suited to the workers were torn down; and the new world technique required was built in their place. Technique has enough of the mechanical in its nature to enable it to cope with the machine, but it surpasses and transcends the machine because it remains in close touch with the human order. The metal monster could not go on forever torturing mankind. It found in technique a rule as hard and inflexible as itself.

Technique integrates the machine into society. It constructs the kind of world the machine needs and introduces order where the incoherent banging of machinery heaped up ruins. It clarifies, arranges, and rationalizes; it does in the domain of the abstract what the machine did in the domain of labor. It is efficient and brings efficiency to everything. Moreover, technique is sparing in the use of the machine, which has traditionally been exploited to conceal defects of organization. "Machines sanctioned social inefficiency," says Mumford. Technique, on the other hand, leads to a more rational and less indiscriminate use of machines. It places machines exactly where they ought to be and requires of them just what they ought to do.

This brings us to two contrasting forms of social growth. Henri Guitton says: "Social growth was formerly reflexive or instinctive, that is to say, unconscious. But new circumstances (the machine) now compel us to recognize a kind of social development that is rational, intelligent, and conscious. We may ask ourselves whether this is the beginning not only of the era of a spatially finite world but also the era of a conscious world." All embracing technique is in fact the consciousness of the mechanized world.

Technique integrates everything. It avoids shock and sensational events.

Man is not adapted to a world of steel; technique adapts him to it. It changes the arrangement of this blind world so that man can be a part of it without colliding with its rough edges, without the anguish of being delivered up to the inhuman. Technique thus provides a model; it specifies attitudes that are valid once and for all. The anxiety aroused in man by the turbulence of the machine is soothed by the consoling hum of a unified society.

As long as technique was represented exclusively by the machine, it was possible to speak of "man *and* the machine." The machine remained an external object, and man (though significantly influenced by it in his professional, private, and psychic life) remained none the less independent. He was in a position to assert himself apart from the machine; he was able to adopt a position with respect to it.

But when technique enters into every area of life, including the human, it ceases to be external to man and becomes his very substance. It is no longer face to face with man but is integrated with him, and it progressively absorbs him. In this respect, technique is radically different from the machine. This transformation, so obvious in modern society, is the result of the fact that technique has become autonomous.

When I state that technique leads to mechanization, I am not referring to the simple fact of human adaptation to the machine. Of course, such a process of adaptation exists, but it is caused by the action of the machine. What we are concerned with here, however, is a kind of mechanization in itself. If we may ascribe to the machine a superior form of "know-how," the mechanization which results from technique is the application of this higher form to *all* domains hitherto foreign to the machine; we can even say that technique is characteristic of precisely that realm in which the machine itself can play no role. It is a radical error to think of technique and machine as interchangeable; from the very beginning we must be on guard against this misconception.

*   *   *   *   *

The enormous effort required to put this technical civilization into motion supposes that all individual effort is directed toward this goal alone and that all social forces are mobilized to attain the mathematically perfect structure of the edifice. ("Mathematically" does not mean "rigidly." The perfect technique is the most adaptable and, consequently, the most plastic one. True technique will know how to maintain the illusion of liberty, choice, and individuality; but these will have been carefully calculated so that they will be integrated into the mathematical reality merely as appearances!) Henceforth, it will be wrong for a man to escape this universal effort. It will be inadmissible for any part of the individual not to be integrated in the drive toward technicization; it will be inadmissible that any man even aspire to escape this necessity of the whole society. The individual will no longer be able, materially or spiritually, to disengage himself from society. Materially, he will not be able to release himself because the technical means are so numerous that they invade his whole life and make it impossible for him to escape the collective phenomena. There is no longer an uninhabited place, or any other geographical locale, for the would-be solitary. It is no longer possible to refuse entrance into a community to a highway, a high-tension line, or a dam. It is vain to aspire to live alone when one is obliged to participate in all collective phenomena and to use all the collective's tools, without which it is impossible to earn a bare subsistence. Nothing is gratis any longer in our society; and to live on charity is less and less possible. "Social advantages" are for the workers alone, not for "useless mouths." The solitary is a useless mouth and will have no ration card—up to the day he is transported to a penal colony. (An attempt was made to institute this procedure during the French Revolution, with deportations to Cayenne.)

Spiritually, it will be impossible for the individual to disassociate himself from society. This is due not to the existence of spiritual techniques which have increasing force in our society, but rather to our situation. We are constrained to be "engaged," as the existentialists say, with technique. Positively or negatively, our spiritual attitude is constantly urged, if not determined, by this situation. Only bestiality, because it is unconscious, would seem to escape this situation, and it is itself only a product of the machine.

Every conscious being today is walking the narrow ridge of a decision with regard to technique. He who maintains that he can escape it is either a hypocrite or unconscious. The autonomy of technique forbids the man of today to choose his destiny. Doubtless, someone will ask if it has not always been the case that social conditions, environment, manorial oppression, and the family conditioned man's fate. The answer is, of course, yes. But there is no common denominator between the suppression of ration cards in an authoritarian state and the family pressure of two centuries ago. In the past, when an individual entered into conflict with society, he led a harsh and miserable life that required a vigor which either hardened or broke him. Today the concentration camp and death await him; technique cannot tolerate aberrant activities.

Because of the autonomy of technique, modern man cannot choose his means any more than his ends. In spite of variability and flexibility according to place and circumstance (which are characteristic of technique) there is still only a single employable technique in the given place and time in which an individual is situated. We have already examined the reasons for this.

At this point, we must consider the major consequences of the autonomy of technique. This will bring us to the climax of this analysis.

Technical autonomy explains the "specific weight" with which technique is endowed. It is not a kind of neutral matter, with no direction, quality, or structure. It is a power endowed with its own peculiar force. It refracts in its own specific sense the wills which make use of it and the ends proposed for it. Indeed, independently of the objectives that man pretends to assign to any given technical means, that means always conceals in itself a finality which cannot be evaded. And if there is a competition between this intrinsic finality and an extrinsic end proposed by man, it is always the intrinsic finality which carries the day. If the technique in question is not exactly adapted to a proposed human end, and if an individual pretends that he is adapting the technique to this end, it is generally quickly evident that it is the end which is being modified, not the technique. Of course, this statement must be qualified by what has already been said concerning the endless refinement of techniques and their adaptation. But this adaptation is effected with reference to the techniques concerned and to the conditions of their applicability. It does not depend on external ends. Perrot has demonstrated this in the case of judicial techniques, and Giedion in the case of mechanical techniques. Concerning the over-all problem of the relation between the ends and the means, I take the liberty of referring to my own work, *Présence au monde moderne.*

Once again we are faced with a choice of "all or nothing." If we make use of technique, we must accept the specificity and autonomy of its ends, and the totality of its rules. Our own desires and aspirations can change nothing.

The second consequence of technical autonomy is that it renders technique at once sacrilegious and sacred. (*Sacrilegious* is not used here in the theological but in the sociological sense.) Sociologists have recognized that the world in which man lives is for him not only a material but also a spiritual world; that forces act in it which are unknown and perhaps unknowable; that there are phenomena in it which man interprets as magical; that there are relations and correspondences between things and beings in which material connections are of little consequence. This whole area is mysterious. Mystery (but not in the Catholic sense) is an element of man's life. Jung has shown that it is catastrophic to make superficially clear what is hidden in man's innermost depths. Man must make allowance for a background, a great deep above which lie his reason and his clear consciousness. The mystery of man perhaps creates the mystery of the world he inhabits. Or perhaps this mystery is a reality in itself. There is no way to decide between these two alternatives. But, one way or the other, mystery is a necessity of human life.

Man cannot live without a sense of the secret. The psychoanalysts agree on this point. But the invasion of technique desacralizes the world in which man is called upon to live. For technique nothing is sacred, there is no mystery, no taboo. Autonomy makes this so. Technique does not accept the existence of rules outside itself, or of any norm. Still less will it accept any judgment upon it. As a consequence, no matter where it penetrates, what it does is permitted, lawful, justified.

To a great extent, mystery is desired by man. It is not that he cannot understand, or enter into, or grasp mystery, but that he does not desire to do so. The sacred is what man decides unconsciously to respect. The taboo becomes compelling from a social standpoint, but there is always a factor of adoration and respect which does not derive from compulsion and fear.

Technique worships nothing, respects nothing. It has a single role: to strip off externals, to bring everything to light, and by rational use to transform everything into means. More than science, which limits itself to explaining the "how," technique desacralizes because it demonstrates (by evidence and not by reason, through use and not through books) that mystery does not exist. Science brings to the light of day everything man had believed sacred. Technique takes possession of it and enslaves it. The sacred cannot resist. Science penetrates to the great depths of the sea to photograph the unknown fish of the deep. Technique captures them, hauls them up to see if they are edible—but before they arrive on deck they burst. And why should technique not act thus? It is autonomous and recognizes as barriers only the temporary limits of its action. In its eyes, this terrain, which is for the moment unknown but not mysterious, must be attacked. Far from being restrained by any scruples before the sacred, technique constantly assails it. Everything which is not yet technique becomes so. It is driven onward by itself, by its character of self-augmentation. Technique denies mystery a priori. The mysterious is merely that which has not been technicized.

*   *   *   *   *

Technique Unchecked. At present there is no counterbalance to technique. In a society in equilibrium, every new cultural tendency, every new impulse, encounters a certain number of obstacles which act as the society's first line of defense. This is not due to the interplay of conservative and revolutionary forces in general, nor in particular to the play between the means of production and the organs of consumption. It is rather due to the simple fact that every new factor must be integrated into the cultural framework, and this process requires a certain period of time because it entails modifications of the two interacting elements. It is never initially clear that the new factor will be acceptable to the cultural complex. On one hand is a kind of process of selection and, on the other, a resistance that gradually abates. A number of different forces play this restraining role. I shall discuss four of them.

The first is morality. Every civilization has rules of precise conduct, which are covered by the term *morality* in either its French or its Anglo-Saxon meaning. They may be conscious and thought out, or unconscious and spontaneous. They determine what is good and what is bad and, consequently, admit or reject a given innovation.

Very close to morality, public opinion comprises a set of much more irrational reactions which are not necessarily related to good and evil. For reasons still poorly understood, public opinion may be impelled in a certain direction under the influence of a given impulse, or it may remain refractory. Obviously, public opinion is decisive in the interaction between morality and a new factor. It can render morality obsolete or lead it to triumph.

A third restraining force is social structure, which includes both social morphology and economic or legal structure. The social structure reacts strongly whenever new factors threaten to modify it. (This, incidentally, is the only one of the four factors retained by Marxism.) Systems or ideas are no longer the sole operative factors; economic relations or sociological factors can disturb the equilibrium even of a situation the stability of which was previously thought assured.

Finally, there is the state, the special organ of defense of a society, which reacts with every means at its disposal against all disturbing forces.

We may now ask what position we are in today with respect to these factors insofar as technique is concerned. Let us put aside the problem of morality and concern ourselves with public opinion. It is completely oriented in favor of technique; only technical phenomena interest modern men. The machine has made itself master of the heart and brain both of the average man and of the mob. What excites the crowd? Performance—whether performance in sports (the result of a certain sporting technique) or economic performance (as in the Soviet Union), in reality these are the same thing. Technique is the instrument of performance. What is important is to go higher and faster; the object of the performance means little. The act is sufficient unto itself. Modern man can think only in terms of figures, and the higher the figures, the greater his satisfaction. He looks for nothing beyond the marvelous escape mechanism that technique has allowed him, to offset the very repressions caused by the life technique forces him to lead. He is reduced, in the process, to a near nullity. Even if he is not a worker on the assembly line, his share of autonomy and individual initiative becomes smaller and smaller. He is constrained and repressed in thought and action by an omnivorous reality which is external to him and imposed upon him. He is no longer permitted to display any personal power. Then, suddenly, he learns that the airplane his factory manufactures has flown at 700 miles an hour! All his repressed power soars into flight in that figure. Into that record speed he sublimates everything that was repressed in himself. He has gone one step further toward fusion with the mob, for it is the mob as a whole that is moved by a performance that incarnates its will to power. Every modern man expresses his will to power in records he has not established himself.

Public opinion is all the more important in that it is a two-pronged element. In the first place, there is modern man's collective worship of the power of fact, which is displayed in every technique and which is manifested in his total devotion to its overwhelming progress. This adoration is not passive but truly mystical. Men sacrifice themselves to it and lose themselves in the search for it. In this sense Mussolini was right in speaking of men realizing themselves in and through the state, the collective instrument of power. The martyrs of science or of the air force or of the atomic pile give us the most profound sense of this worship when we see the deference the crowd pays them. "I have faith in technique," declared Henry Wallace, the former Secretary of Commerce of the United States. His faith indeed dwells in men's hearts. Man is scandalized when he is told that technique causes evil; the scourges engendered by one technique will be made good by still other techniques. This is society's normal attitude.

In the second place, there is the deep conviction that technical problems are the only serious ones. The amused glance people give the philosopher; the lack of interest displayed in metaphysical and theological questions ("Byzantine" quarrels); the rejection of the humanities which comes from the conviction that we are living in a technical age and education must correspond to it; the search for the immediately practical, carrying the implication that history is useless and can serve no practical ends—all these are symptomatic of that "reasonable" conviction which pervades the social hierarchy and is identical for all social classes. "Only technique is not mere gab." It is positive and brings about real achievements.

In these two ways, the mystic and the rational, public opinion is completely oriented toward technique. And at present another precise technique molds public opinion with reference to any given question. This technique has never been fully exploited because public opinion is favorable enough to technique without it. But if a sudden change should occur and public opinion should turn against technique, we would see the propaganda machinery set into motion to recreate a favorable atmosphere, for the whole social edifice would be at stake.

As to the third traditional restraining force—the social structure—the question is whether the social structure of our world acts as a brake on technical evolution. By way of answer, I have shown that progress has been rapid only because social morphology has favored it. This phenomenon has not fluctuated very much; and at present we are witnessing the penetration of social structure by techniques. The life of the modern world is to an ever greater degree dominated by economics, and economics in turn is more and more dominated by technique. The whole of the material world in which we live rests on this technical base. (It is a commonplace of science-fiction writers to imagine what would happen if the use of technical instruments were to be suddenly stopped.) Likewise, our analysis has led us to recognize that as technique progresses in a given society, it tends to reproduce in that society the social structures that gave birth to it.

The individualist and atomized society of the nineteenth century was, from the sociological point of view, favorable to technical development. Today we are witnessing a kind of technical reconstitution of the scattered fragments of society; communities and associations flourish everywhere. Men seem overjoyed at this creation of new social frameworks independent of the state. The social solidification of today contrasts sharply with the fluidity of the nineteenth century. Does this phenomenon then present an effective opposition to techniques? The answer must be in the negative. If we examine these new sociological forms in detail, we find them all organized as functions of techniques. We hardly need to examine industrial associations, but the same applies to all other twentieth-century associations. They may be associations for sport or for culture, the goal of which is clearly recognizable. They may be labor unions, which have their characteristic relation to life through the economy, this last being conditioned by technique. They may be communities like the *Kibbutzim,* whose object is to exploit techniques while allowing man a normal life. In every kind of modern society there is a predominance of techniques. The social morphology of these societies indeed differs radically from that of traditional societies. Traditional societies were centered upon human needs and instincts (for example, in family, clan, seignory). Modern societies, on the other hand, are centered on technical necessity and derivatively, of course, on human adherence. Man, in modern societies, is not situated in relation to other men, but in relation to technique; for this reason the sociological structure of these societies is completely altered. There is no longer any question of autonomous collectivities or groups with specific values and orientations. Modern collectivities and groups have no existence beyond technique—they are representative of the major tendency of our time.

In the transition from the individualist to the collectivist society, there are then two stages of evolution, both of which are favorable to technique, not two different attitudes of society toward technique. Comparably, it is clear that collectivist society cannot be established, or even conceived of, except as growing out of an extreme technical development. This might not be true in a communal society (although the communities that exist today are markedly dependent on technique); but we do not seem to be moving in the direction of such societies.

Hence, we must conclude that our social structures, viewed in any light whatsoever, are unanimously favorable to technique and could hardly act as a check upon it.

Only the state remains, then, as a possible brake upon technique. But we have already seen that the state has abdicated this function, renouncing its directive role in favor of technique. Indeed, since the nineteenth century every social element which traditionally acted as a restraint on innovating forces has been overthrown as far as technique is concerned. *Inverted* might be a better term; the factors which formerly acted as hindrances have today become powerful auxiliaries to technique. (We have only to reflect on public opinion and the expansion of the economy to realize this.) Technique, therefore, encounters no possible obstacles or checks to its progress. It can advance as it will, since it encounters no limiting factors other than its own powers (which seem unlimited and inexhaustible).

A technique without limits is not in itself disquieting. If we look at our technical society without our idealist spectacles, what seems most disquieting is that the character of technique renders it *independent of man himself.* We do not mean by this that the machine tends to replace the human being; that fact is already well known. The important thing is that man, practically speaking, no longer possesses any means of bringing action to bear upon technique. He is unable to limit it or even to orient it. I am well acquainted with the claims of those who think that society has technique under firm control because man is always inventing it anew. I know too of the hopes of those who are always prescribing remedies for this sorcerer's apprentice whom they feel free to invoke without discernment. But these claims and hopes are mere words. The reality is that man no longer has any means with which to subjugate technique, which is not an intellectual, or even, as some would have it, a spiritual phenomenon. It is above all a sociological phenomenon; and in order to cure or change it, one would have to oppose to it checks and barriers of a sociological character. By such means alone man might possibly bring action to bear upon it. But everything of a sociological character has had its character changed by technique. There is, therefore, nothing of a sociological character available to restrain technique, because everything in society is its servant. Technique is essentially independent of the human being, who finds himself naked and disarmed before it. Modern man divines that there is only one reasonable way out: to submit and take what profit he can from what technique otherwise so richly bestows upon him. If he is of a mind to oppose it, he finds himself really alone.

It has been said that modern man surrounded by techniques is in the same situation as prehistoric man in the midst of nature. This is only a metaphor; it cannot be carried very far, even though it is as exact as a metaphor can be. Both environments give life but both place him in utter peril. Both represent terrifying powers, worlds in which man is a participant but which are closed against him. In the joy of conquest, he has not perceived that what he has created takes from him the possibility of being himself. He is like a rich man of many possessions who finds himself a nonentity in his own household. The state, man's last protector, has made common cause with alien powers.

The Role of the State in the Development of Modern Techniques. The state plays a role of prime importance with respect to techniques. We have noted that until recently different techniques were unrelated to one another. This unrelatedness was true of state techniques because they were localized and their domains were not contiguous; it held for private techniques because they were the result of highly uncoordinated activity which, while fruitful, was also anarchical and was dominated, moreover, by specialization.

The basic effect of state action on techniques is to coordinate the whole complex. The state possesses the power of unification, since it is the planning power par excellence in society. In this it plays its true role, that of coordinating, adjusting, and equilibrating social forces. It has played this role with respect to techniques for half a century by bringing hitherto unrelated techniques into contact with one another, for example, economic and propaganda techniques. It relates them by establishing organisms responsible for this function, as, for example, the simple organs of liaison between ministries. It integrates the whole complex of techniques into a plan. Planning itself is the result of well-applied techniques, and only the state is in a position to establish plans which are valid on the national level. We are, at present, beginning to see plans on a continental scale, not only the so-called five-year plans, but the Marshall Plan and plans for assisting underdeveloped countries.

It is only in the framework of planning that such operations are arranged and find their exact place. The state appears less as the brain which orders them organically and more as the relational apparatus which enables the separate techniques to confront one another and to coordinate their movements. We find concrete evidence of this again and again; in the coordination of rail and automobile traffic, the coordination of the production of steel and motor vehicles and aircraft, in the coordination of the medical profession and social security, the coordination of foreign and colonial commerce, and of all commerce with finance, and so forth.

The more closely related the different sectors, the more does a discovery in one involve repercussions in the others, and the more it becomes necessary to create organisms of transmission, cogs and gears, so to speak, connecting the different techniques. This is an impossible task for private enterprise, not only because the phenomenon in question is a global one but because the technicians themselves are specialists. The state alone can undertake the indispensable task of bridging these specializations. The state knows approximately the available resources in men and techniques and can undertake the still embryonic function of coordinator. Since discoveries in one technical sector are so useful in others, the role of coordinator is bound to become more and more important.

Consider, for example, the diversity of techniques necessary for the production of a motion picture. There are financial, literary, and cinematographic techniques; there are lesser techniques, such as make-up techniques and the techniques of light and sound. There are completely new techniques, such as script techniques, and so on. These cinematic techniques, though complicated, can be grasped by the brain of a single man, and hence there are still some cases of one-man management. But consider the magnitude of the task of coordinating, on a national scale, even more complicated clusters of techniques which offer active resistance to being coordinated. In such cases the role of organizer, manager, coordinator—whatever it is called—becomes more necessary in proportion as the state takes over that function. Moreover, the state alone can fulfill it. This state of affairs is already a reality; the state is already engaged in bridging the isolated technical specialties. Individual specialized disciplines—for example, those of the biologist, the engineer, the sociologist, the psychologist—are combined to yield new techniques such as psychotechniques and industrial relations. But these individual disciplines are also joined together in a more organic way, as, for example, when the so-called human techniques, physics and politics, are combined in propaganda.

In addition to coordinating the different techniques, the state furnishes material means far beyond the power of any individuals to supply. An expedition to the North Pole, which only a half century ago was within the resources of one or at most a few private persons, is no longer possible on a private basis. Formerly all that was needed was Eskimo equipment, such as a boat, sledges, dogs—and, above all, courage. Today complicated mechanical equipment is necessary: airplanes (especially equipped for the cold and for ice landings), caterpillar trucks, radio and radio telephones, prefabricated housing, and so on. Every possible means to lessen danger is available to him who dreams of exploring unknown territory. It would doubtless be possible to revive old traditions—by risking one's life. But why reject the new means? Why endanger one's life when one can do a better job without that? Obviously, bravado is unreasonable. One must employ the maximum means to assure optimal results with the least danger. But no private person has the means to set into motion the enormous apparatus that is needed. The means must be requisitioned by the state, which alone is in a position to find indefinite supplies of cash and to exploit financial techniques forbidden to individuals. The same applies in submarine exploration. When one leaves the domain of the merely amateurish and desires to give one's work status, legal or otherwise, it is necessary to solicit the support of the state to cover expenses and to resolve administrative problems.

But the state demands something in return for subventions. The state does not think it important for an individual to go to the North Pole, either for sport's sake or for honors. The state desires tangible *technical* results. It agrees to furnish assistance for purposes of scientific research and for the acquisition of certain rights it hopes to exploit; for example, mineral resources and aviation. The result must be the technical aggrandizement of the state; that is the only condition under which a contract between state and individual is possible.

That the state acts to promote scientific research is not new; in the eighteenth century the state offered recompenses to inventors, and these recompenses had much to do with the discovery of certain navigational methods (compensating chronometer, mathematical tables, and so on). The state thereafter seemed to lose interest, but for the last thirty years it has resumed the policy of recompensating technologists and inventors.

*   *   *   *   *

A Look at the Year 2000. In 1960 the weekly *l'Express* of Paris published a series of extracts from texts by American and Russian scientists concerning society in the year 2000. As long as such visions were purely a literary concern of science-fiction writers and sensational journalists, it was possible to smile at them. Now we have like works from Nobel Prize winners, members of the Academy of Sciences of Moscow, and other scientific notables whose qualifications are beyond dispute. The visions of these gentlemen put science fiction in the shade. By the year 2000, voyages to the moon will be commonplace; so will inhabited artificial satellites. All food will be completely synthetic. The world's population will have increased fourfold but will have been stabilized. Sea water and ordinary rocks will yield all the necessary metals. Disease, as well as famine, will have been eliminated; and there will be universal hygienic inspection and control. The problems of energy production will have been completely resolved. Serious scientists, it must be repeated, are the source of these predictions, which hitherto were found only in philosophic utopias.

The most remarkable predictions concern the transformation of educational methods and the problem of human reproduction. Knowledge will be accumulated in "electronic banks" and transmitted directly to the human nervous system by means of coded electronic messages. There will no longer be any need of reading or learning mountains of useless information; everything will be received and registered according to the needs of the moment. There will be no need of attention or effort. What is needed will pass directly from the machine to the brain without going through consciousness.

In the domain of genetics, natural reproduction will be forbidden. A stable population will be necessary, and it will consist of the highest human types. Artificial insemination will be employed. This, according to Muller, will "permit the introduction into a carrier uterus of an ovum fertilized *in vitro,* ovum and sperm . . . having been taken from persons representing the masculine ideal and the feminine ideal, respectively. The reproductive cells in question will preferably be those of persons dead long enough that a true perspective of their lives and works, free of all personal prejudice, can be seen. Such cells will be taken from cell banks and will represent the most precious genetic heritage of humanity. . . . The method will have to be applied universally. If the people of a single country were to apply it intelligently and intensively . . . they would quickly attain a practically invincible level of superiority. . . ." Here is a future Huxley never dreamed of.

Perhaps, instead of marveling or being shocked, we ought to reflect a little. A question no one ever asks when confronted with the scientific wonders of the future concerns the interim period. Consider, for example, the problems of automation, which will become acute in a very short time. How, socially, politically, morally, and humanly, shall we contrive to get there? How are the prodigious economic problems, for example, of unemployment, to be solved? And, in Muller's more distant utopia, how shall we force humanity to refrain from begetting children naturally? How shall we force them to submit to constant and rigorous hygienic controls? How shall man be persuaded to accept a radical transformation of his traditional modes of nutrition? How and where shall we relocate a billion and a half persons who today make their livings from agriculture and who, in the promised ultrarapid conversion of the next forty years, will become completely useless as cultivators of the soil? How shall we distribute such numbers of people equably over the surface of the earth, particularly if the promised fourfold increase in population materializes? How will we handle the control and occupation of outer space in order to provide a stable modus vivendi? How shall national boundaries be made to disappear? (One of the last two would be a necessity.) There are many other "hows," but they are conveniently left unformulated. When we reflect on the serious although relatively minor problems that were provoked by the industrial exploitation of coal and electricity, when we reflect that after a hundred and fifty years these problems are still not satisfactorily resolved, we are entitled to ask whether there are any solutions to the infinitely more complex "hows" of the next forty years. In fact, there is one and only one means to their solution, a world-wide totalitarian dictatorship which will allow technique its full scope and at the same time resolve the concomitant difficulties. It is not difficult to understand why the scientists and worshippers of technology prefer not to dwell on this solution, but rather to leap nimbly across the dull and uninteresting intermediary period and land squarely in the golden age. We might indeed ask ourselves if we will succeed in getting through the transition period at all, or if the blood and the suffering required are not perhaps too high a price to pay for this golden age.

If we take a hard, unromantic look at the golden age itself, we are struck with the incredible naiveté of these scientists. They say, for example, that they will be able to shape and reshape at will human emotions, desires, and thoughts and arrive scientifically at certain efficient, pre-established collective decisions. They claim they will be in a position to develop certain collective desires, to constitute certain homogeneous social units out of aggregates of individuals, to forbid men to raise their children, and even to persuade them to renounce having any. At the same time, they speak of assuring the triumph of freedom and of the necessity of avoiding dictatorship at any price. They seem incapable of grasping the contradiction involved, or of understanding that what they are proposing, even after the intermediary period, is in fact the harshest of dictatorships. In comparison, Hitler's was a trifling affair. That it is to be a dictatorship of test tubes rather than of hobnailed boots will not make it any less a dictatorship.

When our savants characterize their golden age in any but scientific terms, they emit a quantity of down-at-the-heel platitudes that would gladden the heart of the pettiest politician. Let's take a few samples. "To render human nature nobler, more beautiful, and more harmonious." What on earth can this mean? What criteria, what content, do they propose? Not many, I fear, would be able to reply. "To assure the triumph of peace, liberty, and reason." Fine words with no substance behind them. "To eliminate cultural lag." What culture? And would the culture they have in mind be able to subsist in this harsh social organization? "To conquer outer space." For what purpose? The conquest of space seems to be an end in itself, which dispenses with any need for reflection.

We are forced to conclude that our scientists are incapable of any but the emptiest platitudes when they stray from their specialties. It makes one think back on the collection of mediocrities accumulated by Einstein when he spoke of God, the state, peace, and the meaning of life. It is clear that Einstein, extraordinary mathematical genius that he was, was no Pascal; he knew nothing of political or human reality, or, in fact, anything at all outside his mathematical reach. The banality of Einstein's remarks in matters outside his specialty is as astonishing as his genius within it. It seems as though the specialized application of all one's faculties in a particular area inhibits the consideration of things in general. Even J. Robert Oppenheimer, who seems receptive to a general culture, is not outside this judgment. His political and social declarations, for example, scarcely go beyond the level of those of the man in the street. And the opinions of the scientists quoted by *l'Express* are not even on the level of Einstein or Oppenheimer. Their pomposities, in fact, do not rise to the level of the average. They are vague generalities inherited from the nineteenth century, and the fact that they represent the furthest limits of thought of our scientific worthies must be symptomatic of arrested development or of a mental block. Particularly disquieting is the gap between the enormous power they wield and their critical ability, which must be estimated as null. To wield power well entails a certain faculty of criticism, discrimination, judgment, and option. It is impossible to have confidence in men who apparently lack these faculties. Yet it is apparently our fate to be facing a "golden age" in the power of sorcerers who are totally blind to the meaning of the human adventure. When they speak of preserving the seed of outstanding men, whom, pray, do they mean to be the judges. It is clear, alas, that they propose to sit in judgment themselves. It is hardly likely that they will deem a Rimbaud or a Nietzsche worthy of posterity. When they announce that they will conserve the genetic mutations which appear to them most favorable, and that they propose to modify the very germ cells in order to produce such and such traits; and when we consider the mediocrity of the scientists themselves outside the confines of their specialties, we can only shudder at the thought of what they will esteem most "favorable."

None of our wise men ever pose the question of the end of all their marvels. The "wherefore" is resolutely passed by. The response which would occur to our contemporaries is: for the sake of happiness. Unfortunately, there is no longer any question of that. One of our best-known specialists in diseases of the nervous system writes: "We will be able to modify man's emotions, desires and thoughts, as we have already done in a rudimentary way with tranquilizers." It will be possible, says our specialist to produce a conviction or an impression of happiness without any real basis for it. Our man of the golden age, therefore, will be capable of "happiness" amid the worst privations. Why, then, promise us extraordinary comforts, hygiene, knowledge, and nourishment if, by simply manipulating our nervous systems, we can be happy without them? The last meager motive we could possibly ascribe to the technical adventure thus vanishes into thin air through the very existence of technique itself.

But what good is it to pose questions of motives? of Why? All that must be the work of some miserable intellectual who balks at technical progress. The attitude of the scientists, at any rate, is clear. Technique exists because it is technique. The golden age will be because it will be. Any other answer is superfluous.

from Utopia or Oblivion

R. BUCKMINSTER FULLER

I have been asked: "What would you do if you were building commissioner of the U.S.A. or even of the world?"

I would resign!

It is popularly assumed that democracy's checks and balances—its political and economic institutions—frustrate logical housing solutions.

Many think that housing of man can be accomplished only through a powerful political mandate. They overlook the far vaster prerogatives of the inventor. The inventor has natural and immediate access to all the potentials of the universe. Edison, Bell, Marconi, and the Wrights needed no licenses from anyone to light the night, to shrink the earth and interlink all of humanity.

Yesterday's capitalists were naturally eager to prolong the earnings of profitable machinery investments. They disliked inventors. Inventors made their going machines obsolete. Businessmen were powerful enough to persuade society that inventors were screwballs. All that is changing. Businessmen now find change profitable. Inventors are becoming respectable.

Inventors pay no attention to manmade laws—pay attention only to the physical laws which alone govern what man ultimately may do in universe. If humanity succeeds in becoming a total success it will have been initiated by the Wright- and Bell-type inventions and not by the always debilitating and often lethal biases of politics.

All humans are born inventors. As children we invent games until grownups persuade us that our inventing is futile and that we should conform with yesterday's seemingly proven but usually outworn inventions. But the inventiveness remains latent in us all.

Inventors may employ man's innate capability to think effectively in cosmic terms. As inventor I now ask the cosmic questions. "Is man needed in the universe?" "Does he have a universal function?" "If he is essential what needs to be invented to improve his functioning?" "What are the largest overall trends of human evolution that need accommodations?" If we can answer such questions we will know what to do about housing man on earth or anywhere else.

My answers to the first two questions are that man is needed to employ his mind to put things in order in the areas of universal events in which he finds himself existing. Physical universe is forever expanding and multiplying in ever more disorderly ways. This is called entropy. Biological life is forever sorting, selecting, compacting, and producing more orderly chemical substances. This is called antientropy. Human mind is the most powerful selector and order formulator thus far evidenced in universe. Mind reduces billions of special case experiences recorded by brain to a few hundred generalized principles observed to be always operative in universe. The diffuse multiplication and expansion of *physical* universe is regeneratively countered by the contractive metaphysical capabilities of human intellect. The greatest of our scientists are those who discover additional interrelationships of the comprehensive order always embracing the only at first seeming disorders of the physical. The antientropic metaphysical takes the measure of and progressively commands the entropic physical. Intellect's identification of $E = mc^2$ is irreversible. Energy cannot identify intellect.

According to my speculative reconstruction, the ecological history of humanity around earth has two chapters. In chapter one, humanity—whose bodies are better than 90% water—lived in huts on rafts beside the rivers, lakes, bays, and oceans, for fish were the most plentiful food and the raft kept the humans safe from wild animals on shore. Some of these raft dwellers were blown out to sea and preponderantly eastward around earth's surface, three-quarters of which is water.

In the second chapter of all history, men learned to sail to windward. Seeming to follow the sun, to which they intuitively attributed their metabolic regeneration, men worked westward fighting preponderantly into the headwind seas.

Approximately the whole of the last 10,000 years' span of recorded history takes place during chapter two's preponderantly westbound movement of humanity. In the Eurasian continent, where 76% of humanity exists, this westward motion finally funnels into Western Europe. As humanity converged it crossbred. Western Europe represented an amalgam of a myriad of previously isolated "nations." The "nations" had developed through millenniums of inland inbred adaptations to unique local subsistence patterns. Forced to hibernate and cover up their skin those in the north became bleached and blond, those isolated in the hot equatorial sun darkened and blackened. Further inbreeding heightened the differentiations. Along the waterfronts the sailors crossbred and their skins became pink or swarthy.

Crossbreeding Europe, intermingling with the Angles and Jutes, poured into the British Isles to crossbreed even more. Westbound Indian Ocean people inhabited Africa in ever further westward, tribally inbreeding, ever-darkening skin, inland isolations. Then crossbreeding Western Europeans jumped westward across the Atlantic to the Americas. For 11 successive generations they have settled further westward. As they moved westward they crossbred acceleratingly, not only with their own westbound, chapter-two Eurasian stocks but with the Eurasian stock of chapter one, which had drifted eastward to the American continents between 30,000 and 10,000 years earlier. Into the North and South American continents and their islands there also flowed westward, both by slave trade and migration, a swiftly crossbreeding homogenization of the inbred African tribesmen.

In California, at the midpoint of the western shores of America, cross-breeding man has become so genetically integrated he frequently is unidentifiable with any of the earlier inbred national characteristics of Eurasia. Chapter two climaxes in the emergence of World Man.

In California we have an advanced phase of crossbred world man poised on an epochal springboard to fly both skyward and into the seas' depths around the earth, thus to open chapter three of history—that of Universe Man.

From this pad, humanity is taking off—from its flounder-, snail-, and crablike previous existence, only around the two-dimensional bottom of the skyocean world—into its self-interference-free, four-dimensional occupancy of universe. Man will free himself from local time and geographical bases and will progressively discard encumbrances, giving all heavy, static, and economically nontransportable properties to libraries, museums, and universities or scrapping them as he is able to rent superior devices and services everywhere around the earth.

For the last decade many of the world's responsible scientists have conceded for the first time in human history that Malthus was wrong and that it is physically feasible to employ the earth's energy-income resources and recirculatable metals in such a manner as to make all of humanity physically, economically, and continuously successful within 20 years. This potential is the optimum we are interested in accomplishing.

The best way to solve world housing problems is first to see how many feasible solutions there are for emerging world man and how long each would take and what its logistics are. Having chosen the optimum solutions that may be progressively attained we may see how to get from here to there—from 1966 to Utopia.

The concept of cities as they now exist developed entirely before the existence or the thought of electricity or automobiles, or before any of the millions of inventions registered in the United States Patent Office had occurred. Cities developed as warehouse trading-posts. All warehousing is gone out of the modern city. Warehousing has become dynamic. The warehousing now is mostly on wheels, wings, or in ships. The cities were later used to house vast hordes of immigrants to work in the factories which were also centered in the cities. The factories have now been deployed from the cities along with the warehouses. Cities, as we know them, are obsolete in respect to all of yesterday's functions. Trying to rebuild cities to make them accommodate the new needs of world man is like trying to reconstruct and improve a wrecked ship as the shipwreck rests upon the reef, pounded by the surf. The surf of technical obsolescence is invisible but is more inexorably powerful in its destruction than are pounding waves of the visible ocean.

Mankind is deploying all his physical activity, both the prosaic business of manufacturing and the recreational business (such as mountain and water skiing), completely out and away from cities. Mankind now converges in the old cities essentially for abstract, almost weightless, activity. Cities are great exchanges of abstract, weightless equities. Only a few cities can maintain the prestige of being the great cultural or stock exchange centers—New York, London, Paris, Tokyo, and a handful of others. These great cities will turn into great universities as automation replaces the humans functioning only as automatons.

Columbia University, New York University, Fordham University, and City College of New York are now the prime real-estate holders of New York City. All the cities which do not have the cultural and economic exchange prestige will become totally obsolete.

It is my lifelong resolve to accomplish tasks by reforming the mechanics of the physical environment rather than by trying to reform man. I'm confident that humanity is endowed with extraordinary capabilities.

Only about one-half of the total brain is now employed.

I surmise that our higher potentials are unrealized because inauspicious environmental conditions into which life has been born have heretofore frustrated realization of most of man's potentials. We have learned much however through recent behavioral-science research, for instance that environmental conditions determine how much of the child's total brain potential will blossom successfully into coordinate effectiveness. Fifty percent of a child's total IQ capability has tried to blossom in coordinating competence by the time it is four years old, another 30% by seven, and 12% more by thirteen. At seventeen the blossoming is over. "Blossoming" frustrated by environmental conditions is usually lost.

Scientist Benjamin Bloom of the University of Chicago has demonstrated time and again that if you list the pertinent environmental conditions affecting a life throughout each of its first seventeen years, he can predict within one point of accuracy what any youth's IQ will be at seventeen. He must know—year by year—what kind of home the child lives in, whether the parents are alcoholics, etc.

Bloom validates my commitment to progressively reforming only the environment. Politics undertakes only to reform man.

When I was young, I saw that society undertook to reduce automobile accidents by attempting to reform the drivers with arrests, fines, propaganda, behavioral exhortations, and laws. I saw that instead it was physically possible to prevent accidents by split-level crossings, banked turns, and divided highways. In 1906 people said, "You can't do that, it would cost millions." After trying unsuccessfully for 60 years to reform the drivers and after a greater mortality on the U.S. highways than in World Wars I and II combined, society has at last undertaken to reform the environment with a $100 billion national highway program which has already safely multiplied the 1906 auto speeds fivefold while greatly reducing the accident rate per each accomplished passenger-mile.

Inventions alone have upped the numbers enjoying an advanced standard of living—one now superior to the best known to any sovereign before 1900—from 1% in 1900 to 40% of all humanity in 1966—despite continually decreasing metals per each human being. That same advantaged 40% are also living three times the number of years that man lived a century ago. All of that has come about through inventions which have induced appropriate social reforms but only as accessories after the facts of invention.

Take away all the inventions from humanity and within six months half of humanity will die of starvation and disease. Take away all the politicians and all political ideologies and leave all the inventions in operation and more will eat and prosper than now while racing on to take care of 100% of humanity.

My task as inventor is to employ the earth's resources and energy income in such a way as to support all humanity while also enabling all people to enjoy the whole earth, all its historical artifacts and its beautiful places without one man interfering with the other, and without any man enjoying life around earth at the cost of another. Always the cost must be prepaid by design-science competence in modifying the environment.

Man now sprawls horizontally upon the land—uncheckable by planners who enjoy only the right to "suggest." Visionless realtors, backed by government funds, operate indiscriminately in acquiring low-cost options on farmland upon which they install speculator houses. This continually reduces the productive land per capita and unbalances the ecological regeneration of life on earth. Despite the fact that the average American family now moves out of town every four years man is forced by the government-backed realtors to buy his home on 30-year mortgages which never get amortized. Man was designed with legs—not roots. He is destined to ever-increasing freedom of individually selected motions, articulated in preferred directions, as his spaceship, *Earth,* spinning its equator at 1000 miles per hour, orbits the sun at one million miles per day, as all the while the quadrillions of atomic components of which man is composed inter-gyrate and transform at seven million miles per hour. Both man and universe are indeed complex aggregates of motion.

Over ten million humans have now traveled more than three million miles around their spinning orbiting spaceship *Earth's* surface in contrast to the 30,000 miles per lifetime averaged by all humanity prior to the year 1900. So ignorantly, myopically, and statically conceived and so obsolete is the whole housing art that its death led the Crash of 1929, since when its ghost script has been kept in rehearsal by U.S. government subsidy at a total underwriting cost to date of $200 billion.

If we take inventor heed of all the foregoing conditions and trends and if we build vertically, both outwardly and inwardly of the earth's surface, we may use less land and return good soil lands to metabolic productivity. We can also install vertical habitations upon and within the three-quarters of the earth covered by water.

The *Queen Elizabeth* is a luxuriously comfortable abode either at sea or in port. She is a mobile city. She is shaped to get passengers across oceans in a hurry. If such floating cities didn't have to speed and were designed only to be towed to an anchorage, having their occupants boated or flown to them, they might have an efficiently symmetrical shape. It is eminently feasible and economical to develop floatable organic cities of immense size.

It has been discovered also that it costs no more to go into the ground and remove earth than it does to go skyward. The great atom-war-anticipating government cave building of the last 20 years cost the same per cubic foot as building fireproof skyscrapers.

Frank Lloyd Wright designed a proposed one-mile-high tower building. His magnificent drawings excited people. But there was no engineering analysis to show whether his structure would stand under adverse conditions such as earthquakes and tornadoes. A one-mile tower is four times the height of the Empire State Building which is, as yet, in 1966, the tallest occupied building man has erected. However, in recent months calculations, only feasible by computers, have been made on a 2 1/4-mile-high tower habitation which will be approximately ten times the height of the Empire State. It is as high as Mount Fuji. The calculations show such a tower is physically feasible—assuming winds up to 600 m.p.h. and the tower members all encased in ice one foot thick in all directions as it is shaken by earthquakes. Though the project is feasible, the amount of steel required is formidable.

To visualize the various design-controlling conditions under which such a high building can be constructed pinch a camera tripod's legs together in parallel. Take hold of the very bottom of the tripod in one hand and try to hold it vertically on the top of an automobile going at 70 miles an hour over rough terrain. But as we open the legs of the tripod, each time we spread them, the tripod gets steadier and steadier. This is the stabilizing effect obtained when tension stays are rigged from top to bottom on three sides of a mast, as with radio towers. It is equally effective to have the legs spread outwardly as in the Eiffel Tower. When the three legs are spread apart so that the length of the edges of their base triangle equals the length of each of the legs the tripod attains its maximum stability. This conformation of the tripod and its base triangle is that of the regular or equilateral tetrahedron. As the tripod's legs go further apart than the regular tetrahedron, its top can support less and less load. Thus we learn that the most stable structure is the regular tetrahedron.

Following that design-science clue we find that a tetrahedral city to house a million people is both technologically and economically feasible. Such a vertical-tetrahedronal city can be constructed with all of its 300,000 families each having balconied "outside" apartments of 2000 square feet, i.e., 200 square meters, of floor space each. All of the organic machinery necessary to its operation will be housed inside the tetrahedron. It is found that such a one-million-passenger tetrahedronal city is so structurally efficient, and therefore so relatively light, that together with its hollow box-sectioned reinforced-concrete foundations it can float.

Such tetrahedronal floating cities would measure two miles to an edge. That is, each of the three base legs will be two miles long. This means that their reinforced-concrete, box-sectioned, and frequently partitioned bottom foundations will be 200 feet in depth and several hundreds of feet wide. Such a tetrahedronal floating city can be floated in a triangularly patterned canal. The structure can be assembled on the floating foundations. This will make the whole structure earthquake-proof. The whole city can be floated out into the ocean to any point and anchored. The depth of its foundation will go below the turbulence level of the seas so that the floating tetrahedronal island will be, in effect, a floating triangular atoll. Its two-mile-long "boat" foundation, on each of its three bottom edges, will constitute landing strips for jet airplanes. Its interior two-mile harbor will provide refuge for the largest and smallest ocean vessels. The total structural and mechanical materials involved in production of a number of such one-million-inhabitant tetrahedronal cities are within feasibility magnitude of the already operating steel and other metals manufacturing capabilities of any one company of the several major industrial nations around the earth.

Tetrahedra are geometrically unique in that they can be added to on any one of their four surfaces while increasing symmetrically in size. The tetrahedron city can grow symmetrically by adding to any one of its faces. Tetrahedronal cities will be symmetrically growable as are biological systems. They may start with a thousand occupants and grow to hold millions without changing overall shape though always providing each family with 2000 square feet of floor space.

Withdrawal of materials from obsolete buildings on the land will permit the production of enough of these floating cities to support frequently spaced floating cities of various sizes around the oceans of the earth at distances negotiable by relatively small boats such as operate safely between Miami, Florida, and Nassau on the Bahama Islands.

At the present time, ocean cargoes must go from one country to another, e.g., from Buenos Aires to London because ships cannot dock beside one another on the ever-heaving ocean to transfer cargo. Because the depth of their "foundations" goes below wave turbulence, permitting dropped thresholds over which the deepest draft ships may pass, such floating tetrahedron cities will permit midocean cargo transferring within their harbors and therewith extraordinary increase of efficiency of the interdistribution of the world's raw and finished products as well as of the passenger traffic. Such tetrahedronal cities floated upon the oceans will generate their own energy with atomic reactors whose by-product heat will be used to desalinate the city's water supply. All major ships of the sea already desalinate their water.

Such ocean-passage-shortening habitats of ever-transient humanity will permit his individual flying, sailing, economic steppingstone travel around the whole earth in many directions. Three-quarters of the earth is covered by water. Man is clearly intent on penetrating those world-around ocean waters in every way to work both their ocean bottoms and their marine-life and chemistry resources.

When we double the length of an airplane fuselage, we increase its surface area by four and increase its volume by eight. This means that every time we double the length of a ship we eightfold its useful cargo and passenger space while only fourfolding its surface. The amount of surface of a ship governs its friction and drag. The larger the ship, the more economically its cargo may be carried. Yesterday's limitation in relation to the bigness of airplanes was occasioned by their horizontal speeds requiring longer and longer landing strips. The new generation of large airplanes emerging, which will carry 700 to 1000 passengers and "up," are all equipped for vertical takeoff and landing, which does away altogether with the necessity for prepared landing strips. With the long landing-strip limitation removed, the size of the airplanes will multiply very rapidly.

To take advantage of the progressive economy gains of increasing size, leading airplane manufacturers already have airplanes on their engineering boards of a size adequate to carry 10,000 passengers or their equivalent in cargo. The 10,000-passenger ship has a length equivalent to that of the Empire State Building. The leading aircraft manufacturers realize that it will be possible to produce Empire State Building-size skyscrapers in horizontal position under factory-controlled conditions in mass-production jigs with mass-production tools.

Working on scaffolds, the Empire State Building was erected under approximately noncontrolled conditions of wind, rain, heat, and cold in the heart of New York City's traffic. One man was killed for every floor of the Empire State Building's 102 stories. No men should be killed in the production of the horizontal skyscraper in the airplane factory. Such skyscraper-size airplanes may then be taken from their factory and with vertical takeoffs and temporarily applied wings will be flown horizontally with minimum effort, to any position around the world and horizontally landed. Using their vertical takeoff equipment they will be upended to serve as skyscrapers, anchored, and braced. Thus we see that whole cities can be flown to any location around the world and also removed in one day to another part of the world just as fleets of ships can come in to port and anchor in one day, or be off for other parts of the world.

In 1954, the United States Marine Corps helicopter-lifted, at 60 miles per hour, a geodesic dome large enough to house an American family. This dome had a floor area of 1000 square feet. In 1955, the Marines air-delivered geodesic domes twice that size, from aircraft carriers to the land, fully skinned and ready to occupy, also at 60 miles per hour. In 1962, the Ford Motor Company helicopter lift delivered a geodesic dome covering a five-times-larger-again floor area of 10,000 square feet. The latest helicopters being built for Vietnam can air-deliver geodesic domes, at 60 miles per hour, large enough to cover an American football field including the end zones, the quarter-mile running track and side bleachers. By 1970, it will be possible to air-deliver geodesic domes large enough to cover small cities. It is now possible with a number of separate helicopter lifts to deliver large subassemblies to complete a geodesic dome large enough to cover a large city and do so within three months' time.

Domed-over cities have extraordinary economic advantage. A two-mile diameter dome has been calculated to cover mid-Manhattan Island, spanning west to east at 42nd Street from the Hudson River to the East River, and spanning south to north from 22nd Street to 62nd Street.

When we wish to make a good air-cooled engine, we design it with many thin fins and spicules to carry away the heat by providing the greatest possible external surface area. The dome calculated for mid-Manhattan has a surface which is only 1/85 the total area of the buildings which it would cover. It would reduce the energy losses either in winter heating or summer cooling to 1/85 the present energy cost obviating snow removals. The cost saving in ten years would pay for the dome.

Domed cities are going to be essential to the occupation of the Arctic and the Antarctic. The Russians are already experimenting with them in the Arctic. The Canadians are also studying them. Mining of the great resources of the Antarctic will require domed-over cities. Domed-over cities will be used in desert areas to shield new growth from the sun while preventing wasteful evaporation of piped in, desalinized water. Gradually the success of new domed cities in remote places will bring about their use in covering old cities, particularly where antiquities are to be protected.

The domed-over cities will be so high and their structural members so delicate that their structural members will be approximately invisible. They will operate like a controlled cloud to bring shadow when shadow is desirable and bring sun when sun is desirable, always keeping out rain, snow, and storms as well as exterior industrial fumes, while collecting all the rainwater in reservoirs. The temperature inside the dome will be so stabilized that a semitropical atmosphere will exist. Inasmuch as there will be no rain or snow in the area, people will live in gardens, or upon garden-terrace skyscrapers needing only local screening for privacy.

There are already 5000 geodesic domes in 50 countries around the world, many so light and strong as to have been air-delivered.

* * * * *

The great historical applications of science have been fundamentally underwritten by the munitions industries and the weapons programs of great nations. When scientists designed the cannon, they didn't have to do anything about the man who fired the cannon. He could sleep beside the cannon and there was air for him to breathe; there was water near at hand, inclement temperature could be offset by clothing. Science produced bigger guns, floated by battleships. Men then could sleep on the deck. However, now that scientific warfare has gone into space, men who handle the warfaring apparatus in space find no air to breathe and no water or food waiting to drink and eat. For the first time in history, it has been necessary for science to upgrade environmental and metabolic regeneration conditions of man and to package them for economic delivery by rockets. To do so requires that science understand man as a process. When the astronauts go beyond the thermos-bottle-and-sandwich excursion limits and live for protracted periods on the moon or elsewhere in space all the regenerative conditions provided by the great biological interactions within the biosphere around earth's surface will have to be reproduced in a miniaturized and capsulized human ecology which will emulate all the chemical and physical transactions necessary to sustain the process "Man." All the apparatus to do so will be contained in a little black box weighing about 500 pounds and measuring about 20 cubic feet. Man in space with the little black box will be able to regenerate his many organic processes, needing only small annual additions to the recirculating chemistry and physical transforming.

The first men living comfortably in space, by virtue of the little black box, will be watched by TV through every moment of their time by continuously rotating audiences of two billion humans on Earth. The whole of humanity will be swiftly educated on the uses and success of living with an entirely new set of environmental control mechanics.

To be successful, the new apparatus will have to operate as unconsciously, on the astronauts' part, as do all of humans' internal organic processes. Men are only aware of their internal organisms when they get a pain in the tummy, or of their eyes when they get a cinder in them.

The little 500-pound black box will have to be produced on earth. The astronauts will not be asked to produce their own black box in space. Though the first black box will probably cost the United States and Russia, combined, well over $7 billion, it will be mass-reproducible on earth at around $2 per pound. This means that a $1000 box could be rented profitably at $200 a year. Any individuals, and their families, could take their black box, costing approximately $18 a month, and go to any remote "dollar-a-year" or wilderness park lands part of earth— mountaintop or island—and enjoy essential services superior to those now available in any city complex because the sewers and energy lines will all be displaced and improved upon by the little autonomously recirculating black box.

The black box as domestic technology fallout from the space and munitions programs will constitute the first wholesale application of science directly to making man a physical and economic success anywhere in universe which of course includes "on earth." It will swiftly divert firsthand application of science from almost exclusive development of weapons and their support and the latter's heretofore almost inexorable nosedive toward self-extermination.

In 1972, a single-family dwelling machine was engineeringly proposed whose structure was similar to that of a wire wheel—laid horizontally on its side—with its axle elongated vertically to act as a supporting mast around which the circular dwelling was supported. This high carousellike dwelling machine had advanced living apparatus suitable for a family of six. It had a top sundeck above and an airplane hangar and garage below the dwelling zone. It was finally prototyped in the aircraft industry in 1944. It weighed only three tons which was approximately 3% of the weight of the equivalent facilities when provided by conventional structures and mechanics. It was popularly hailed. All that was lacking was the little black box to make this air-deliverable dwelling machine the world's most luxurious, remotely installable, and economic family habitat.

* * * * *

A one-hundred-foot-diameter geodesic sphere weighing 3 tons encloses 7 tons of air. The air to structural weight ratio is 2:1. When we double the size so that geodesic sphere is 200 feet in diameter the weight of the structure goes up to 7 tons while the weight of the air goes up to 56 tons—the air to structure ratio changes to 8:1. When we double the size again to a 400-foot geodesic sphere—the size of several geodesic domes now operating—the weight of the air inside goes to about 500 tons while the weight of the structure goes up to 15 tons. The air to structure weight ratio is now 33:1. When we get to a geodesic sphere one-half mile in diameter, the weight of the air enclosed is so great that the weight of the structure itself becomes of relatively negligible magnitude, for the ratio is 1000:1.

When the sun shines on an open-frame aluminum geodesic sphere of one-half-mile diameter the sun penetrating through the frame and reflected from the concave far side bounces back into the sphere and gradually heats the interior atmosphere to a mild degree. When the interior temperature of the sphere rises only 1° Fahrenheit, the weight of air pushed out of the sphere is greater than the weight of the spherical-frame geodesic structure. This means that the total weight of the interior air, plus the weight of the structure, is much less than the surrounding atmosphere. This means that the total assemblage of the geodesic sphere and its contained air will have to float outwardly into the sky, being displaced by the heavy atmosphere around it. When a great bank of mist lies in a valley in the morning and the sun shines upon the mist, the sun heats the air inside the bank of mist. The heated air expands and therefore pushes some of itself outside the mist bank. The total assembly of the mist bank weighs less than the atmosphere surrounding it and the mist bank floats aloft into the sky. Thus are clouds manufactured.

As geodesic spheres get larger than one-half mile in diameter they become floatable cloud structures. If their surfaces were draped with outwardly hung polyethylene curtains to retard the rate at which air would come back in at night, the sphere and its internal atmosphere would continue to be so light as to remain aloft. Such sky-floating geodesic spheres may be designed to float at preferred altitudes of thousands of feet. The weight of human beings added to such pre-fabricated "cloud nines" would be relatively negligible. Many thousands of passengers could be housed aboard one-mile-diameter and larger cloud structures. The passengers could come and go from cloud to cloud, or cloud to ground, as the clouds float around the earth or are anchored to mountaintops. While the building of such floating clouds is several decades hence, we may foresee that along with the floating tetrahedronal cities, air-deliverable skyscrapers, submarine islands, subdry-surface dwellings, domed-over cities, flyable dwelling machines, rentable, autonomous-living black boxes, that man may be able to converge and deploy at will around the earth, in great numbers, without further depletion of the productive surface of the earth.

It may be that after we get to the large skyscraper-size airplanes that they may be economically occupiable and economically flyable from here to there with passengers living aboard as on cruise ships.

It may be that human beings will begin to live in completely mobile ways on sky ships and sea ships as they now occupy cruise ships in large numbers, for months, while traveling around the water and sky oceans. As people live completely around the earth, changing from "summer" to "winter" in hours, the old concept of man as a cold-area or warm-area dweller or as a fixed, static dweller anywhere, and all the old concepts of seasons, or even of work as related only to daylight hours, will gradually be eradicated from man's conditioned reflexes.

Man will come to occupy mobile habitats which may at will be anchored habitats and live independently of day and night and season schedules. This will mean a much higher occupancy in use rate of environment-control facilities. Nowadays, at international airport hotels, people with one-to-eight-hour flight-transfer waitovers follow one another in rooms and beds which are made up freshly as one occupant follows the other. The rooms are occupied, not on a noon-to-noon schedule, but on a use schedule which we may call a frequency-modulation schedule. Such frequency-modulated occupancy of rented space in mobile hotels or in dwelling machines will become the fundamental patterning of man's living around the earth.

On the old farmstead there were a great many buildings to be seen—the great barn, containing hay and cows, the stables, corncribs, silos full of wet fermenting ensilage, the woodshed, pigsty, the carriage house, the cold cellar and the warm cellar. All these buildings and many others on the farms are disappearing or have disappeared because machinery in the house has displaced the functions carried on by the so-called "buildings." The small electric refrigerating device took the place of ice, the icehouse and icebox system. The electric current took the place of the wood, the woodshed and stove system, etc. In two decades the windmills, formerly on every farm, have gone.

In this way, we discover that the buildings, which controlled energy conditions of heat, cold, dry, and wet, were in effect machines because machines process and control energy. All those machines known erroneously as "buildings" have now been replaced by machines more readily recognized by us as machinery. Now however the recognizable components are decreasing as technology employs more and more of the invisible capabilities of electronics. What we are witnessing is the disappearance of the ever less economic "housing" or slow-motion phase of machinery as its functions are taken over by the high-speed machinery that brings about and maintains the preferred environment conditions at ever less cost and personal effort. This evolution is well underway, but we hide it from our awareness through semantic error, typical of which is society's noncomprehension of what Le Corbusier meant when he said, "A house is a machine for living."

When the early homesteaders went on the land with few or no tools, they had to work in the fields or build their energy-controlling structures during every minute of daylight. Spent, in 12 hours of hard labor, they slept from twilight to dawn. The design of their farmhouses told the story—little boxes with vertical walls going down into the ground. There were no porches or stoops. There were a few windows, enough for the farmer's wife to see where he was around the farm and to see if the Indians were coming. When tools, and more tools, came to shorten the time taken to do a given job, the farmer gained more time of his own. Finally, he had enough time before twilight to sit and look at the scenery, and he built porches around his house. As he began to have more and more time, he began to put screens on the porches. With ever more time, he began to put glass windows on the porches. Sitting on his porches, he watched other people go by. Then came the automobile, which in effect put wheels under his glassed-in front porch, so instead of waiting to see people go by he drove down the street to see the people. In a very real sense, the automobile was part of the house, broken off, like hydra cells going off on a life of their own. The young people who used to court in the parlor, then on the glassed-in front porch, now began to do their courting in the automobile, or the porch with wheels. Today, the young people do their courting in their parlor on wheels, driving it to the drive-in theater. Because we are conditioned to think of the house as static, we fail to realize that the automobile is as much a part of the house as is the addition of a woodshed.

In 1920, 85% of the cost of production of a single-family dwelling in the United States went into the house's shell and foundation. Only 15% of the general contract went into what we call "mechanical inclusions." In North America, that 15% covered a kitchen sink and a furnace. There was no electrical refrigeration at that time. Only a small percentage of houses had indoor toilets. A very small percentage had electric wiring. Due to the high mechanization of World War I, the postwar "fallout" of advanced technology brought one mechanical inclusion after another to be incorporated in the general contract for a single-family dwelling. Then came the electric refrigerator, the oil-burner furnace, the hot-water heater, the radio, etc.

In 1929, 28% of the general contract for a single-family dwelling went into mechanical inclusions.

In 1940, 45% of the general contract went into mechanical inclusions.

At the present time, 65% of the general contract goes into mechanical inclusions, which embraces electric wiring and plumbing, as well as the obvious machinery.

During this same time, the size of the various domestic machines has continually decreased. As an instance, the electric sewing machine decreased from a very big device to a small one. As transistors and other miniaturizations occurred, the machinery of the general contract continually produced more service with less apparatus and effort. Through the years, the cost of the electrical current to operate the mechanization continually decreased despite the increase of costs in almost all other directions.

Concurrently, the size of the houses greatly decreased as servants were replaced with machines, which eliminated servants' rooms. Sizes of families decreased as life expectancy increased. Despite the continual decrease in the size of individual homes, the cost per cubic foot of the enclosing structure has rocketed upward.

Clearly the machinery is giving man more-and-more for less-and-less, while the structural arts are giving man less-and-less for more-and-more.

The great city electric generators and the great chemical factories were once housed in vast Georgian-architecture brick factories. The chemical industries learned how to make machinery so that it would not deteriorate in the open air. The electrical industry did the same. Today we see enormous petroleum refineries and other chemical plants with their machinery completely exposed to the atmosphere—no walls. This is invisible architecture. We see the electrical switchyards entirely outdoors, with only high fences around them. We can correlate these trends—of the single-family dwelling's swiftly transferring tasks to machinery from the relatively inefficient structural shells—with the trend of the front parlor onto wheels to go off down the street to be called the "automobile."

Because of these trends, what we now call "home trailers" are simply modern, lightweight, aluminum boxes, full of the mechanical package which constitutes the improved standard of living—minus the expensive house—compacted into usable array which mobile home packages prosper as the "regular" static home market has never prospered, despite the lack of esthetic appeal, and despite cultural inertias.

The home-trailer business has rocketed into a major industry without any federal subsidies and mortgages, while the whole home-building business has been kept going only by the 40-year government mortgage-loan guarantees, and is now in fundamental decline.

The environment always consists of energy—energy as matter, energy as radiation, energy as gravity, and energy as "events." Housing is an energetic environment-controlling mechanism. Thinking correctly of all housing as machinery we begin to realize the complete continuity of interrelationship of such technological evolution as that of the home bedroom into the railway sleeping car, into the automobile with seat-to-bed conversions, into the filling-station toilets, which are accessories of the parlor-on-wheels; the trailer, the motels, hotels, and ocean liners. All this living machinery complements the inherently transient nature of world society and its progressive emancipation from the local shackles of physical-property "machines" which were so inefficient and so enormous as to be nonportable and therefore to have imposed a static property condition upon world society which misled man into thinking of himself as geographically rooted. The new pushbutton-operating, energy-processing machinery makes operative preferred conditions on wheels, on boats, on wings, or on temporarily anchored earth beds anywhere around the earth and outwardly in space, permitting man to rest or go where he wills.

But the conditioned reflexes of society make laws that force the mobile home owner to emulate only the realtors' static horizontality. The realtors' zoned trailer parks grow up everywhere to capture the swiftly multiplying mechanical house packages. The rapidly expanding fiberglass-plastic-and-metal boat production is turning out houseboats, motor cruisers, sailing cruisers all with living machinery of the highest order of efficiently and livably compact packaging. Mooring or storing of these boats operates horizontally in harbors or marinas.

The tetrahedronal city which can be expanded from a 100,000- to a 300,000-family-supporting device consists structurally of a complex of trusses. Such tetrahedronal cities make it a practical matter for power cranes to pick up the mechanical package in the form of trailers, houseboats, or cruisers and park them on the open terraces of the tetrahedronal trusses.

One reason that we allowed 2000 square feet (200 square meters) per family on the vertically paralleled terraces of the tetrahedronal floating cities is to permit the storage of mobile trailers, houseboats, and mobile homes in general on the terraces, leaving an additional thousand square feet for a garden for each mobile tenant. These devices will be all weatherproofed and therefore require no additional "walls" or external skins to be fastened onto the tetrahedron city. Such a two-mile-high tetrahedronal city will consist of an open-truss-framework "structural mountain" whose sides are covered with parked mobile homes which at night will be ablaze with light as are the great petroleum refineries.

There will be no brick- or stone-sided tetrahedronal "mountain" cities. There will be delicate, fireproof, prestressed-concrete open-framework tetrahedronal cities consisting of hundreds or even thousands of decks one above the other on which the floatable, flyable, roadable mobile-home mechanical containers will be economically parked as their occupants dwell locally for periods during their world-around peregrinations. Each mobile home safely locked in place on its mechanical mountain terrace will provide its own all-weather skin.

As we consider these fundamental transitions in types of machinery from what seemed to be "buildings" to obvious mechanics, we realize the complete evolutionary continuity of all these trends. We realize also that the transition to the faster technologies, which will open up all oceans and skies to man's support and enjoyment, is an inevitable consequence of what is already irrevocably and inexorably underway, but has been mistakenly identified by the wrong names, wrong conceptions, and wrong categories with which man has processed his experiences.

By and large, the great world housing problem is an *educational problem*. By and large, man's inertias are only overcome by virtue of his own personal discoveries, discernment, and understanding of what it is that is happening to him. There will be no instant world housing solutions. There are fundamental rates at which the educational gestation takes place.

Publishers who try to exploit man's imagination by giving him only the end-product concepts, without showing how man will get from here to there, postpone the opportunities for helping man to educate himself on how these events may come to pass and the advantages which will be gained.

I, for one, am unwilling to allow anyone to be only amused by startling concepts of tetrahedronal cities and air-deliverable Empire State buildings while keeping from society the opportunity to understand the complex of factors that lead to such tangible results.

The comprehensive introduction of automation everywhere around the earth will free man from being an automaton and will generate so fast a mastery and multiplication of energy wealth by humanity that we will be able to support all of humanity in ever greater physical and economic success anywhere around his little spaceship *Earth*.

Quite clearly, man enabled to enjoy his total earth, enabled to research the bottom of his ocean, and to reexplore earlier patterns of man around earth, will also be swiftly outwardbound to occupy ever greater ranges of universe.

Within decades we will know whether man is going to be a physical success around earth, able to function in ever greater patterns of local universe or whether he is going to frustrate his own success with his negatively conditioned reflexes of yesterday and will bring about his own extinction around the planet earth. My intuitions foresee his success despite his negative inertias. This means things are going to move fast.

The Role of Technology in Society

EMMANUEL G. MESTHENE

SOCIAL CHANGE

Three Unhelpful Views about Technology. While a good deal of research
is aimed at discerning the particular effects of technological change on industry, government, or education, systematic inquiry devoted to seeing these
effects together and to assessing their implications for contemporary society
as a whole is relatively recent and does not enjoy the strong methodology and
richness of theory and data that mark more established fields of scholarship.
It therefore often has to contend with facile or one-dimensional views about
what technology means for society. Three such views, which are prevalent at
the present time, may be mildly caricatured somewhat as follows.

The first holds that technology is an unalloyed blessing for man and society. Technology is seen as the motor of all progress, as holding the solution to
most of our social problems, as helping to liberate the individual from the
clutches of a complex and highly organized society, and as the source of permanent prosperity; in short, as the promise of utopia in our time. This view
has its modern origins in the social philosophies of such 19th-century thinkers
as Saint-Simon, Karl Marx, and Auguste Comte. It tends to be held by many
scientists and engineers, by many military leaders and aerospace industrialists,
by people who believe that man is fully in command of his tools and his destiny, and by many of the devotees of modern techniques of "scientific management."

A second view holds that technology is an unmitigated curse. Technology
is said to rob people of their jobs, their privacy, their participation in democratic government, and even, in the end, their dignity as human beings. It is
seen as autonomous and uncontrollable, as fostering materialistic values and
as destructive of religion, as bringing about a technocratic society and bureaucratic state in which the individual is increasingly submerged, and as threatening, ultimately, to poison nature and blow up the world. This view is akin to
historical "back-to-nature" attitudes toward the world and is propounded
mainly by artists, literary commentators, popular social critics, and existen-
tialist philosophers. It is becoming increasingly attractive to many of our

youth, and it tends to be held, understandably enough, by segments of the population that have suffered dislocation as a result of technological change.

The third view is of a different sort. It argues that technology as such is not worthy of special notice, because it has been well recognized as a factor in social change at least since the Industrial Revolution, because it is unlikely that the social effects of computers will be nearly so traumatic as the introduction of the factory system in 18th-century England, because research has shown that technology has done little to accelerate the rate of economic productivity since the 1880s, because there has been no significant change in recent decades in the time period between invention and widespread adoption of new technology, and because improved communications and higher levels of education make people much more adaptable than heretofore to new ideas and to new social reforms required by technology.

While this view is supported by a good deal of empirical evidence, however, it tends to ignore a number of social, cultural, psychological, and political effects of technological change that are less easy to identify with precision. It thus reflects the difficulty of coming to grips with a new or broadened subject matter by means of concepts and intellectual categories designed to deal with older and different subject matters. This view tends to be held by historians, for whom continuity is an indispensable methodological assumption, and by many economists, who find that their instruments measure some things quite well while those of the other social sciences do not yet measure much of anything.

Stripped of caricature, each of these views contains a measure of truth and reflects a real aspect of the relationship of technology and society. Yet they are oversimplifications that do not contribute much to understanding. One can find empirical evidence to support each of them without gaining much knowledge about the actual mechanism by which technology leads to social change or significant insight into its implications for the future. All three remain too uncritical or too partial to guide inquiry. Research and analysis lead to more differentiated conclusions and reveal more subtle relationships.

Some Countervailing Considerations. Two of the projects of the Harvard University Program on Technology and Society serve, respectively, to temper some exaggerated claims made for technology and to replace gloom with balanced judgment. Professor Anthony G. Oettinger's study of information technology in education[1] has shown that, in the schools at least, technology is not

1. Unless otherwise noted, studies such as Oettinger's which are referred to in this article are described in the Fourth Annual Report (1967–68) of the Harvard University Program on Technology and Society.

likely to bring salvation with it quite so soon as the U.S. Office of Education, leaders of the education industry, and enthusiastic computermen and systems analysts might wish. Neither educational technology nor the school establishment seems ready to consummate the revolution in learning that will bring individualized instruction to every child, systematic planning and uniform standards across 25,000 separate school districts, an answer to bad teachers and unmovable bureaucracies, and implementation of a national policy to educate every American to his full potential for a useful and satisfying life. Human fallibility and political reality are still here to keep utopia at bay, and neither promises soon to yield to a quick technological fix. Major institutional change that can encourage experimentation, flexibility, variety, and competition among educational institutions seems called for before the new technology can contribute significantly to education. Application of the technology itself, moreover, poses problems of scale-up, reliability, and economics that have scarcely been faced as yet.

By contrast, Professor Manfred Stanley's study of the value presuppositions that underlie the pessimistic arguments about technology suggests that predictions of inevitable doom are premature and that a number of different social outcomes are potential in the process of technological change. In other words, the range of possibility and of human choice implicit in technology is much greater than most critics assume. The problem—here, as well as in the application of educational technology—is how to organize society to free the possibility of choice.

Finally, whether modern technology and its effects constitute a subject matter deserving of special attention is largely a matter of how technology is defined. The research studies of the Harvard Program on Technology and Society reflect an operating assumption that the meaning of technology includes more than machines. As most serious investigators have found, understanding is not advanced by concentrating single-mindedly on such narrowly drawn yet imprecise questions as "What are the social implications of computers, or lasers, or space technology?" Society and the influences of technology upon it are much too complex for such artificially limited approaches to be meaningful. The opposite error, made by some, is to define technology too broadly by identifying it with rationality in the broadest sense. The term is then operationally meaningless and unable to support fruitful inquiry.

We have found it more useful to define technology as tools in a general sense, including machines, but also including linguistic and intellectual tools and contemporary analytic and mathematical techniques. That is, we define technology as the organization of knowledge for practical purposes. It is in this broader meaning that we can best see the extent and variety of the effects of technology on our institutions and values. Its pervasive influence on our very culture would be unintelligible if technology were understood as no more than hardware.

It is in the pervasive influence of technology that our contemporary situation seems qualitatively different from that of past societies, for three reasons. (1) Our tools are more powerful than any before. The rifle wiped out the buffalo, but nuclear weapons can wipe out man. Dust storms lay whole regions waste, but too much radioactivity in the atmosphere could make the planet uninhabitable. The domestication of animals and the invention of the wheel literally lifted the burden from man's back, but computers could free him from all need to labor. (2) This quality of finality of modern technology has brought our society, more than any before, to explicit awareness of technology as an important determinant of our lives and institutions. (3) As a result, our society is coming to a deliberate decision to understand and control technology to good social purpose and is therefore devoting significant effort to the search for ways to measure the full range of its effects rather than only those bearing principally on the economy. It is this prominence of technology in many dimensions of modern life that seems novel in our time and deserving of explicit attention.

How Technological Change Impinges on Society. It is clearly possible to sketch a more adequate hypothesis about the interaction of technology and society than the partial views outlined above. Technological change would appear to induce or "motor" social change in two principal ways. New technology creates new opportunities for men and societies, and it also generates new problems for them. It has both positive and negative effects, and it usually has the two *at the same time and in virtue of each other.* Thus, industrial technology strengthens the economy, as our measures of growth and productivity show. As Dr. Anne P. Carter's study on structural changes in the American economy has helped to demonstrate, however, it also induces changes in the relative importance of individual supplying sectors in the economy as new techniques of production alter the amounts and kinds of materials, parts and components, energy, and service inputs used by each industry to produce its output. It thus tends to bring about dislocations of businesses and people as a result of changes in industrial patterns and in the structure of occupations.

The close relationship between technological and social change itself helps to explain why any given technological development is likely to have both positive and negative effects. The usual sequence is that (1) technological advance creates a new opportunity to achieve some desired goal; (2) this requires (except in trivial cases) alterations in social organization if advantage is to be taken of the new opportunity, (3) which means that the functions of existing social structures will be interfered with, (4) with the result that other goals which were served by the older structures are now only inadequately achieved.

As the Meyer-Kain study has shown, for example, improved transportation technology and increased ownership of private automobiles have increased the mobility of businesses and individuals. This has led to altered patterns of industrial and residential location, so that older unified cities are being increasingly transformed into larger metropolitan complexes. The new opportunities for mobility are largely denied to the poor and black populations of the core cities, however, partly for economic reasons, and partly as a result of restrictions on choice of residence by Negroes, thus leading to persistent Negro unemployment despite a generally high level of economic activity. Cities are thus increasingly unable to perform their traditional functions of providing employment opportunities for all segments of their populations and an integrated social environment that can temper ethnic and racial differences. The new urban complexes are neither fully viable economic units nor effective political organizations able to upgrade and integrate their core populations into new economic and social structures. The resulting instability is further aggravated by modern mass communications technology, which heightens the expectations of the poor and the fears of the well-to-do and adds frustration and bitterness to the urban crisis.

An almost classic example of the sequence in which technology impinges on society is provided by Professor Mark Field's study of changes in the system and practice of medical care. Recent advances in biomedical science and technology have created two new opportunities: (1) they have made possible treatment and cures that were never possible before, and (2) they provide a necessary condition for the delivery of adequate medical care to the population at large as a matter of right rather than privilege. In realization of the first possibility, the medical profession has become increasingly differentiated and specialized and is tending to concentrate its best efforts in a few major, urban centers of medical excellence. This alters the older social organization of medicine that was built around the general practitioner. The second possibility has led to big increases in demand for medical services, partly because a healthy population has important economic advantages in a highly industrialized society. This increased demand accelerates the process of differentiation and multiplies the levels of paramedical personnel between the physician at the top and the patient at the bottom of the hospital pyramid.

Both of these changes in the medical system are responsive to the new opportunities for technical excellence that have been created by biomedical technology. Both also involve a number of well-known costs in terms of some older desiderata of medical care. The increasing scarcity of the general practitioner in many sections of the country means that people in need often have neither easy access to professional care nor the advantage of a "medical general manager" who can direct them to the right care at the right place at the right time, which can result both in poor treatment and a waste of medical resources. Also, too exclusive a concentration on technical excellence can lead to neglect of the patient's psychological well-being, and even the possibility of technical error increases as the "medical assembly line" gets longer.

The pattern illustrated by the preceding examples tends to be the general one. Our most spectacular technological successes in America in the last quarter of a century have been in national defense and in space exploration. They have brought with them, however, enthusiastic advocates and vested interests who claim that the development of sophisticated technology is an intrinsic good that should be pursued for its own sake. They thus contribute to the self-reinforcing quality of technological advance and raise fears of an autonomous technology uncontrollable by man. Mass communications technology has also made rapid strides since World War II, with great benefit to education, journalism, commerce, and sheer convenience. It has also been accompanied by an aggravation of social unrest, however, and may help to explain the singular rebelliousness of a youth that can find out what the world is like from television before home and school have had the time to instill some ethical sense of what it could or should be like.

In all such cases, technology creates a new opportunity and a new problem at the same time. That is why isolating the opportunity or the problem and construing it as the whole answer is ultimately obstructive of rather than helpful to understanding.

How Society Reacts to Technological Change. The heightened prominence of technology in our society makes the interrelated tasks of profiting from its opportunities and containing its dangers a major intellectual and political challenge of our time.

Failure of society to respond to the opportunities created by new technology means that much actual or potential technology lies fallow, that is, is not used at all or is not used to its full capacity. This can mean that potentially solvable problems are left unsolved and potentially achievable goals unachieved, because we waste our technological resources or use them inefficiently. A society has at least as much stake in the efficient utilization of technology as in that of its natural or human resources.

There are often good reasons, of course, for not developing or utilizing a particular technology. The mere fact that it can be developed is not sufficient reason for doing so. The costs of development may be too high in the light of the expected benefits, as in the case of the project to develop a nuclear-powered aircraft. Or, a new technological device may be so dangerous in itself or so inimical to other purposes that it is never developed, as in the cases of Herman Kahn's "Doomsday Machine" and the recent proposal to "nightlight" Vietnam by reflected sunlight.

But there are also cases where technology lies fallow because existing social structures are inadequate to exploit the opportunities it offers. This is revealed clearly in the examination of institutional failure in the ghetto by Professor Richard S. Rosenbloom and his colleagues. At point after point, their analyses confirm what has been long suspected, that is, that existing institutions and traditional approaches are by and large incapable of coming to grips with the new problems of our cities—many of them caused by technological change, as the Meyer-Kain study has reminded us—and unable to realize the possibilities for resolving them that are also inherent in technology. Vested economic and political interests serve to obstruct adequate provision of low-cost housing. Community institutions wither for want of interest and participation by residents. City agencies are unable to marshal the skills and take the systematic approach needed to deal with new and intensified problems of education, crime control, and public welfare. Business corporations, finally, which are organized around the expectation of private profit, are insufficiently motivated to bring new technology and management know-how to bear on urban projects where the benefits will be largely social. All these factors combine to dilute what may otherwise be a genuine desire to apply our best knowledge and adequate resources to the resolution of urban tensions and the eradication of poverty in the nation.

There is also institutional failure of another sort. Government in general and agencies of public information in particular are not yet equipped for the massive task of public education that is needed if our society is to make full use of its technological potential, although the federal government has been making significant strides in this direction in recent years. Thus, much potentially valuable technology goes unused because the public at large is insufficiently informed about the possibilities and their costs to provide support for appropriate political action. As noted, we have done very well with our technology in the face of what were or were believed to be crisis situations, as with our military technology in World War II and with our space efforts when beating the Russians to the moon was deemed a national goal of first priority. We have also done very well when the potential benefits of technology were close to home or easy to see, as in improved health care and better and more varied consumer goods and services. We have done much less well in developing and applying technology where the need or opportunity has seemed neither so clearly critical nor so clearly personal as to motivate political action, as in the instance of urban policy already cited. Technological possibility continues to lie fallow in those areas where institutional and political innovation is a precondition of realizing it.

Containing the Negative Effects of Technology. The kinds and magnitude of the negative effects of technology are no more independent of the institutional structures and cultural attitudes of society than is realization of the new opportunities that technology offers. In our society, there are individuals or individual firms always on the lookout for new technological opportunities, and large corporations hire scientists and engineers to invent such opportunities. In deciding whether to develop a new technology, individual entrepreneurs engage in calculations of expected benefits and expected costs to themselves, and proceed if the former are likely to exceed the latter. Their calculations do not take adequate account of the probable benefits and costs of the new developments to others than themselves or to society generally. These latter are what economists call external benefits and costs.

The external benefits potential in new technology will thus not be realized by the individual developer and will rather accrue to society as a result of deliberate social action, as has been argued above. Similarly with the external costs. In minimizing only expected costs to himself, the individual decision maker helps to contain only some of the potentially negative effects of the new technology. The external costs and therefore the negative effects on society at large are not of principal concern to him and, in our society, are not expected to be.

Most of the consequences of technology that are causing concern at the present time—pollution of the environment, potential damage to the ecology of the planet, occupational and social dislocations, threats to the privacy and political significance of the individual, social and psychological malaise—are negative externalities of this kind. They are with us in large measure because it has not been anybody's explicit business to foresee and anticipate them. They have fallen between the stools of innumerable individual decisions to develop individual technologies for individual purposes without explicit attention to what all these decisions add up to for society as a whole and for people as human beings. This freedom of individual decision making is a value that we have cherished and that is built into the institutional fabric of our society. The negative effects of technology that we deplore are a measure of what this traditional freedom is beginning to cost us. They are traceable, less to some mystical autonomy presumed to lie in technology, and much more to the autonomy that our economic and political institutions grant to individual decision making.

When the social costs of individual decision making in the economic realm achieved crisis proportions in the great depression of the 1930s, the federal government introduced economic policies and measures many of which had the effect of abridging the freedom of individual decision. Now that some of the negative impacts of technology are threatening to become critical, the government is considering measures of control that will have the analogous effect of constraining the freedom of individual decision makers to develop and apply new technologies irrespective of social consequence. Congress is actively seeking to establish technology-assessment boards of one sort or another which it hopes may be able to foresee potentially damaging effects of technology on nature and man. In the executive branch, attention is being directed (1) to development of a system of social indicators to help gauge the social effects of technology, (2) to establishment of some body of social advisers to the president to help develop policies in anticipation of such effects, and generally (3) to strengthening the role of the social sciences in policy making.

Measures to control and mitigate the negative effects of technology, however, often appear to threaten freedoms that our traditions still take for granted as inalienable rights of men and good societies, however much they may have been tempered in practice by the social pressures of modern times: the freedom of the market, the freedom of private enterprise, the freedom of the scientist to follow truth wherever it may lead, and the freedom of the individual to pursue his fortune and decide his fate. There is thus set up a tension between the need to control technology and our wish to preserve our values, which leads some people to conclude that technology is inherently inimical to human values. The political effect of this tension takes the form of inability to adjust our decision-making structures to the realities of technology so as to take maximum advantage of the opportunities it offers and so that we can act to contain its potential ill effects before they become so pervasive and urgent as to seem uncontrollable.

To understand why such tensions are so prominent a social consequence of technological change, it becomes necessary to look explicitly at the effects of technology on social and individual values.

VALUES

Technology's Challenge to Values. Despite the practical importance of the techniques, institutions, and processes of knowledge in contemporary society, political decision making and the resolution of social problems are clearly not dependent on knowledge alone. Numerous commentators have noted that ours is a "knowledge" society, devoted to rational decision making and an "end of ideology," but none would deny the role that values play in shaping the course of society and the decisions of individuals. On the contrary, questions of values become more pointed and insistent in a society that organizes itself to control technology and that engages in deliberate social planning. Planning demands explicit recognition of value hierarchies and often brings into the open value conflicts which remain hidden in the more impersonal working of the market.

In economic planning, for example, we have to make choices between the values of leisure and increased productivity, without a common measure to help us choose. In planning education, we come face to face with the traditional American value dilemma of equality versus achievement: do we opt for equality and nondiscrimination and give all students the same basic education, or do we foster achievement by tailoring education to the capacity for learning, which is itself often conditioned by socioeconomic background?

The new science-based decision-making techniques also call for clarity: in the specification of goals, thus serving to make value preferences explicit. The effectiveness of systems analysis, for example, depends on having explicitly stated objectives and criteria of evaluation to begin with, and the criteria and objectives of specific actions invariably relate to the society's system of values. That, incidentally, is why the application of systems analysis meets with less relative success in educational or urban planning than in military planning: the value conflicts are fewer in the latter and the objectives and criteria easier to specify and agree on. This increased awareness of conflicts among our values contributes to a general questioning attitude toward traditional values that appears to be endemic to a high-technology, knowledge-based society: "A society in which the store of knowledge concerning the consequences of action is large and is rapidly increasing is a society in which received norms and their 'justifying' values will be increasingly subjected to questioning and reformulation."[2]

2. Robin Williams, "Individual and Group Values," *Annals of the American Academy of Political and Social Science* 37 (May 1967): 30.

This is another way of pointing to the tension alluded to earlier, between the need for social action based on knowledge on the one hand, and the pull of our traditional values on the other. The increased questioning and reformulation of values that Williams speaks of, coupled with a growing awareness that our values are in fact changing under the impact of technological change, leads many people to believe that technology is by nature destructive of values. But this belief presupposes a conception of values as eternal and unchanging and therefore tends to confuse the valuable with the stable. The fact that values come into question as our knowledge increases and that some traditional values cease to function adequately when technology leads to changes in social conditions does not mean that values per se are being destroyed by knowledge and technology.

What does happen is that values change through a process of accommodation between the system of existing values and the technological and social changes that impinge on it. The projects of the Harvard Program in the area of technology and values are devoted to discovering the specific ways in which this process of accommodation occurs and to tracing its consequences for value changes in contemporary American society. The balance of this section is devoted to a more extended discussion of the first results of these projects.

Technology as a Cause of Value Change. Technology has a direct impact on values by virtue of its capacity for creating new opportunities. By making possible what was not possible before, it offers individuals and society new options to choose from. For example, space technology makes it possible for the first time to go to the moon or to communicate by satellite and thereby adds those two new options to the spectrum of choices available to society. By adding new options in this way, technology can lead to changes in values in the same way that the appearance of new dishes on the heretofore standard menu of one's favorite restaurant can lead to changes in one's tastes and choices of food. Specifically, technology can lead to value change either (1) by bringing some previously unattainable goal within the realm of choice or (2) by making some values easier to implement than heretofore, that is, by changing the costs associated with realizing them.

Dr. Irene Taviss is exploring the ways in which technological change affects intrinsic sources of tension and potential change in value systems. When technology facilitates implementation of some social ideal and society fails to act upon this new possibility, the conflict between principle and practice is sharpened, thus leading to new tensions. For example, the economic affluence that technology has helped to bring to American society makes possible fuller implementation than heretofore of our traditional values of social and economic equality. Until it is acted upon, that possibility gives rise to the tensions we associate with the rising expectations of the underprivileged and provokes both the activist response of the radical left and the hippie's rejection of society as "hypocritical."

Another example related to the effect of technological change on values is implicit in our concept of democracy. The ideal we associate with the old New England town meeting is that each citizen should have a direct voice in political decisions. Since this has not been possible, we have elected representatives to serve our interests and vote our opinions. Sophisticated computer technology, however, now makes possible rapid and efficient collection and analysis of voter opinion and could eventually provide for "instant voting" by the whole electorate on any issue presented to it via television a few hours before. It thus raises the possibility of instituting a system of direct democracy and gives rise to tensions between those who would be violently opposed to such a prospect and those who are already advocating some system of participatory democracy.

This new technological possibility challenges us to clarify what we mean by democracy. Do we construe it as the will of an undifferentiated majority, as the resultant of transient coalitions of different interest groups representing different value commitments, as the considered judgment of the people's elected representatives, or as by and large the kind of government we actually have in the United States, minus the flaws in it that we would like to correct? By bringing us face to face with such questions, technology has the effect of calling society's bluff and thereby preparing the ground for changes in its values.

In the case where technological change alters the relative costs of implementing different values, it impinges on inherent contradictions in our value system. To pursue the same example, modern technology can enhance the values we associate with democracy. But it can also enhance another American value—that of "secular rationality," as sociologists call it—by facilitating the use of scientific and technical expertise in the process of political decision making. This can in turn further reduce citizen participation in the democratic process. Technology thus has the effect of facing us with contradictions in our own value system and of calling for deliberate attention to their resolution.

The Value Implications of Economic Change. In addition to the relatively direct effects of technology on values, as illustrated above, value change often comes about through the intermediation of some more general social change produced by technology, as in the tension imposed on our individualistic values by the external benefits and costs of technological development that was alluded to in the earlier discussion of the negative effects of technology. Professor Nathan Rosenberg is exploring the closely allied relationship between such values and the need for society to provide what economists call public goods and services.

As a number of economists have shown, such public goods differ from private consumer goods and services in that they are provided on an all-or-none basis and consumed in a joint way, so that more for one consumer does not mean less for another. The clearing of a swamp or a flood-control project, once completed, benefits everyone in the vicinity. A meteorological forecast, once made, can be transmitted by word of mouth to additional users at no additional cost. Knowledge itself may thus be thought of as the public good par excellence, since the research expenses needed to produce it are incurred only once, unlike consumer goods of which every additional unit adds to the cost of production.

As noted earlier, private profit expectation is an inadequate incentive for the production of such public goods, because their benefit is indiscriminate and not fully appropriate to the firm or individual that might incur the cost of producing them. Individuals are therefore motivated to dissimulate by understating their true preferences for such goods in the hope of shifting their cost to others. This creates a "free-loader" problem, which skews the mechanism of the market. The market therefore provides no effective indication of the optimal amount of such public commodities from the point of view of society as a whole. If society got only as much public health care, flood control, or knowledge as individual profit calculations would generate, it would no doubt get less of all of them than it does now or than it expresses a desire for by collective political action.

This gap between collective preference and individual motivation imposes strains on a value system, such as ours, which is primarily individualistic rather than collective or "societal" in its orientation. That system arose out of a simpler, more rustic, and less affluent time, when both benefits and costs were of a much more private sort than now. It is no longer fully adequate for our society, which industrial technology has made productive enough to allocate significant resources to the purchase of public goods and services, and in which modern transportation and communications as well as the absolute magnitude of technological effects lead to extensive ramifications of individual actions on other people and on the environment.

The response to this changed experience on the part of the public at large generally takes the form of increased government intervention in social and economic affairs to contain or guide these wider ramifications, as noted previously. The result is that the influence of values associated with the free reign of individual enterprise and action tends to be counteracted, thus facilitating a change in values. To be sure, the tradition that ties freedom and liberty to a laissez-faire system of decision making remains very strong, and the changes in social structures and cultural attitudes that can touch it at its foundations are still only on the horizon.

Religion and Values. Much of the unease that our society's emphasis on technology seems to generate among various sectors of society can perhaps be explained in terms of the impact that technology has on religion. The formulations and institutions of religion are not immune to the influences of technological change, for they too tend toward an accommodation to changes in the social milieu in which they function. But one way in which religion functions is as an ultimate belief system that provides legitimation, that is, a "meaning" orientation, to moral and social values. This ultimate meaning orientation, according to Professor Harvey Cox, is even more basic to human existence than the value orientation. When the magnitude or rapidity of social change threatens the credibility of that belief system, therefore, and when the changes are moreover seen as largely the results of technological change, the meanings of human existence that we hold most sacred seem to totter and technology emerges as the villain.

Religious change thus provides another mediating mechanism through which technology affects our values. That conditions are ripe for religious change at the present time has been noted by many observers, who are increasingly questioning whether our established religious syntheses and symbol systems are adequate any longer to the religious needs of a scientific and secular society that is changing so fundamentally as to strain traditional notions of eternity. If they are not, how are they likely to change? Professor Cox is addressing himself to this problem with specific attention to the influence of technology in guiding the direction of change.

He notes that religion needs to come to terms with the pluralism of belief systems that is characteristic of the modern world. The generation of knowledge and the use of technology are so much a part of the style and self-image of our own society that men begin to experience themselves, their power, and their relationships to nature and history in terms of open possibility, hope, action, and self-confidence. The symbolism of such traditional religious postures as subservience, fatefulness, destiny, and suprarational faith begin then to seem irrelevant to our actual experience. They lose credibility, and their religions function is weakened. Secular belief systems arise to compete for the allegiance of men: political belief systems, such as communism; or scientific ones, such as modern-day humanism; or such inexplicit, noninstitutionalized belief complexes as are characteristic of agnosticism.

This pluralism poses serious problems for the ultimate legitimation or "meaning" orientation for moral and social values that religion seeks to provide, because it demands a religions synthesis that can integrate the fact of variant perspectives into its own symbol system. Western religions have been notoriously incapable of performing this integrating function and have rather gone the route of schism and condemnation of variance as heresy. The institutions and formulations of historical Christianity in particular, which once served as the foundations of Western society, carry the added burden of centuries of conflict with scientific world views as these have competed for ascendancy in the same society. This makes it especially difficult for traditional Christianity to accommodate to a living experience so infused by scientific knowledge and attitudes as ours and helps explain why its adequacy is coming under serious question at the present time.

Cox notes three major traditions in the Judeo-Christian synthesis and finds them inconsistent in their perceptions of the future: an "apocalyptic" tradition foresees imminent catastrophe and induces a negative evaluation of this world; a "teleological" tradition sees the future as the certain unfolding of a fixed purpose inherent in the universe itself; a "prophetic" tradition, finally, sees the future as an open field of human hope and responsibility and as becoming what man will make of it.[3]

Technology, as noted, creates new possibilities for human choice and action but leaves their disposition uncertain. What its effects will be and what ends it will serve are not inherent in the technology, but depend on what man will do with technology. Technology thus makes possible a future of open-ended options that seems to accord well with the presuppositions of the prophetic tradition. It is in that tradition above others, then, that we may seek the beginnings of a religious synthesis that is both adequate to our time and continuous with what is most relevant in our religious history. But this requires an effort at deliberate religious innovation for which Cox finds insufficient theological ground at the present time. Although it is recognized that

3. See Harvey Cox, "Tradition and the Future," pts. 1 and 2, in *Christianity and Crisis* 27, nos. 16 and 17 (October 2 and 16, 1968): 218–20 and 227–31.

religions have changed and developed in the past, conscious innovation in religion has been condemned and is not provided for by the relevant theologies. The main task that technological change poses for theology in the next decades, therefore, is that of deliberate religious innovation and symbol reformulation to take specific account of religious needs in a technological age.

What consequences would such changes in religion have for values? Cox approaches this question in the context of the familiar complaint that, since technology is principally a means, it enhances merely instrumental values at the expense of expressive, consummatory, or somehow more "real" values. The appropriate distinction, however, is not between technological instrumental values and nontechnological expressive values, but among the expressive values that attach to different technologies. The horse-and-buggy was a technology too, after all, and it is not prima facie clear that its charms were different in kind or superior to the sense of power and adventure and the spectacular views that go with jet travel.

Further, technological advance in many instances is a condition for the emergence of new creative or consummatory values. Improved sound boxes in the past and structural steel and motion photography in the present have made possible the artistry of Jascha Heifetz, Frank Lloyd Wright, and Charles Chaplin, which have opened up wholly new ranges of expressive possibility without, moreover, in any way inhibiting a concurrent renewal of interest in medieval instruments and primitive art. If religious innovation can provide a meaning orientation broad enough to accommodate the idea that new technology can be creative of new values, a long step will have been taken toward providing a religious belief system adequate to the realities and needs of a technological age.

Individual Man in a Technological Age. What do technological change and the social and value changes that it brings with it mean for the life of the individual today? It is not clear that their effects are all one-way. For example, we are often told that today's individual is alienated by the vast proliferation of technical expertise and complex bureaucracies, by a feeling of impotence in the face of "the machine," and by a decline in personal privacy. It is probably true that the social pressures placed on individuals today are more complicated and demanding than they were in earlier times. Increased geographical and occupational mobility and the need to function in large organizations place difficult demands on the individual to conform or "adjust." It is also evident that the privacy of many individuals tends to be encroached upon by sophisticated eavesdropping and surveillance devices, by the accumulation of more and more information about individuals by governmental and many private agencies, and by improvements in information-handling technologies such as the proposed institution of centralized statistical data banks. There is little doubt, finally, that the power, authority, influence, and scope of government are greater today than at any time in the history of the United States.

But, as Professor Edward Shils points out in his study on technology and the individual, there is another, equally compelling side of the coin. First, government seems to be more shy and more lacking in confidence today than ever before. Second, while privacy may be declining in the ways indicated above, it also tends to decline in a sense that most individuals are likely to approve. The average man in Victorian times, for example, probably "enjoyed" much more privacy than today. No one much cared what happened to him, and he was free to remain ignorant, starve, fall ill, and die in complete privacy; that was the "golden age of privacy," as Shils puts it. Compulsory universal education, social security legislation, and public health measures—indeed, the very idea of a welfare state—are all antithetical to privacy in this sense, and it is the rare individual today who is loath to see that kind of privacy go.

It is not clear, finally, that technological and social complexity must inevitably lead to reducing the individual to "mass" or "organization" man. Economic productivity and modern means of communication allow the individual to aspire to more than he ever could before. Better and more easily available education not only provides him with skills and with the means to develop his individual potentialities, but also improves his self-image and his sense of value as a human being. This is probably the first age in history in which such high proportions of people have *felt* like individuals; no 18th-century English factory worker, so far as we know, had the sense of individual worth that underlies the demands on society of the average resident of the black urban ghetto today. And, as Shils notes, the scope of individual choice and action today are greater than in previous times, all the way from consumer behavior to political or religious allegiance. Even the much-maligned modern organization may in fact "serve as a mediator or buffer between the individual and the full raw impact of technological change," as an earlier study supported by the Harvard Program has concluded.

Recognition that the impact of modern technology on the individual has two faces, both negative and positive, is consistent with the double effect of technological change that was discussed above. It also suggests that appreciation of that impact in detail may not be achieved in terms of old formulas, such as more or less privacy, more or less government, more or less individuality. Professor Shils is therefore attempting to couch his inquiry in terms of the implications of technological change for the balance that every individual must strike between his commitment to private goals and satisfactions and his desires and responsibilities as a public citizen. The citizens of ancient Athens seem to have been largely public beings in this sense, while certain segments of today's hippie population seem to pursue mainly private gratifications. The political requirements of our modern technological society would seem to call for a relatively greater public commitment on the part of individuals than has been the case in the past, and it is by exploring this hypothesis that we may enhance our understanding of what technology does to the individual in present-day society. . . .

ECONOMIC AND POLITICAL ORGANIZATION

The Enlarged Scope of Public Decision Making. When technology brings about social changes (as described in the first section of this essay) which impinge on our existing system of values (in ways reviewed in the second section), it poses for society a number of problems that are ultimately political in nature. The term "political" is used here in the broadest sense: it encompasses all of the decision-making structures and procedures that have to do with the allocation and distribution of wealth and power in society. The political organization of society thus includes not only the formal apparatus of the state but also industrial organizations and other private institutions that play a role in the decision-making process. It is particularly important to attend to the organization of the entire body politic when technological change leads to a blurring of once clear distinctions between the public and private sectors of society and to changes in the roles of its principal institutions.

It was suggested above that the political requirements of our modern technological society call for a relatively greater public commitment on the part of individuals than in previous times. The reason for this, stated most generally, is that technological change has the effect of enhancing the importance of public decision making in society, because technology is continually creating new possibilities for social action as well as new problems that have to be dealt with.

A society that undertakes to foster technology on a large scale, in fact, commits itself to social complexity and to facing and dealing with new problems as a normal feature of political life. Not much is yet known with any precision about the political imperatives inherent in technological change, but

one may nevertheless speculate about the reasons why an increasingly technological society seems to be characterized by enlargement of the scope of public decision making.

For one thing, the development and application of technology seems to
require large-scale, and hence increasingly complex, social concentrations,
whether these be large cities, large corporations, big universities, or big government. In instances where technological advance appears to facilitate reduction of such first-order concentrations, it tends instead to enlarge the relevant
system of social organization, that is, to lead to increased centralization.
Thus, the physical dispersion made possible by transportation and communications technologies, as Meyer and Kain have shown, enlarges the urban complex that must be governed as a unit.

A second characteristic of advanced technology is that its effects cover
large distances, in both the geographical and social senses of the term. Both
its positive and negative features are more extensive. Horsepowered transportation technology was limited in its speed and capacity, but its nuisance value
was also limited, in most cases to the owner and to the occupant of the next
farm. The supersonic transport can carry hundreds across long distances in
minutes, but its noise and vibration damage must also be suffered willy-nilly
by everyone within the limits of a swath 3,000 miles long and several miles
wide.

The concatenation of increased density (or enlarged system) and extended
technological "distance" means that technological applications have increasingly wider ramifications and that increasingly large concentrations of people
and organizations become dependent on technological systems. A striking illustration of this was provided by the widespread effects of the power blackout
in the northeastern part of the United States. The result is not only that more
and more decisions must be social decisions taken in public ways, as already
noted, but that, once made, decisions are likely to have a shorter useful life
than heretofore. That is partly because technology is continually altering the
spectrum of choices and problems that society faces, and partly because any
decision taken is likely to generate a need to take ten more.

These speculations about the effects of technology on public decision
making raise the problem of restructuring our decision-making mechanisms—
including the system of market incentives—so that the increasing number and
importance of social issues that confront us can be resolved equitably and
effectively.

Private Firms and Public Goods. Among these issues, as noted earlier, is that created by the shift in the composition of demand in favor of public goods and services—such as education, health, transportation, slum clearance, and recreational facilities—which, it is generally agreed, the market has never provided effectively and in the provision of which government has usually played a role of some significance. This shift in demand raises serious questions about the relationship between technological change and existing decision-making structures in general and about the respective roles of government and business in particular. [A] project initiated . . . under the direction of Dr. Robin Marris is designed to explore those questions in detail.

In Western industrialized countries, new technological developments generally originate in and are applied through joint stock companies whose shares are widely traded on organized capital markets. Corporations thus play a dominant role in the development of new methods of production, of new methods of satisfying consumer wants, and even of new wants. Most economists appear to accept the thesis originally proposed by Schumpeter that corporations play a key role in the actual process of technological innovation in the economy. Marris himself has recently characterized this role as a perceiving of latent consumer needs and of fostering and regulating the rate at which these are converted into felt wants.[4]

There is no similar agreement about the implications of all this for social policy. J. K. Galbraith, for example, argues that the corporation is motivated by the desire for growth subject to a minimum profit constraint and infers (1) a higher rate of new-want development than would be the case if corporations were motivated principally to maximize profit, (2) a bias in favor of economic activities heavy in "technological content" in contrast to activities requiring sophisticated social organization, and (3) a bias in the economy as a whole in favor of development and satisfaction of private needs to the neglect of public needs and at the cost of a relatively slow rate of innovation in the public sector.

But Galbraith's picture is not generally accepted by economists, and his model of the corporation is not regarded as established economic theory. There is, in fact, no generally accepted economic theory of corporate behavior, as Marris points out, so that discussions about the future of the system of corporate enterprise usually get bogged down in an exchange of unsubstantiated assertions about how the existing system actually operates. What seems needed at this time, then, is less a new program of empirical research than an attempt to synthesize what we know for the purpose of arriving at a more

4. Robin Marris, *The Economic Theory of "Managerial" Capitalism* (New York, 1964).

adequate theory of the firm. This is the objective of phase 1 of the Marris project.

On the basis of the resulting theoretical clarification, phase 2 will go on to address such questions as (1) the costs of a policy of economic growth, (2) the incommensurability of individual incentive and public will, (3) the desirable balance between individual and social welfare when the two are inconsistent with each other, (4) changes in the roles of government and industrial institutions in the political organization of American society, and (5) the consequences of those changes for the functions of advertising and competing forms of communication in the process of public education. In particular, attention will be directed to whether existing forms of company organization are adequate for marshaling technology to social purposes by responding to the demand for public goods and services, or whether new productive institutions will be required to serve that end.

We can hope to do no more than raise the level of discussion of such fundamental and difficult questions, of course, but even that could be a service.

The Promise and Problems of Scientific Decision Making. There are two further consequences of the expanding role of public decision making. The first is that the latest information-handling of devices and techniques tend to be utilized in the decision-making process. This is so (1) because public policy can be effective only to the degree that it is based on reliable knowledge about the actual state of the society, and thus requires a strong capability to collect, aggregate, and analyze detailed data about economic activities, social patterns, popular attitudes, and political trends, and (2) because it is recognized increasingly that decisions taken in one area impinge on and have consequences for other policy areas often thought of as unrelated, so that it becomes necessary to base decisions on a model of society that sees it as a system and that is capable of signaling as many as possible of the probable consequences of a contemplated action.

As Professor Alan F. Westin points out, reactions to the prospect of more decision making based on computerized data banks and scientific management techniques run the gamut of optimism to pessimism mentioned in the opening of this essay. Negative reactions take the form of rising political demands for greater popular participation in decision making, for more equality among different segments of the population, and for greater regard for the dignity of individuals. The increasing dependence of decision making on scientific and technological devices and techniques is seen as posing a threat to these goals, and pressures are generated in opposition to further "rationalization" of decision-making processes. These pressures have the paradoxical effect, however, not of deflecting the supporters of technological decision making from their course, but of spurring them on to renewed effort to save the society before it explodes under planlessness and inadequate administration.

The paradox goes further, and helps to explain much of the social discontent that we are witnessing at the present time. The greater complexity and the more extensive ramifications that technology brings about in society tend to make social processes increasingly circuitous and indirect. The effects of actions are widespread and difficult to keep track of, so that experts and sophisticated techniques are increasingly needed to detect and analyze social events and to formulate policies adequate to the complexity of social issues. The "logic" of modern decision making thus appears to require greater and greater dependence on the collection and analysis of data and on the use of technological devices and scientific techniques. Indeed, many observers would agree that there is an "increasing relegation of questions which used to be matters of political debate to professional cadres of technicians and experts which function almost independently of the democratic political process."[5] In recent times, that process has been most noticeable, perhaps, in the areas of economic policy and national security affairs.

This "logic" of modern decision making, however, runs counter to that element of traditional democratic theory that places high value on direct participation in the political processes and generates the kind of discontent referred to above. If it turns out on more careful examination that direct participation is becoming less relevant to a society in which the connections between causes and effects are long and often hidden—which is an increasingly "indirect" society, in other words—elaboration of a new democratic ethos and of new democratic processes more adequate to the realities of modern society will emerge as perhaps the major intellectual and political challenge of our time.

The Need for Institutional Innovation. The challenge is, indeed, already upon us, for the second consequence of the enlarged scope of public decision making is the need to develop new institutional forms and new mechanisms to replace established ones that can no longer deal effectively with the new kinds of problems with which we are increasingly faced. Much of the political ferment of the present time—over the problems of technology assessment, the introduction of statistical data banks, the extension to domestic problems of techniques of analysis developed for the military services, and the modifica-

5. Harvey Brooks, "Scientific Concepts and Cultural Change," in G. Holton, ed., *Science and Culture* (Boston, 1965), p. 71.

tion of the institutions of local government—is evidence of the need for new institutions. It will be recalled that Professor Oettinger's study concludes that innovation is called for in the educational establishment before instructional technology can realize the promise that is potential in it. Our research in the biomedical area has repeatedly confirmed the need for institutional innovation in the medical system, and Marris has noted the evolution that seems called for in our industrial institutions. The Rosenbloom research group, finally, has documented the same need in the urban area and is exploring the form and course that the processes of innovation might take.

Direct intervention by business or government to improve ghetto conditions will tend to be ineffective until local organizations come into existence which enable residents to participate in and control their own situation. Such organizations seem to be a necessary condition for any solution of the ghetto problem that is likely to prove acceptable to black communities. Professors Richard S. Rosenbloom, Paul R. Lawrence, and their associates are therefore engaged in the design of two types of organization suited to the peculiar problems of the modern ghetto. These are (1) a state- or area-wide urban development corporation in which business and government join to channel funds and provide technical assistance to (2) a number of local development corporations, under community control, which can combine social service with sound business management.

Various "ghetto enrichment" strategies are being proposed at the present time, all of which stress the need for institutional innovation of some kind and in many of which creation of one sort or another of community development corporation is a prominent feature. In none of these respects does our approach claim any particular originality. What does seem promising, however, is our effort to design a local development corporation that is at once devoted to social service and built on sound business principles.

These characteristics point to large and powerful organizations that can serve as engines of indigenous ghetto development. They would of course interact with "outside" institutions, not only those at various levels of government, but especially their counterpart state or area urban development corporations. They would not be dependent principally on such outside institutions, however, since they would be engines that, once started, could keep running largely on their own power. In economic terms, the local development corporations would become "customers" of business. In political terms, they would be partners of existing governmental structures. In broader social terms, they could become vehicles for integrating underprivileged urban communities into the mainstream of American society.

The design for the state or area urban development corporation, in Professor Rosenbloom's description, would be a new form of public-private partnership serving to pull together the resources and programs of the business sector, of universities and research institutions, of public agencies, and of community organizations. This corporation could act as a surrogate for the "invisible hand" of the market, able to reward the successes of the local development corporations through command of a pool of unrestricted funds. Since there is no necessary relationship between profitability and social benefit for economic ventures in the ghetto, however, success would need to be measured, not in usual profit-and-loss terms, but in terms of such social indicators as employment levels, educational attainment, health statistics, and the like.

The collaborative arrangements we have entered into in New Jersey and in Boston offer us a welcome opportunity to test and develop some of our hypotheses and designs. In both of these programs, our research group is in a position to contribute know-how and advice, based on its understanding of organizational and corporate behavior, and to acquire insight and primary data for research that can prove useful in other contexts. As long ago as our first annual report, we announced the hope and expectation that the Harvard Program could supplement its scholarly production by adding a dimension of action research. New Jersey and Boston are providing us with our first opportunity to realize that objective.

CONCLUSION

As we review what we are learning about the relationship of technological and social change, a number of conclusions begin to emerge. We find, on the one hand, that the creation of new physical possibilities and social options by technology tends toward and appears to require the emergence of new values, new forms of economic activity, and new political organizations. On the other hand, technological change also poses problems of social and psychological displacement.

The two phenomena are not unconnected, nor is the tension between them new: man's technical prowess always seems to run ahead of his ability to deal with and profit from it. In America, especially, we are becoming adept at extracting the new techniques, the physical power, and the economic productivity that are inherent in our knowledge and its associated technologies. Yet we have not fully accepted the fact that our progress in the technical realm does not leave our institutions, values, and political processes unaffected. Individuals will be fully integrated into society only when we can extract from our knowledge not only its technological potential but also its implications for a system of values and a social, economic, and political organization appropriate to a society in which technology is so prevalent. . . .

Technology: The Opiate
of the Intellectuals

JOHN McDERMOTT

If religion was formerly the opiate of the masses, then surely technology is the opiate of the educated public today, or at least of its favorite authors. No other single subject is so universally invested with high hopes for the improvement of mankind generally and of Americans in particular. The content of these millennial hopes varies somewhat from author to author, though with considerable overlap. A representative but by no means complete list of these promises and their prophets would include: an end to poverty and the inauguration of permanent prosperity (Leon Keyserling), universal equality of opportunity (Zbigniew Brzezinski), a radical increase in individual freedom (Edward Shils), the replacement of work by leisure for most of mankind (Robert Theobald), fresh water for desert dwellers (Lyndon Baines Johnson), permanent but harmless social revolution (Walt Rostow), the final comeuppance of Mao Tse-tung and all his ilk (same prophet), the triumph of wisdom over power (John Kenneth Galbraith), and, lest we forget, the end of ideology (Daniel Bell).

These hopes for mankind's, or technology's, future, however, are not unalloyed. Technology's defenders, being otherwise reasonable men, are also aware that the world population explosion and the nuclear missiles race are also the fruit of the enormous advances made in technology during the past half century or so. But here too a cursory reading of their literature would reveal widespread though qualified optimism that these scourges too will fall before technology's might. Thus population (and genetic) control and permanent peace are sometimes added to the already imposing roster of technology's promises. What are we to make of such extravagant optimism?

[In early 1968] Harvard University's Program on Technology and Society, ". . . an inquiry in depth into the effects of technological change on the economy, on public policies, and on the character of society, as well as into the reciprocal effects of social progress on the nature, dimension, and directions of scientific and technological development," issued its Fourth Annual Report to the accompaniment of full front-page coverage in *The New York Times* (January 18). Within the brief (fewer than 100) pages of that report and most clearly in the concluding essay by the Program's Director, Emmanuel G. Mesthene, one can discern some of the important threads of belief which bind together much current writing on the social implications of technology. Mesthene's essay is worth extended analysis because these beliefs are of interest in themselves and, of greater importance, because they form the basis not of a new but of a newly aggressive right-wing ideology in this country, an ideology whose growing importance was accurately measured by the magnitude of the *Times*'s news report.

At the very beginning of Mesthene's essay, which attempts to characterize the relationships between technological and social change, the author is careful to dissociate himself from what he believes are several extreme views of those relationships. For example, technology is neither the relatively "unalloyed blessing" which, he claims, Marx, Comte, and the Air Force hold it to be, nor an unmitigated curse, a view he attributes to "many of our youth." (This is but the first of several reproofs Mesthene casts in the direction of youth.) Having denounced straw men to the right and left of him he is free to pursue that middle or moderate course favored by virtually all political writers of the day. This middle course consists of an extremely abstract and—politically speaking—sanitary view of technology and technological progress.

For Mesthene, it is characteristic of technology that it:

. . . creates new possibilities for human choice and action but leaves their disposition uncertain. What its effects will be and what ends it will serve are not inherent in the technology, but depend on what man will do with technology. Technology thus makes possible a future of open-ended options . . . .

This essentially optimistic view of the matter rests on the notion that technology is merely ". . . the organization of knowledge for practical purposes . . ." and therefore cannot be purely boon or wholly burden. The matter is somewhat more complex:

New technology creates new opportunities for men and societies and it also generates new problems for them. It has both positive and negative effects, and it usually has the two *at the same time and in virtue of each other.*

This dual effect he illustrates with an example drawn from the field of medicine. Recent advances there

have created two new opportunities: (1) they have made possible treatment and cures that were never possible before, and (2) they provide a necessary condition for the delivery of adequate medical care to the population at large as a matter of right rather than privilege.

Because of the first, however,

the medical profession has become increasingly differentiated and specialized and is tending to concentrate its best efforts in a few major, urban centers of medical excellence.

Mesthene clearly intends but does not state the corollary to this point, namely that the availability of adequate medical care is declining elsewhere.[1] Moreover, because of the second point, there have been

. . . big increases in demand for medical services, partly because a healthy population has important economic advantages in a highly industrialized society. This increased demand accelerates the process of differentiation and multiplies the levels of paramedical personnel between the physician at the top and the patient at the bottom of the hospital pyramid.

Similarly, Mesthene points out that marvelous improvements in auto and air transportation have aggravated social and other problems in the inner city. Furthermore,

Mass communications technology has also made rapid strides since World War II, with great benefit to education, journalism, commerce and sheer convenience. It has also been accompanied by an aggravation of social unrest, however, and may help to explain the singular rebelliousness of a youth that can find out what the world is like from television before home and school have had the time to instill some ethical sense of what it could or should be like.

Mesthene believes there are two distinct problems in technology's relation to society, a positive one of taking full advantage of the opportunities it offers

1. This is almost certainly true of persons living in rural areas or in smaller towns and cities. However, a New York based New Left project, the Health-Policy Advisory Center, has argued with considerable documentation, that roughly half of New York City's population is now medically indigent and perhaps 80 percent of the population is indigent with respect to major medical care.

and the negative one of avoiding unfortunate consequences which flow from the exploitation of those opportunities. Positive opportunities may be missed because the costs of technological development outweigh likely benefits (e.g., Herman Kahn's "Doomsday Machine"). Mesthene seems convinced, however, that a more important case is that in which

... technology lies fallow because existing social structures are inadequate to exploit the opportunities it offers. This is revealed clearly in the examination of institutional failure in the ghetto carried on by [the Program]. At point after point, . . . analyses confirm . . . that existing institutions and traditional approaches are by and large incapable of coming to grips with the new problems of our cities—many of them caused by technological change . . . —and unable to realize the possibilities for resolving them that are also inherent in technology. Vested economic and political interests serve to obstruct adequate provision of low-cost housing. Community institutions wither for want of interest and participation by residents. City agencies are unable to marshall the skills and take the systematic approach needed to deal with new and intensified problems of education, crime control, and public welfare. Business corporations, finally, which are organized around the expectation of private profit, are insufficiently motivated to bring new technology and management know-how to bear on urban projects where the benefits will be largely social.

His diagnosis of these problems is generous in the extreme:

All these factors combine to dilute what may be otherwise a genuine desire to apply our best knowledge and adequate resources to the resolution of urban tensions and the eradication of poverty in the nation.

Moreover, because government and the media ". . . are not yet equipped for the massive task of public education that is needed . . ." if we are to exploit technology more fully, many technological opportunities are lost because of the lack of public support. This too is a problem primarily of "institutional innovation."

Mesthene believes that institutional innovation is no less important in combatting the negative effects of technology. Individuals or individual firms which decide to develop new technologies normally do not take "adequate account" of their likely social benefits or costs. His critique is anti-capitalist in spirit, but lacks bite, for he goes on to add that

... [most of the negative] consequences of technology that are causing concern at the present time—pollution of the environment, potential damage to the ecology of the planet, occupational and social dislocations, threats to the privacy and political significance of the individual, social and psychological malaise—are *negative externalities of this kind.* They are with us in large measure because it has not been anybody's explicit business to foresee and anticipate them. [Italics added.]

Mesthene's abstract analysis and its equally abstract diagnosis in favor of "institutional innovation" places him in a curious and, for us, instructive position. If existing social structures are inadequate to exploit technology's full potential, or if, on the other hand, so-called negative externalities assail us because it is nobody's business to foresee and anticipate them, doesn't this say that we should apply technology to this problem too? That is, we ought to apply and organize the appropriate *organizational* knowledge for the practical purpose of solving the problems of institutional inadequacy and "negative externalities."[2] Hence, in principle, Mesthene is in the position of arguing that the cure for technology's problems, whether positive or negative, is still more technology. This is the first theme of the technological school of writers and its ultimate First Principle.

Technology, in their view, is a self-correcting system. Temporary oversight or "negative externalities" will and should be corrected by technological means. Attempts to restrict the free play of technological innovation are, in the nature of the case, self-defeating. Technological innovation exhibits a distinct tendency to work for the general welfare in the long run. *Laissez innover!*

I have so far deliberately refrained from going into any greater detail than does Mesthene on the empirical character of contemporary technology (see below) for it is important to bring out the force of the principle of *laissez innover* in its full generality. Many writers on technology appear to deny in their definition of the subject—organized knowledge for practical purposes—that contemporary technology exhibits distinct trends which can be identified or projected. Others, like Mesthene, appear to accept these trends, but

---

2. Practicing what it preaches, the Program sponsors a Research Project on Technology, Business, and the City which has begun for urban areas ". . . an exploration into what organizational innovations might produce the social and economic development programs that might take maximum advantage of the opportunities offered by modern technology while exploiting the advantages and *reducing the weaknesses of both traditional business institutions and traditional government organizations*" (italics added). The Project has proposed ". . . (1) a state- or area-wide Urban Development Corporation in which business and government join to channel funds and provide technical assistance to (2) a number of Local Development Corporations, *under community control,* which can *combine social service with sound business management*" (italics added).

Mesthene comments that the Urban Development Corporation ". . . could act as a surrogate for the 'invisible hand' of the market, able to reward the success of the Local Development Corporation through command of a pool of unrestricted funds." Community control is to be strengthened and business weaknesses reduced by linking the two together and providing the latter with a "pool of unrestricted funds." It's all very participatory, though a trifle weak on democracy.

then blunt the conclusion by attributing to technology so much flexibility and "scientific" purity that it becomes an abstraction infinitely malleable in behalf of good, pacific, just, and egalitarian purposes. Thus the analogy to the *laissez-faire* principle of another time is quite justified. Just as the market or the free play of competition provided in theory the optimum long-run solution for virtually every aspect of virtually every social and economic problem, so too does the free play of technology, according to its writers. Only if technology or innovation (or some other synonym) is allowed the freest possible reign, they believe, will the maximum social good be realized.

What reasons do they give to believe that the principle of *laissez innover* will normally function for the benefit of mankind rather than, say, merely for the benefit of the immediate practitioners of technology, their managerial cronies, and for the profits accruing to their corporations? As Mesthene and other writers of his school are aware, this is a very real problem, for they all believe that the normal tendency of technology is, and ought to be, the increasing concentration of decision-making power in the hands of larger and larger scientific-technical bureaucracies. *In principle,* their solution is relatively simple, though not often explicitly stated.[3]

Their argument goes as follows: the men and women who are elevated by technology into commanding positions within various decision-making bureaucracies exhibit no generalized drive for power such as characterized, say, the landed gentry of pre-industrial Europe or the capitalist entrepreneur of the last century. For their social and institutional position and its supporting culture as well are defined solely by the fact that these men are problem solvers. (Organized knowledge for practical purposes again.) That is, they gain advantage and reward only to the extent that they can bring specific technical knowledge to bear on the solution of specific technical problems. Any more general drive for power would undercut the bases of their usefulness and legitimacy.

Moreover their specific training and professional commitment to solving technical problems creates a bias against ideologies in general which inhibits any attempts to formulate a justifying ideology for the group. Consequently, they do not constitute a class and have no general interests antagonistic to those of their problem-beset clients. We may refer to all of this as the disinterested character of the scientific-technical decision-maker, or, more briefly and cynically, as the principle of the Altruistic Bureaucrat.

3. For a more complete statement of the argument which follows, see Suzanne Keller, *Beyond the Ruling Class* (Random House, 1963).

As if not satisfied by the force of this (unstated) principle, Mesthene like many of his school fellows spends many pages commenting around the belief that the concentration of power at the top of technology's organizations is a problem, but that like other problems technology should be able to solve it successfully through institutional innovation. You may trust in it; the principle of *laissez innover* knows no logical or other hurdle.

This combination of guileless optimism with scientific toughmindedness might seem to be no more than an eccentric delusion were the American technology it supports not moving in directions that are strongly antidemocratic. To show why this is so we must examine more closely Mesthene's seemingly innocuous distinction between technology's positive opportunities and its "negative externalities." In order to do this I will make use of an example drawn from the very frontier of American technology, the Vietnam War.

II

At least two fundamentally different bombing programs [have been] carried out in South Vietnam. There are fairly conventional attacks against targets which consist of identified enemy troops, fortifications, medical centers, vessels, and so forth. The other program is quite different and, at least since March, 1968, infinitely more important. With some oversimplification it can be described as follows:

Intelligence data is gathered from all kinds of sources, of all degrees of reliability, on all manner of subjects, and fed into a computer complex located, I believe, at Bien Hoa. From this data and using mathematical models developed for the purpose, the computer then assigns probabilities to a range of potential targets, probabilities which represent the likelihood that the latter contain enemy forces or supplies. These potential targets might include: a canal-river crossing known to be used occasionally by the NLF; a section of trail which would have to be used to attack such and such an American base, now overdue for attack; a square mile of plain rumored to contain enemy troops; a mountainside from which camp fire smoke was seen rising. Again using models developed for the purpose, the computer divides pre-programmed levels of bombardment among those potential targets which have the highest probability of containing actual targets. Following the raids, data provided by further reconnaissance is fed into the computer and conclusions are drawn (usually optimistic ones) on the effectiveness of the raids. This estimate of effectiveness then becomes part of the data governing current and future operations, and so on.

Two features must be noted regarding this program's features which are superficially hinted at but fundamentally obscured by Mesthene's distinction between the abstractions of positive opportunity and "negative externality." First, when considered from the standpoint of its planners, the bombing program is extraordinarily rational, for it creates previously unavailable "opportunities" to pursue their goals in Vietnam. It would make no sense to bomb South Vietnam simply at random, and no serious person or Air Force General would care to mount the effort to do so. So the system employed in Vietnam significantly reduces, though it does not eliminate, that randomness. That canal-river crossing which is bombed at least once every eleven days or so is a very poor target compared to an NLF battalion observed in a village. But it is an infinitely more promising target than would be selected by throwing a dart at a grid map of South Vietnam. In addition to bombing the battalion, why not bomb the canal crossing to the frequency and extent that it *might* be used by enemy troops?

Even when we take into account the crudity of the mathematical models and the consequent slapstick way in which poor information is evaluated, it is a "good" program. No single raid will definitely kill an enemy soldier but a whole series of them increases the "opportunity" to kill a calculable number of them (as well, of course, as a calculable but not calculated number of non-soldiers). This is the most rational bombing system to follow if American lives are very expensive and American weapons and Vietnamese lives very cheap. Which, of course, is the case.

Secondly, however, considered from the standpoint of goals and values not programmed in by its designers, the bombing program is incredibly irrational. In Mesthene's terms, these "negative externalities" would include, in the present case, the lives and well-being of various Vietnamese as well as the feelings and opinions of some less important Americans. Significantly, this exclusion of the interests of people not among the managerial class is based quite as much on the so-called technical means being employed as on the political goals of the system. In the particular case of the Vietnamese bombing system, the political goals of the bombing system clearly exclude the interests of certain Vietnamese. After all, the victims of the bombardment are communists or their supporters, they are our enemies, they resist US intervention. In short, their interests are fully antagonistic to the goals of the program and simply must be excluded from consideration. The technical reasons for this exclusion require explanation, being less familiar and more important, especially in the light of Mesthene's belief in the malleability of technological systems.

Advanced technological systems such as those employed in the bombardment of South Vietnam make use not only of extremely complex and expensive equipment but, quite as important, of large numbers of relatively scarce and expensive-to-train technicians. They have immense capital costs; a thousand aircraft of a very advanced type, literally hundreds of thousands of spare parts, enormous stocks of rockets, bombs, shells and bullets, in addition to tens of thousands of technical specialists; pilots, bombardiers, navigators, radar operators, computer programmers, accountants, engineers, electronic and mechanical technicians, to name only a few. In short, they are "capital intensive."

Moreover, the coordination of this immense mass of esoteric equipment and its operators in the most effective possible way depends upon an extremely highly developed technique both in the employment of each piece of equipment by a specific team of operators and in the management of the program itself. Of course, all large organizations standardize their operating procedures, but it is peculiar to advanced technological systems that their operating procedures embody a very high degree of information drawn from the physical sciences, while their managerial procedures are equally dependent on information drawn from the social sciences. We may describe this situation by saying that advanced technological systems are both "technique intensive" and "management intensive."

It should be clear, moreover, even to the most casual observer that such intensive use of capital, technique, and management spills over into almost every area touched by the technological system in question. An attack program delivering 330,000 tons of munitions more or less selectively to several thousand different targets monthly would be an anomaly if forced to rely on sporadic intelligence data, erratic maintenance systems, or a fluctuating and unpredictable supply of heavy bombs, rockets, jet fuel, and napalm tanks. Thus it is precisely because the bombing program requires an intensive use of capital, technique, and management that the same properties are normally transferred to the intelligence, maintenance, supply, coordination and training systems which support it. Accordingly, each of these supporting systems is subject to sharp pressures to improve and rationalize the performance of its machines and men, the reliability of its techniques, and the efficiency and sensitivity of the management controls under which it operates. Within integrated technical systems, higher levels of technology drive out lower, and the normal tendency is to integrate systems.

From this perverse Gresham's Law of Technology follow some of the main social and organizational characteristics of contemporary technological systems:

the radical increase in the scale and complexity of operations that they demand and encourage; the rapid and widespread diffusion of technology to new areas; the great diversity of activities which can be directed by central management; an increase in the ambition of management's goals; and, as a corollary, especially to the last, growing resistance to the influence of so-called negative externalities.

Complex technological systems are extraordinarily resistant to intervention by persons or problems operating outside or below their managing groups, and this is so regardless of the "politics" of a given situation. Technology creates its own politics. The point of such advanced systems is to minimize the incidence of personal or social behavior which is erratic or otherwise not easily classified, of tools and equipment with poor performance, of improvisory techniques, and of unresponsiveness to central management.

For example, enlisted men who are "unrealistically soft" on the subject of civilian casualties and farmers in contested districts pose a mortal threat to the integral character of systems like that used in Vietnam. In the case of the soldier this means he must be kept under tight military discipline. In the case of the farmer, he must be easily placed in one of two categories; collaborator or enemy. This is done by assigning a probability to him, his hamlet, his village, or his district, and by incorporating that probability into the targeting plans of the bombing system. Then the enlisted man may be controlled by training and indoctrination as well as by highly developed techniques of command and coercion, and the farmers may be bombed according to the most advanced statistical models. In both cases the system's authority over its farmer subjects or enlisted men is a technical one. The technical means which make that system rational and efficient in its aggregate terms, i.e., as viewed from the top, themselves tend by design to filter out the "non-rational" or "non-efficient" elements of its components and subjects, i.e., those rising from the bottom.

To define technology so abstractly that it obscures these observable characteristics of contemporary technology—as Mesthene and his school have done—makes no sense. It makes even less sense to claim some magical malleability for something as undefined as "institutional innovation." Technology, in its concrete, empirical meaning, refers fundamentally to systems of rationalized control over large groups of men, events, and machines by small groups of technically skilled men operating through organizational hierarchy. The latent "opportunities" provided by that control and its ability to filter out discordant "negative externalities" are, of course, best illustrated by extreme cases. Hence the most instructive and accurate example should be of a technology able to suppress the humanity of its rank-and-file and to commit genocide as a by-product of its rationality. The Vietnam bombing program fits technology to a "T."

III

It would certainly be difficult to attempt to translate in any simple and direct way the social and organizational properties of highly developed technological systems from the battlefields of Vietnam to the different cultural and institutional setting of the US. Yet before we conclude that any such attempt would be futile or even absurd, we might consider the following story.

In early 1967 I stayed for several days with one of the infantry companies of the US Fourth Division whose parent battalion was then based at Dau Tieng. From the camp at Dau Tieng the well-known Black Lady Mountain, sacred to the Cao Dai religious sect, was easily visible and in fact dominated the surrounding plain and the camp itself. One afternoon when I began to explain the religious significance of the mountain to some GI friends, they interrupted my somewhat academic discourse to tell me a tale beside which even the strange beliefs of the Cao Dai sect appeared prosaic.

According to GI reports which the soldiers had heard and believed, the Viet Cong had long ago hollowed out most of the mountain in order to install a very big cannon there. The size of the cannon was left somewhat vague— "huge, fucking . . ."—but clearly the GI's imagined that it was in the battleship class. In any event, this huge cannon had formerly taken a heavy toll of American aircraft and had been made impervious to American counterattacks by the presence of two—"huge, fucking"—sliding steel doors, behind which it retreated whenever the Americans attacked. Had they seen this battleship cannon, and did it ever fire on the camp, which was easily within its range? No, they answered, for a brave flyer, recognizing the effectiveness of the cannon against his fellow pilots, had deliberately crashed his jet into those doors one day, jamming them, and permitting the Americans to move into the area unhindered.

I had never been in the army, and at the time of my trip to Vietnam had not yet learned how fantastic GI stories can be. Thus I found it hard to understand how they could be convinced of so improbable a tale. Only later, after talking to many soldiers and hearing many other wild stories from them as well, did I realize what the explanation for this was. Unlike officers and civilian correspondents who are almost daily given detailed briefings on a unit's situation capabilities and objectives, GI's are told virtually nothing of this sort by the Army. They are simply told what to do, where, and how, and it is a rare officer, in my experience anyway, who thinks they should be told any more than this. Officers don't think soldiers are stupid; they simply assume it, and act accordingly. For the individual soldier's personal life doesn't make too much difference; he still has to deal with the facts of personal feelings, his own well-being, and that of his family.

But for the soldier's group life this makes a great deal of difference. In their group life, soldiers are cut off from sources of information about the situation of the group and are placed in a position where their social behavior is governed largely by the principle of blind obedience. Under such circumstances, reality becomes elusive. Because the soldiers are not permitted to deal with facts in their own ways, facts cease to discipline their opinions. Fantasy and wild tales are the natural outcome. In fact, it is probably a mark of the GI's intelligence to fantasize, for it means that he has not permitted his intellectual capacity to atrophy. The intelligence of the individual is thus expressed in the irrationality of the group.

It is this process which we may observe when we look to the social effect of modern technological systems in America itself. Here the process is not so simple and clear as in Vietnam, for it involves not simply the relations of today's soldiers to their officers and to the Army but the historical development of analogous relations between the lower and upper orders of our society. Moreover, these relations are broadly cultural rather than narrowly social in nature. It is to a brief review of this complex subject that I now wish to turn.

IV

Among the conventional explanations for the rise and spread of the democratic ethos in Europe and North America in the seventeenth, eighteenth, and nineteenth centuries, the destruction of the gap in political culture between the mass of the population and that of the ruling classes is extremely important. There are several sides to this explanation. For example, it is often argued that the invention of the printing press and the spread of Protestant Christianity encouraged a significant growth in popular literacy. In its earliest phases this literacy was largely expended on reading the Old and New Testaments, but it quickly broadened to include other religious works such as Bunyan's *Pilgrim's Progress,* and after that to such secular classics as *Gulliver's Travels.* The dating of these developments is, in the nature of the case, somewhat imprecise. But certainly by the middle of the eighteenth century, at least in Britain and North America, the literacy of the population was sufficient to support a variety of newspapers and periodicals not only in the larger cities but in the smaller provincial towns as well. The decline of Latin as the first language of politics and religion paralleled this development, of course. Thus, even before the advent of Tom Paine, Babeuf, and other popular tribunes, literacy and the information it carried were widely and securely spread throughout the population and the demystification of both the religious and the political privileges of the ruling classes was well developed. Common townsmen had closed at least one of the cultural gaps between themselves and the aristocracy of the large cities.

Similarly, it is often argued that with the expansion and improvement of road and postal systems, the spread of new tools and techniques, the growth in the number and variety of merchants, the consequent invigoration of town life, and other numerous and familiar related developments, the social experiences of larger numbers of people became richer, more varied, and similar in fact to those of the ruling classes. This last, the growth in similarity of the social experiences of the upper and lower classes, is especially important. Social skills and experiences which underlay the monopoly of the upper classes over the processes of law and government were spreading to important segments of the lower orders of society. For carrying on trade, managing a commercial—not a subsistence—farm, participating in a vestry of workingmen's guild, or working in an up-to-date manufactory or business, unlike the relatively narrow existence of the medieval serf or artisan, were experiences which contributed to what I would call the social rationality of the lower orders.

Activities which demand frequent intercourse with strangers, accurate calculation of near means and distant ends, and a willingness to devise collective ways of resolving novel and unexpected problems demand and reward a more discriminating attention to the realities and deficiencies of social life, and provide thereby a rich variety of social experiences analogous to those of the governing classes. As a result not only were the processes of law and government, formerly treated with semi-religious veneration, becoming demystified but, equally important, a population was being fitted out with sufficient skills and interests to contest their control. Still another gap between the political cultures of the upper and lower ends of the social spectrum was being closed.

The same period also witnesses a growth in the organized means of popular expression. In Britain, these would include the laboring people's organizations whose development is so ably described in Edward Thompson's *The Making of the English Working Class.* In America, the increase in the organized power of the populace was expressed not only in the growing conflict between the colonies and the Crown but more sharply and fundamentally in the continuous antagonism between the coastal areas and the backwoods, expressed, for example, in Shay's rebellion in western Massachusetts in 1786. Clearly these organizational developments were related to the two foregoing as both cause and effect. For the English workingmen's movement and the claims to local self-government in America spurred, and were spurred by, the growth in individual literacy and in social rationality among the lower classes. They were in fact its organizational expression.

These same developments were also reflected in the spread of egalitarian and republican doctrines such as those of Richard Price and Thomas Paine, which pointed up the arbitrary character of what had heretofore been considered the rights of the higher orders of society, and thus provided the popular ideological base which helped to define and legitimate lower-class demands.[4]

4. Mesthene is blind on this point. He writes, for example, that "This is probably the first age in history in which such high proportions of people have *felt* like individuals; no eighteenth century English factory worker, so far as we know, had the sense of individual worth that underlies the demands on society of the average resident of the black urban ghetto today." Contrast the following account from Edward Thompson's *The Making of the English Working Class* (Vintage Books, 1967), one of several hundred of the same character.

During a wave of repression against various workingmen's organizations in May, 1794, Prime Minister William Pitt himself, in the presence of the Lord Chancellor, the Home Secretary and, we may presume, a full battery of police spies and other officials, interrogated a number of Jacobite working men. Thompson relates that at one point Pitt ". . . summoned for interrogation a fourteen-year-old lad, Henry Eaton, who had been living with [the family of one of the accused]. But the boy stood his ground and [as a contemporary account relates] " 'entered into a political harangue, in which he used very harsh language against Mr. Pitt; upbraiding him with having taxed the people to an enormous extent. . . .' " (p. 19).

As Thompson richly documents, the boy was not speaking out of personal cheek. He was part of a movement of Englishmen of the lower orders whose culture had long been developing broad conceptions of working-class rights and dignity in opposition to the repressive culture of the aristocracy and the bourgeoisie. The sources of that culture were very diverse and included religious elements as well as political ones. Thompson shows, for example, that the religious traditions of some lower-class Britons included the view that worldly success was a mark of the Devil, and poverty often a sign of virtue. Thus no very great effort was required to see through the social, no less than the religious, legitimacy of the upper classes. Only a slight shift of understanding was required to change sin into social vice and the Devil himself into the capitalist system, while the poor's sense of their own moral worth became a fundamental support of their belief in the rightness and worth of the working class movement.

One wonders just what Mesthene's conception of the history of the rise of the democratic ethos consists in. I suspect that he, like many other intellectuals, assumed without thinking that its impulse derives more from blind developments in technology and from ideological inputs from elite intellectuals, than from any processes which exemplify merit and intelligence in the lower classes. How flattering to intellectuals to assume that their benevolence is more important in these matters than the labors, struggles, and experiences of vital popular cultures.

This description by no means does justice to the richness and variety of the historical process underlying the rise and spread of what has come to be called the democratic ethos. But it does, I hope, isolate some of the important structural elements and, moreover, it enables us to illuminate some important ways in which the new technology, celebrated by Mesthene and his associates for its potential contributions to democracy, contributes instead to the erosion of that same democratic ethos. For if, in an earlier time, the gap between the political cultures of the higher and lower orders of society was being widely attacked and closed, this no longer appears to be the case. On the contrary, I am persuaded that the direction has been reversed and that we now observe evidence of a growing separation between ruling and lower-class culture in America, a separation which is particularly enhanced by the rapid growth of technology and the spreading influence of its *laissez innover* ideologues.

Certainly, there has been a decline in popular literacy, that is to say, in those aspects of literacy which bear on an understanding of the political and social character of the new technology. Not one person in a hundred is even aware of, much less understands, the nature of technologically highly advanced systems such as are used in the Vietnam bombing program. People's ignorance in these things is revealed in their language. No clearer illustration of this ignorance is needed than the growing and already enormous difference between the speech of organizational and technical specialists and that of the man in the street, including many of the educated ones. To the extent that technical forms of speech within which the major business of American society is carried on are not understood or are poorly understood, there is a decline in one of the essentials of democracy.

This is not to say that the peculiar jargon which characterizes the speech of, say, aerospace technicians, crisis managers, or economic mandarins is intrinsically superior to the vocabulary of ordinary conversation, though sometimes this is indeed the case. What is important about technical language is that the words, being alien to ordinary speech, hide their meaning from ordinary speakers; terms like foreign aid or technical assistance have a good sound in ordinary speech; only the initiate recognizes them as synonyms for the old-fashioned, nasty word, imperialism. Such instances can be corrected but when almost all of the public's business is carried on in specialized jargon correction makes little difference. Like Latin in the past, the new language of social and technical organization is divorced from the general population, which continues to speak in the vulgar tongue of, say, *The New Republic,* the *Saturday Review of Literature,* or *The Reader's Digest.*

Secondly, the social organization of this new technology, by systematically denying to the general population experiences which are analogous to those of its higher management, contributes very heavily to the growth of social irrationality in our society. For example, modern technological organization defines the roles and values of its members, not vice versa. An engineer or a sociologist is one who does all those things but only those things called for by the "table of organization" and the "job description" used by his employer. Professionals who seek self-realization through creative and autonomous behavior without regard to the defined goals, needs, and channels of their respective departments have no more place in a large corporation or government agency than squeamish soldiers in the Army. Naturally some tolerance would normally be extended to very gifted or personable individuals. This is especially true in universities. But for the common garden variety employee (or junior faculty member) company sanctions on job behavior, style of work, and related matters must have the force of law.

However, those at the top of technology's more advanced organizations hardly suffer the same experience. For reasons which are clearly related to the principle of the Altruistic Bureaucracy the psychology of an individual's fulfillment through work has been incorporated into management ideology. As the pages of *Fortune, Time,* or *Business Week* or the memoirs of out-of-office Kennedyites serve to show, the higher levels of business and government are staffed by men and women who spend killing hours looking after the economic welfare and national security of the rest of us. The rewards of this life are said to be very few: the love of money would be demeaning and, anyway, taxes are said to take most of it; its sacrifices are many, for failure brings economic depression to the masses or gains for communism as well as disgrace to the erring managers. Even the essential high-mindedness or altruism of our managers earns no reward, for the public is distracted, fickle, and, on occasion, vengeful. (The extensive literature on the "ordeal" of Lyndon Johnson is a case in point.) Hence for these "real revolutionaries of our time," as Walt Rostow has called them, self-fulfillment through work and discipline is the only reward. The managerial process is seen as an expression of the vital personalities of our leaders and the right to it an inalienable right of the national elite.

In addition to all of this, their lonely and unrewarding eminence in the face of crushing responsibility, etc., tends to create an air of mystification around technology's managers. When the august mystery of science and the perquisites of high office are added to their halos, they glow very blindingly indeed. Thus, in ideology as well as in reality and appearance, the experiences of the higher managers tend to separate and isolate themselves from those of the managed. Again the situation within the US is not so severe nor so stark as in the Army in Vietnam but the effect on those who are excluded from self-management is very similar. Soldiers in Vietnam are not alone in believing huge, secret guns threaten them from various points; that same feeling is a national malady in the US.

It seems fundamental to the social organization of modern technology that the quality of the social experience of the lower orders of society declines as the level of technology grows no less than does their literacy. And, of course, this process feeds on itself, for with the consequent decline in the real effectiveness and usefulness of local and other forms of organization open to easy and direct popular influence their vitality declines still further, and the cycle is repeated.

The normal life of men and women in the lower and, I think, middle levels of American society now seems cut off from those experiences in which near social means and distant social ends are balanced and rebalanced, adjusted, and readjusted. But it is from such widespread experience with effective balancing and adjusting that social rationality derives. To the degree that it is lacking, social irrationality becomes the norm, and social paranoia a recurring phenomenon.

Those who seek an explanation for the infatuation of local government with anti-fluoridation campaigns several years ago need look no further. A similar irrationality is now being exhibited toward the war in Vietnam and the anti-war Movement. With no great effort and using no great skill, Presidents Johnson and Nixon have managed to direct disorganized popular frustration over the continuation of the war and popular abhorrence over its unremitting violence on to precisely that element in the population most actively and effectively opposed to the war and its violence. As for paranoia, consider the widespread reaction of whites to the murder of Dr. King. Their demand for force and more force to be used against the Black population was consistent only with the hypothesis that Dr. King murdered James Earl Ray, just as SNCC members had lynched Klansmen only a few years before.

People often say that America is a sick society when what they really mean is that it has lots of sick individuals. But they were right the first time: the society is so sick that individual efforts to right it and individual rationality come to be expressed in fundamentally sick ways. Like the soldiers in Vietnam, we try to avoid atrophy of our social intelligence only to be led into fantasy and, often, violence. It is a good thing to want the war in Vietnam over for, as everyone now recognizes, it hurts us almost as much as the Vietnamese who are its intended victims. But for many segments of our population, especially those cut off from political expression because of their own social disorganization, the rationality of various alternatives for ending the war is fundamentally obscure. Thus their commendable desire to end the war is expressed in what they believe is the clearest and most certain alternative: use the bomb!

Mesthene himself recognizes that such "negative externalities" are on the increase. His list includes ". . . pollution of the environment, potential damage to the ecology of the planet, occupational and social dislocations, threats to the privacy and political significance of the individual, social and psychological malaise. . . ." Minor matters all, however, when compared to the marvelous opportunities *laissez innover* holds out to us: more GNP, continued free world leadership, supersonic transports, urban renewal on a regional basis, institutional innovation, and the millennial promises of his school.

This brings us finally to the ideologies and doctrines of technology and their relation to what I have argued is a growing gap in political culture between the lower and upper classes in American society. Even more fundamentally than the principles of *laissez innover* and the altruistic bureaucrat, technology in its very definition as the organization of knowledge for practical purposes assumes that the primary and really creative role in the social processes consequent on technological change is reserved for a scientific and technical elite, the elite which presumably discovers and organizes that knowledge. But if the scientific and technical elite and their indispensable managerial cronies are the really creative (and hardworking and altruistic) element in American society, what is this but to say that the common mass of men are essentially drags on the social weal? This is precisely the implication which is drawn by the *laissez innover* school. Consider the following quotations from an article which appeared in *The New Republic* in December 1967, written by Zbigniew Brzezinski, one of the intellectual leaders of the school.

Brzezinski is describing a nightmare which he calls the "technetronic society" (the word like the concept is a pastiche of technology and electronics). This society will be characterized, he argues, by the application of ". . . the principle of equal opportunity for all but . . . special opportunity for the singularly talented few." It will thus combine ". . . continued *respect* for the popular will with an increasing *role* in the key decision-making institutions of individuals with special intellectual and scientific attainments." (Italics added.) Naturally, "The educational and social systems [will make] it increasingly attractive and easy for those meritocratic few to develop to the fullest of their special potential."

However, while it will be "... necessary to require everyone at a sufficiently responsible post to take, say, two years of [scientific and technical]
retraining every ten years ... ," the rest of us can develop a new "... interest
in the cultural and humanistic aspects of life, *in addition to purely hedonistic
preoccupations.*" (Italics added.) The latter, he is careful to point out, "would
serve as a social valve, reducing tensions and political frustration."

Is it not fair to ask how much *respect* we carefree pleasure lovers and culture consumers will get from the hard-working bureaucrats, going to night
school two years in every ten, while working like beavers in the "key decision-
making institutions"? The altruism of our bureaucrats has a heavy load to
bear.

Stripped of their euphemisms these are simply arguments which enhance
the social legitimacy of the interests of new technical and scientific elites and
detract from the interests of the rest of us; that is to say, if we can even formulate those interests, blinded as we will be by the mad pursuit of pleasures
(and innovation??!) heaped up for us by advanced technology. Mesthene and
his schoolfellows try to argue around their own derogation of the democratic
ethos by frequent references, as we have seen, to their own fealty to it. But it
is instructive in this regard to note that they tend, with Brzezinski, to find the
real substance of that democratic ethos in the principle of the equality of opportunity. Before we applaud, however, we ought to examine the role which
that principle plays within the framework of the advanced technological society they propose.

As has already been made clear the *laissez innover* school accepts as inevitable and desirable the centralizing tendencies of technology's social organization, and they accept as well the mystification which comes to surround
the management process. Thus equality of opportunity, as they understand it,
has precious little to do with creating a more egalitarian society. On the contrary, it functions as an indispensable feature of the highly stratified society
they envision for the future. For in their society of meritocratic hierarchy,
equality of opportunity assures that talented young meritocrats (the word is
no uglier than the social system it refers to) will be able to climb into the
"key decision-making" slots reserved for trained talent, and thus generate the
success of the new society, and its cohesion against popular "tensions and
political frustration."

The structures which formerly guaranteed the rule of wealth, age, and
family will not be destroyed (or at least not totally so). They will be firmed
up and rationalized by the perpetual addition of trained (and, of course, ac-
culturated) talent. In technologically advanced societies, equality of oppor-

tunity functions as a hierarchical principle, in opposition to the egalitarian social goals it pretends to serve. To the extent that it has already become the kind of "equality" we seek to institute in our society, it is one of the main factors contributing to the widening gap between the cultures of upper- and lower-class America.

V

Approximately a century ago, the philosophy of *laissez faire* began its period of hegemony in American life. Its success in achieving that hegemony clearly had less to do with its merits as a summary statement of economic truth than with its role in the social struggle of the time. It helped to identify the interests of the institutions of entrepreneurial capitalism for the social classes which dominated them and profited from them. Equally, it sketched in bold strokes the outlines of a society within which the legitimate interests of all could supposedly be served only by systematic deference to the interests of entrepreneurial capitalists, their institutions, and their social allies. In short, the primary significance of *laissez faire* lay in its role as ideology, as the cultural or intellectual expression of the interests of a class.

Something like the same thing must be said of *laissez innover*. As a summary statement of the relationship between social and technological change it obscures far more than it clarifies, but that is often the function and genius of ideologues. *Laissez innover* is now the premier ideology of the technological impulse in American society, which is to say, of the institutions which monopolize and profit from advanced technology and of the social classes which find in the free exploitation of *their* technology the most likely guarantee of their power, status, and wealth.

This said, it is important to stress both the significance and limitations of what has in fact been said. Here Mesthene's distinction between the positive opportunities and negative "externalities" inherent in technological change is pivotal; for everything else which I've argued follows inferentially from the actual social meaning of that distinction. As my analysis of the Vietnam bombing program suggested, those technological effects which are sought after as positive opportunities and those which are dismissed as negative externalities are decisively influenced by the fact that this distinction between positive and negative within advanced technological organizations tends to be made among the planners and managers themselves. Within these groups there are, as was pointed out, extremely powerful organizational, hierarchical, doctrinal, and other *"technical"* factors, which tend by design to filter out "irrational" demands from below, substituting for them the "rational" demands of technology itself. As a result, technological rationality is as socially neutral today as market rationality was a century ago.

Turning from the inner social logic of advanced technological organizations and systems to their larger social effect, we can observe a significant convergence. For both the social tendency of technology and the ideology (or rhetoric) of the *laissez innover* school converge to encourage a political and cultural gap between the upper and lower ends of American society. As I have pointed out, these can now be characterized as those who manage and those who are managed by advanced technological systems.

This analysis lends some weight (though perhaps no more than that) to a number of wide-ranging and unorthodox conclusions about American society today and the directions in which it is tending. It may be useful to sketch out the most important of those conclusions in the form of a set of linked hypotheses, not only to clarify what appear to be the latent tendencies of America's advanced technological society but also to provide more useful guides to the investigation of the technological impulse than those offered by the obscurantism and abstractions of the school of *laissez innover.*

First, and most important, technology should be considered as an institutional system, not more and certainly not less. Mesthene's definition of the subject is inadequate, for it obscures the systematic and decisive social changes, especially their political and cultural tendencies, that follow the widespread application of advanced technological systems. At the same time, technology is less than a social system per se, though it has many elements of a social system, viz., an elite, a group of linked institutions, an ethos, and so forth. Perhaps the best summary statement of the case resides in an analogy— with all the vagueness and precision attendant on such things: today's technology stands in relation to today's capitalism as, a century ago, the latter stood to the free market capitalism of the time.

The analogy suggests, accurately enough I believe, the likelihood that the institutional links and shared interests among the larger corporations, the federal government, especially its military sector, the multiversity and the foundations, will grow rather than decline. It suggests further a growing entanglement of their elites, probably in the neo-corporations of technology, such as urban development corporations and institutes for defense analysis, whose importance seems likely to increase markedly in the future.

Finally, it suggests a growing convergence in the ethos and ideology of technology's leading classes along lines which would diminish slightly the relative importance of rhetoric about "property" and even about "national security," while enhancing the rhetoric of *laissez innover*. This does not necessarily imply any sacrifice in the prerogatives of either the private sector or of the crisis managers and the military, for one can readily understand how the elite strictures of *laissez innover* may be applied to strengthen the position of the corporate and military establishments.[5]

A word about the elites: a number of writers of the *laissez innover* school, for example, J. K. Galbraith in his *The New Industrial State*, have argued that the enhanced importance of scientific and technical knowledge within advanced technological systems implies an enhanced socio-political power for the people who have such knowledge. Galbraith in particular has argued that these people, whom he calls "the educational and scientific estate," now constitute an elite class whose interests diverge quite sharply from those of other elites. Since I have argued at length elsewhere against this view,[6] let me limit myself here to only a few critical observances.

5. An interesting illustration of this point is provided by the major change in national security policy brought about in the first years of the Kennedy Administration, a change in which many *laissez innover* writers—Walt Rostow comes immediately to mind—played a prominent intellectual and policy-making role. One of the goals of the new policy was to assign an enhanced importance to American efforts to aid in the development of the so-called underdeveloped world. The leading ideas of the policy were very much influenced by *laissez innover*, for the process of development in the third world nations was largely conceived of as a process of nurturing a technologically advanced sector in the host economy to the point at which it would be able to dominate, economically, socially, politically the remainder of the society. At that "take-off" point American efforts could presumably be relaxed for the further development of the country would be assured, along with its integration into an international economy dominated by the US.

Superficially this might appear as a policy change in which the interests of the American military were sacrificed, at least partially, to those of AID and the State Department. Certainly, slogans to that effect—"less military aid; more economic aid"—seemed to indicate this. But in practice the nation-builders quickly found that the military of the third world nations were their best allies. Theory was quickly adjusted to the needs of practice.

The military in a non-industrialized economy have an abiding interest in the development of a modern economic infrastructure, not least because such an infrastructure is essential to support the modern weaponry amply supplied by the US—a fact about social leverage not lost on our policymakers. The social cohesion even of a swollen officers corps tends to offset the general social fractionation resulting from the changes of modernization and, of course, officers tend to be stalwartly anti-communist.

Thus, in spite of a change in rhetoric under Kennedy, the reality of the AID program very much served the interests of our own military; by strengthening the military capacity of other nations, by providing an expanding advisory role for our officers corps, and, not least important, by maintaining a growing market for American military equipment, both new and used. As an added fillip, the burst of nation-building activity under Kennedy also provided, as in Vietnam, a host of new overseas "commitments," which of course necessitated a major rearmament program for our conventional (i.e., limited war) forces.

6. "Knowledge is Power," *The Nation*, April 14, 1969. Galbraith's "educational and scientific estate" seems but a variant of Keller's strategic elites. . . . In fairness to Gal-

Galbraith's concept of an "educational and scientific" elite class overlooks the peculiar relationship which the members of that supposed class have to advanced technology. Specifically, it overlooks the fact that most technical, scientific, and educational people are employed at relatively specialized tasks within very large organizations whose managing and planning levels are hardly less insulated from their influence than from the influence of the technically unskilled.

The obvious growth in status and, I think, power of such men as Ithiel de Sola Pool, Herman Kahn, Samuel Huntington, Daniel Patrick Moynihan, Henry Kissinger, Charles Hitch, and Paul Samuelson hardly represents the triumph of wisdom over power—an implication not absent from Galbraith's analysis. An examination of the role which these men now play in our national life should emphasize that they are scientific and technical entrepreneurs whose power is largely based on their ability to mobilize *organized* intellectual, scientific, and technical manpower and other resources, including foundation grants and university sponsorship, in behalf of the objectives of going institutions. They are much more like managers than like intellectuals, much more like brokers than like analysts.

The same hardly applies to the thousands of E.E.'s, Ph.D.'s, M.S.'s, and so forth who make up the resources over which these mandarins preside and whose skills are so much at their disposal. But in recognizing the managerial and brokerage functions which predominate in the mandarin role we must also recognize that mandarin interests are more likely than not to converge

braith it should be pointed out that he too is concerned with the authoritarianism and anti-humanism of the technology. His "educational and scientific estate" is supposed to reintroduce democratic and humanist values into society because it, being highly educated, has these things in overabundance. On the whole this seems a dubious proposition. Democracy is vital only when it expresses some sort of social equilibrium; elite ideologies attack the legitimacy of social equilibrium and reduce democracy or democratic values thereby to some sort of elite benevolence toward the unwashed. Similarly, a humanist technology seems not likely to come from a class of humanist masters of technology. Mastership usually interferes with humanism in such cases. Humanist values become like Sunday School values; very good in themselves but not much in use during the week.

Any discussion of a reorganization of technology to serve human needs seems, at this point, so utopian that it robs one of the conviction necessary to shape a believable vision. Perhaps in a period of greater technological stability it would be possible to conjure up an alternate vision, but now, when the rush to technological centralization is so powerful and rapid the task seems beyond us.

My own feeling is that the fundamental point to take account of in constructing an alternate vision is the fact that technology itself and its need for a skilled and knowledgeable population has created within the population ample resources for self-management even of the most complicated activities. For further discussion of this basic contradiction, see below.

toward the interests of other segments of the national elite. This conclusion is diametrically opposed to the one argued by Galbraith.

A second major hypothesis would argue that the most important dimension of advanced technological institutions is the social one, that is, the institutions are agencies of highly centralized and intensive social control. Technology conquers nature, as the saying goes. But to do so it must first conquer man. More precisely, it demands a very high degree of control over the training, mobility, and skills of the work force. The absence (or decline) of direct controls or of coercion should not serve to obscure from our view the reality and intensity of the social controls which are employed (such as the internalized belief in equality of opportunity, indebtedness through credit, advertising, selective service channeling, and so on).

Advanced technology has created a vast increase in occupational specialties, many of them requiring many, many years of highly specialized training. It must motivate this training. It has made ever more complex and "rational" the ways in which these occupational specialties are combined in our economic and social life. It must win passivity and obedience to this complex activity. Formerly, technical rationality had been employed only to organize the production of rather simple physical objects, for example, aerial bombs. Now technical rationality is increasingly employed to organize all of the processes necessary to the utilization of physical objects, such as bombing systems. For this reason it seems a mistake to argue that we are in a "postindustrial" age, a concept favored by the *laissez innover* school. On the contrary, the rapid spread of technical rationality into organizational and economic life and, hence, into social life is more aptly described as a second and much more intensive phase of the industrial revolution. One might reasonably suspect that it will create analogous social problems.

Accordingly, a third major hypothesis would argue that there are very profound social antagonisms or contradictions not less sharp or fundamental than those ascribed by Marx to the development of nineteenth-century industrial society. The general form of the contradictions might be described as follows: a society characterized by the employment of advanced technology requires an ever more socially disciplined population, yet retains an ever declining capacity to enforce the required discipline.

One may readily describe four specific forms of the same general contradiction. Occupationally, the work force must be over-trained and under-utilized. Here, again, an analogy to classical industrial practice serves to shorten and simplify the explanation. I have in mind the assembly line. As a device in the organization of the work process the assembly line is valuable mainly in that it gives management a high degree of control over the pace of the work and, more to the point in the present case, it divides the work process into units so simple that the quality of the work performed is readily predictable. That is, since each operation uses only a small fraction of a worker's skill, there is a very great likelihood that the operation will be performed in a minimally acceptable way. Alternately, if each operation taxed the worker's skill there would be frequent errors in the operation, frequent disturbance of the work flow, and a thoroughly unpredictable quality to the end product. The assembly line also introduces standardization in work skills and thus makes for a high degree of interchangeability among the work force.

For analogous reasons the work force in advanced technological systems must be relatively over-trained or, what is the same thing, its skills relatively under-used. My impression is that this is no less true now of sociologists than of welders, of engineers than of assemblers. The contradiction emerges when we recognize that technological progress requires a continuous increase in the skill levels of its work force, skill levels which frequently embody a fairly rich scientific and technical training, while at the same time the advance of technical rationality in work organization means that those skills will be less and less fully used.

Economically, there is a parallel process at work. It is commonly observed that the work force within technologically advanced organizations is asked to work not less hard but more so. This is particularly true for those with advanced training and skills. Brzezinski's conjecture that technical specialists undergo continuous retraining is off the mark only in that it assumes such retraining only for a managing elite. To get people to work harder requires growing incentives. Yet the prosperity which is assumed in a technologically advanced society erodes the value of economic incentives (while of course, the values of craftsmanship are "irrational"). Salary and wage increases and the goods they purchase lose their over-riding importance once necessities, creature comforts, and an ample supply of luxuries are assured. As if in confirmation of this point, *Fortune* has pointed out (January 1969) that among young people one can already observe a radical weakening in the power of such incentives as money, status, and authority.

Politically, the advance of technology tends to concentrate authority within its managing groups in the ways I have described. But at the same time the increasing skill and educational levels of the population create latent capacities for self-management in the work place and in society. This aspect of the contradictions inherent in technology seems especially noteworthy in much of the current dissent within the armed forces. Of course, there has always been griping in the Army, but the fact that the griping now attaches itself to political problems—the war, the rights of servicemen, and so on—clearly speaks to the fact that GI educational levels have increased very radically.

A similar explanation casts light on the campus revolt. As Lionel Trilling has pointed out (*Partisan Review,* Summer 1968), the cultural and intellectual level of today's university students is far higher than that of their predecessors, if only because of television and the fact that a good part of traditional college work is now completed in the better high schools. The claim to greater self-management by university students is the natural outcome of this change. At the same time, however, the university has been developing the power and status of its own elites. These include the research elites whose power and status are based on consultantships, on their ability to win research grants and contracts and thus prestige for their universities, as well as the more general category of professional elite, i.e., those whose power within the university is buttressed by their prestige in the national professional associations and expressed in their control of the major academic departments. In spite of the apparent decentralization within the university organization, one must recognize that there has been a very tangible increase in the influence of these elites. Within the university (as elsewhere) power has become more centralized, that is, it has gravitated toward an identifiable collection of research and professional mandarins. It is the power of the latter over curriculum, admissions, research and consulting policy, hiring and advancement that is being challenged by student dissidence.[7]

It should be added here that even the "irrationality" of the student revolt is clarified by the general lines of this explanation, i.e., its common failure to formulate coherent social programs and its tendency to enter battle under extremely vague symbolic banners. As we have seen social irrationality can be

7. The foregoing explanation is confirmed, I believe, by some salient aspects of the history of the student movement. Most of the radical student groups began and grew to prominence on elite campuses, i.e., on campuses where the contradiction between the cultural level of the students and the institutional power of the mandarins was most sharp. The New Left began at the University of Michigan and, after winning control over the SDS organization, organized first at Harvard, Swarthmore, Chicago, Berkeley, and other elite campuses. Only in the past two years has it reached out in any significant degree to non-elite campuses and in this it was very much aided by its militant stand against the war and the draft. Even today, *on attitudes toward the university* (as opposed to the war or racism, etc.) the most militant chapters are found in elite schools, Columbia, Chicago, Berkeley, and Harvard. The major exception to this statement is in California, especially San Francisco State, and my impression is that this has to do with the fact that the California system of higher education is, in general, at a further stage of development toward institutional hierarchy than those of most other states.

explained as a normal effect of the social and organizational patterns of advanced technological systems and, if anything, is increased by the personal intelligence of the people trapped in those systems.

Finally, there is a profound social contradiction between the highly stratified society implicit in, say, Brzezinski's meritocracy and the spread of educational opportunity. Yet each appears equally required by advanced technology.

These are brief and, I believe, barely adequate reviews of extremely complex hypotheses. But, in outline, each of these contradictions appears to bear on roughly the same group of the American population, a technological underclass. If we assume this to be the case, a fourth hypothesis would follow, namely that technology is creating the basis for new and sharp class conflict in our society. That is, technology is creating its own working and managing classes just as earlier industrialization created its working and owning classes. Perhaps this suggests a return to the kind of class-based politics which characterized the US in the last quarter of the nineteenth century, rather than the somewhat more ambiguous politics which was a feature of the second quarter of this century. I am inclined to think that this is the case, though I confess the evidence for it is as yet inadequate.

This leads to a final hypothesis, namely that *laissez innover* should be frankly recognized as a conservative or right-wing ideology. This is an extremely complex subject for the hypothesis must confront the very difficult fact that the intellectual genesis of *laissez innover* is traceable much more to leftist and socialist theorizing on the wonders of technical rationality and social planning than it is to the blood politics of a De Maistre or the traditionalism of a Burke. So be it. Much more important is the fact that *laissez innover* is now the most powerful and influential statement of the demands and program of the technological impulse in our society, an impulse rooted in its most powerful institutions. More than any other statement, it succeeds in identifying and rationalizing the interests of the most authoritarian elites within this country, and the expansionism of their policies overseas. Truly it is no accident that the leading figures of *laissez innover,* the Rostows, Kahn, Huntington, Brzezinski, to name but a few, are among the most unreconstructed cold warriors in American intellectual life.

The point of this final hypothesis is not primarily to re-impress the language of European politics on the American scene. Rather it is to summarize the fact that many of the forces in American life hostile to the democratic ethos have enrolled under the banner of *laissez innover.* Merely to grasp this is already to take the first step toward a politics of radical reconstruction and

against the malaise, irrationality, powerlessness, and official violence that
characterize American life today.

Can Technology Be Humane?

PAUL GOODMAN

On March 4, 1969 there was a "work stoppage" and teach-in initiated by dissenting professors at the Massachusetts Institute of Technology, and followed
at thirty other major universities and technical schools across the country,
against misdirected scientific research and the abuse of scientific technology.
Here I want to consider this event in a broader context than the professors
did, indeed as part of a religious crisis. For an attack on the American scientific establishment is an attack on the world-wide system of belief. I think we
are on the eve of a new protestant Reformation, and no institution or status
will go unaffected.

March 4 was, of course, only [one] of a series of protests in the [over]
twenty-five years since the Manhattan Project to build the atom bomb, during
which time the central funding of research and innovation has grown so enormously and its purposes have become so unpalatable. In 1940 the Federal
budget for research and development was less than 100 million dollars, in
1967, 17 billion. Hitler's war was a watershed of modern times. We are accustomed, as H. R. Trevor-Roper has pointed out, to write Hitler off as an aber-
ration, of little political significance. But, in fact, the military emergency that
he and his Japanese allies created confirmed the worst tendencies of the giant
states, till now they are probably irreversible by ordinary political means.

After Hiroshima, there was the conscience-stricken movement of the
Atomic Scientists and the founding of their Bulletin. The American Association for the Advancement of Science pledged itself to keep the public informed about the dangerous bearings of new developments. There was the
Oppenheimer incident. Ads of the East Coast scientists successfully stopped
the bomb shelters, warned about the fall-out, and helped produce the test
ban. There was a scandal about the bombardment of the Van Allen belt. Sci-

entists and technologists formed a powerful (and misguided) *ad hoc* group for Johnson in the 1964 election. In some universities, sometimes with bitter struggle, classified contracts have been excluded. There is a Society for Social Responsibility in Science. Rachel Carson's book on the pesticides caused a stir, until the Department of Agriculture rescued the manufacturers and plantation-owners. Ralph Nader has been on his rampage. Thanks to spectacular abuses like smog, strip-mining, asphalting, pesticides, and oil pollution, even ecologists and conservationists have been getting a hearing. Protest against the boom has slowed up the development of the supersonic transport[, particularly in the United States]. Most recent has been the concerted outcry against the anti-ballistic missiles.

The target of protest has become broader and the grounds of complaint deeper. The target is now not merely the military, but the universities, commercial corporations, and government. It is said that money is being given by the wrong sponsors to the wrong people for the wrong purposes. In some of the great schools, such funding is the main support, e.g., at MIT, 90 percent of the research budget is from the government, and 65 percent of that is military.

Inevitably, such funding channels the brainpower of most of the brightest science students, who go where the action is, and this predetermines the course of American science and technology for the foreseeable future. At present nearly 200,000 American engineers and scientists spend all their time making weapons, which is a comment on, and perhaps explanation for, the usual statement that more scientists are now alive than since Adam and Eve. And the style of such research and development is not good. It is dominated by producing hardware, figuring logistics, and devising salable novelties. Often there is secrecy, always nationalism. Since the grants go overwhelmingly through a very few corporations and universities, they favor a limited number of scientific attitudes and preconceptions, with incestuous staffing. There is a premium on "positive results"; surprising "failures" cannot be pursued, so that science ceases to be a wandering dialogue with the unknown.

The policy is economically wasteful. A vast amount of brains and money is spent on crash programs to solve often essentially petty problems, and the claim that there is a spin-off of useful discoveries is derisory, if we consider the sums involved. The claim that research is neutral, and it doesn't matter what one works on, is shabby, if we consider the heavy funding in certain directions. Social priorities are scandalous: money is spent on overkill, supersonic planes, brand-name identical drugs, annual model changes of cars, new detergents, and color television, whereas water, air, space, food, health, and foreign aid are neglected. And much research is morally so repugnant, e.g., chemical and biological weapons, that one dares not humanly continue it.

The state of the behavioral sciences is, if anything, worse. Their claim to moral and political neutrality becomes, in effect, a means of diverting attention from glaring social evils, and they are in fact used—or would be if they worked—for warfare and social engineering, manipulation of people for the political and economic purposes of the powers that be. This is an especially sad betrayal since, in the not-too-distant past, the objective social sciences were developed largely to dissolve orthodoxy, irrational authority, and taboo. They were heretical and intellectually revolutionary, as the physical sciences had been in their own Heroic Age, and they weren't getting government grants.

This is a grim indictment. Even so, I do not think the dissenting scientists understand how deep their trouble is. They still take themselves too much for granted. Indeed, a repeated theme of the March 4 [1969] complaints was that the science budget was being cut back, especially in basic research. The assumption was that though the sciences are abused, Science would rightly maintain and increase its expensive pre-eminence among social institutions. Only Science could find the answers.

But underlying the growing dissent there is an historical crisis. There has been a profound change in popular feeling, more than among the professors. Put it this way: Modern societies have been operating as if religion were a minor and moribund part of the scheme of things. But this is unlikely. Men do not do without a system of "meanings" that everybody believes and puts his hope in even if, or especially if, he doesn't know anything about it; what Freud called a "shared psychosis," meaningful because shared, and with the power that resides in dream and longing. In fact, in advanced countries it is science and technology themselves that have gradually and finally triumphantly become the system of mass faith, not disputed by various political ideologies and nationalism that have also been mass religions. Marxism called itself "scientific socialism" as against moral and utopian socialisms; and movements of national liberation have especially promised to open the benefits of industrialization and technological progress when once they have gotten rid of the imperialists.

For three hundred years, science and scientific technology had an unblemished and justified reputation as a wonderful adventure, pouring out practical benefits, and liberating the spirit from the errors of superstition and traditional faith. During this century they have finally been the only generally credited system of explanation and problem-solving. Yet in our generation they have come to seem to many, and to very many of the best of the young, as essentially inhuman, abstract, regimenting, hand-in-glove with Power, and even diabolical. Young people say that science is anti-life, it is a Calvinist obsession, it has been a weapon of white Europe to subjugate colored races, and manifestly—in view of recent scientific technology—people who think that way become insane. With science, the other professions are discredited; and the academic "disciplines" are discredited.

The immediate reasons for this shattering reversal of values are fairly obvious. Hitler's ovens and his other experiments in eugenics, the first atom bombs and their frenzied subsequent developments, the deterioration of the physical environment and the destruction of the biosphere, the catastrophes impending over the cities because of technological failures and psychological stress, the prospect of a brainwashed and drugged 1984. Innovations yield diminishing returns in enhancing life. And instead of rejoicing, there is now widespread conviction that beautiful advances in genetics, surgery, computers, rocketry, or atomic energy will surely only increase human woe.

In such a crisis, in my opinion, it will not be sufficient to ban the military from the universities; and it will not even be sufficient, as liberal statesmen and many of the big corporations envisage, to beat the swords into ploughshares and turn to solving problems of transportation, desalinization, urban renewal, garbage disposal, and cleaning up the air and water. If the present difficulty is religious and historical, it is necessary to alter the entire relationship of science, technology, and social needs both in men's minds and in fact. This involves changes in the organization of science, in scientific education, and in the kinds of men who make scientific decisions.

In spite of the fantasies of hippies, we are certainly going to continue to live in a technological world. The question is a different one: is that workable?

PRUDENCE

Whether or not it draws on new scientific research, technology is a branch of moral philosophy, not of science. It aims at prudent goods for the commonweal and to provide efficient means for these goods. At present, however, "scientific technology" occupies a bastard position in the universities, in funding, and in the public mind. It is half tied to the theoretical sciences and half treated as mere know-how for political and commercial purposes. It has no principles of its own. To remedy this—so Karl Jaspers in Europe and Robert Hutchins in America have urged—technology must have its proper place on the faculty as a learned profession important in modern society, along with medicine, law, the humanities, and natural philosophy, learning from them and having something to teach them. As a moral philosopher, a technician should be able to criticize the programs given him to implement. As a professional in a community of learned professionals, a technologist must have a different kind of training and develop a different character than we see at present among technicians and engineers. He should know something of the social sciences, law, the fine arts, and medicine, as well as relevant natural sciences.

Prudence is foresight, caution, utility. Thus it is up to the technologists, not to regulatory agencies of the government, to provide for safety and to think about remote effects. This is what Ralph Nader is saying and Rachel Carson used to ask. An important aspect of caution is flexibility, to avoid the pyramiding catastrophe that occurs when something goes wrong in interlocking technologies, as in urban power failures. Naturally, to take responsibility for such things often requires standing up to the front office and urban politicians, and technologists must organize themselves in order to have power to do it.

Often it is clear that a technology has been oversold, like the cars. Then even though the public, seduced by advertising, wants more, technologists must balk, as any professional does when his client wants what isn't good for him. We are now repeating the same self-defeating congestion with the planes and airports: the more the technology is oversold, the less immediate utility it provides, the greater the costs, and the more damaging the remote effects. As this becomes evident, it is time for technologists to confer with sociologists and economists and ask deeper questions. Is so much travel necessary? Are there ways to diminish it? Instead, the recent history of technology has consisted largely of a desperate effort to remedy situations caused by previous over-application of technology.

Technologists should certainly have a say about simple waste, for even in an affluent society there are priorities—consider the supersonic transport, which has little to recommend it. But the moon shot has presented the more usual dilemma of authentic conflicting claims. I myself believe that space exploration is a great human adventure, with immense aesthetic and moral benefits, whatever the scientific or utilitarian uses. Yet it is amazing to me that the scientists and technologists involved have not spoken more insistently for international cooperation instead of a puerile race. But I have heard some say that except for this chauvinist competition, Congress would not vote any money at all.

Currently, perhaps the chief moral criterion of a philosophic technology is modesty, having a sense of the whole and not obtruding more than a particular function warrants. Immodesty is always a danger of free enterprise, but when the same disposition is financed by big corporations, technologists rush into production with neat solutions that swamp the environment. This applies to packaging products and disposing of garbage, to freeways that bulldoze neighborhoods, high-rises that destroy landscape, wiping out a species for a passing fashion, strip mining, scrapping an expensive machine rather than making a minor repair, draining a watershed for irrigation because (as in Southern California) the cultivable land has been covered by asphalt. Given this disposition, it is not surprising that we defoliate a forest in order to expose a guerrilla and spray teargas from a helicopter on a crowded campus.

Since we are technologically over-committed, a good general maxim in advanced countries at present is to innovate in order to simplify the technical system, but otherwise to innovate as sparingly as possible. Every advanced country is over-technologized; past a certain point, the quality of life diminishes with new "improvements." Yet no country is rightly technologized, making efficient use of available techniques. There are ingenious devices for unimportant functions, stressful mazes for essential functions, and drastic dislocation when anything goes wrong, which happens with increasing frequency. To add to the complexity, the mass of people tend to become incompetent and dependent on repairmen—indeed, unrepairability except by experts has become a desideratum of industrial design.

When I speak of slowing down or cutting back, the issue is not whether research and making working models should be encouraged or not. They should be, in every direction, and given a blank check. The point is to resist the temptation to apply every new device without a second thought. But the big corporate organization of research and development makes prudence and modesty very difficult; it is necessary to get big contracts and rush into production in order to pay the salaries of the big team. Like other bureaucracies, technological organizations are run to maintain themselves but they are more dangerous because, in capitalist countries, they are in a competitive arena.

I mean simplification quite strictly, to simplify the *technical* system. I am unimpressed by the argument that what is technically more complicated is really economically or politically simpler, e.g., by complicating the packaging we improve the supermarkets; by throwing away the machine rather than repairing it, we give cheaper and faster service all around; or even by expanding the economy with trivial innovations, we increase employment, allay discontent, save on welfare. Such ideas may be profitable for private companies or political parties, but for society they have proved to be an accelerating rat race. The technical structure of the environment is too important to be a political or economic pawn; the effect on the quality of life is too disastrous; and the hidden social costs are not calculated, the auto graveyards, the torn-up streets, the longer miles of commuting, the advertising, the inflation, etc. As I pointed out in *People or Personnel,* a country with a fourth of our per capita income, like Ireland, is not necessarily less well off; in some respects it is much richer, in some respects a little poorer. If possible, it is better to solve political problems by political means. For instance, if teaching machines and audio-visual aids are indeed educative, well and good; but if they are used just to save money on teachers, then not good at all—nor do they save money.

Of course, the goals of right technology must come to terms with other values of society. I am not a technocrat. But the advantage of raising technology to be a responsible learned profession with its own principles is that it can have a voice in the debate and argue for *its* proper contribution to the community. Consider the important case of modular sizes in building, or prefabrication of a unit bathroom: these conflict with the short-run interests of manufacturers and craft-unions, yet to deny them is technically an abomination. The usual recourse is for a government agency to set standards; such agencies accommodate to interests that have a strong voice, and at present technologists have no voice.

The crucial need for technological simplification, however, is not in the advanced countries—which can afford their clutter and probably deserve it—but in underdeveloped countries which must rapidly innovate in order to diminish disease, drudgery, and deepening starvation. They cannot afford to make mistakes. It is now widely conceded that the technological aid we have given to such areas according to our own high style—a style usually demanded by the native ruling groups—has done more harm than good. Even when, as frequently if not usually, aid has been benevolent, without strings attached, not military, and not dumping, it has nevertheless disrupted ways of life, fomented tribal wars, accelerated urbanization, decreased the food supply, gone wasted for lack of skills to use it, developed a do-nothing élite.

By contrast, a group of international scientists called Intermediate Technology argue that what is needed is techniques that use only native labor, resources, traditional customs, and teachable know-how, with the simple aim of remedying drudgery, disease, and hunger, so that people can then develop further in their own style. This avoids cultural imperialism. Such intermediate techniques may be quite primitive, on a level unknown among us for a couple of centuries, and yet they may pose extremely subtle problems, requiring exquisite scientific research and political and human understanding, to devise a very simple technology. Here is a reported case (which I trust I remember accurately): In Botswana, a very poor country, pasture was over-grazed, but the economy could be salvaged if the land were fenced. There was no local material for fencing, and imported fencing was prohibitively expensive. The solution was to find the formula and technique to make posts out of mud, and a pedagogic method to teach people how to do it.

In *The Two Cultures,* C. P. Snow berated the humanists for their irrelevance when two-thirds of mankind are starving and what is needed is science and technology. They have perhaps been irrelevant; but unless technology is itself more humanistic and philosophical, it is of no use. There is only one culture.

Finally, let me make a remark about amenity as a technical criterion. It is discouraging to see the concern about beautifying a highway and banning billboards, and about the cosmetic appearance of the cars, when there is no regard for the ugliness of bumper-to-bumper traffic and the suffering of the drivers. Or the concern for preserving an historical landmark while the neighborhood is torn up and the city has no shape. Without moral philosophy, people have nothing but sentiments.

ECOLOGY

The complement to prudent technology is the ecological approach to science. To simplify the technical system and modestly pinpoint our artificial intervention in the environment makes it possible for the environment to survive in its complexity evolved for a billion years, whereas the overwhelming instant intervention of tightly interlocked and bulldozing technology has already disrupted many of the delicate sequences and balances. The calculable consequences are already frightening, but of course we don't know enough, and won't in the foreseeable future, to predict the remote effects of much of what we have done. The only possible conclusion is to be prudent; when there is serious doubt, to do nothing.

Cyberneticists—I am thinking of Gregory Bateson—come to the same cautious conclusion. The use of computers has enabled us to carry out crashingly inept programs on the bases of willful analyses. But we have also become increasingly alert to the fact that things respond, systematically, continually, cumulatively; they cannot simply be manipulated or pushed around. Whether bacteria or weeds or bugs or the technologically unemployed or unpleasant thoughts, they cannot be eliminated and forgotten; repressed, the nuisances return in new forms. A complicated system works most efficiently if its parts readjust themselves decentrally, with a minimum of central intervention or control, except in case of breakdown. Usually there is an advantage in a central clearing house of information about the gross total situation, but decision and execution require more minute local information. The fantastically simulated moon landing hung on a last split-second correction on the spot. In social organization, deciding in headquarters means relying on information that is cumulatively abstract and irrelevant, and chain-of-command execution applies standards that cumulatively do not fit the concrete situation. By and large it is better, given a sense of the whole picture, for those in the field to decide what to do and do it (cf. *People or Personnel,* Chapter 3).

But with organisms too, this has long been the bias of psychosomatic medicine, the Wisdom of the Body, as Cannon called it. To cite a classical experiment of Ralph Hefferline of Columbia: a subject is wired to suffer an annoying regular buzz, which can be delayed and finally eliminated if he makes a precise but unlikely gesture, say by twisting his ankle in a certain way; then it is found that he adjusts quicker if he is *not* told the method and it is left to his spontaneous twitching than if he is told and tries deliberately to help himself. He adjusts better without conscious control, his own or the experimenter's.

Technological modesty, fittingness, is not negative. It is the ecological wisdom of cooperating with Nature rather than trying to master her. (The personification of "Nature" is linguistic wisdom.) A well-known example is the long-run superiority of partial pest-control in farming by using biological deterrents rather than chemical ones. The living defenders work harder, at the right moment, and with more pin-pointed targets. But let me give another example because it is so lovely—though I have forgotten the name of my informant: A tribe in Yucatan educates its children to identify and pull up all weeds in the region; then what is left is a garden of useful plants that have chosen to be there and now thrive.

In the life sciences there is at present a suggestive bifurcation in methodology. The rule is still to increase experimental intervention, but there is also a considerable revival of old-fashioned naturalism, mainly watching and thinking, with very modest intervention. Thus, in medicine, there is new diagnostic machinery, new drugs, spectacular surgery; but there is also a new respect for family practice with a psychosomatic background, and a strong push, among young doctors and students, for a social-psychological and sociological approach, aimed at preventing disease and building up resistance. In psychology, the operant conditioners multiply and refine their machinery to give maximum control of the organism and the environment (I have not heard of any dramatic discoveries, but perhaps they have escaped me). On the other hand, the most interesting psychology in recent years has certainly come from animal naturalists, e.g., pecking order, territoriality, learning to control aggression, language of the bees, overcrowding among rats, trying to talk to dolphins.

On a fair judgment, both contrasting approaches give positive results. The logical scientific problem that arises is, What is there in the nature of things that makes a certain method, or even moral attitude, work well or poorly in a given case? This question is not much studied. Every scientist seems to know what "the" scientific method is.

Another contrast of style, extremely relevant at present, is that between Big Science and old-fashioned shoe-string science. There is plenty of research, with corresponding technology, that can be done only by Big Science; yet much, and perhaps most, of science will always be shoe-string science, for which it is absurd to use the fancy and expensive equipment that has gotten to be the fashion.

Consider urban medicine. The problem, given a shortage of doctors and facilities, is how to improve the level of mass health, the vital statistics, and yet to practice medicine, which aims at the maximum possible health for each person. Perhaps the most efficient use of Big Science technology for the general health would be compulsory biennial checkups, as we inspect cars, for early diagnosis and to forestall chronic conditions with accumulating costs. Then an excellent machine would be a total diagnostic bus to visit the neighborhoods, as we do chest X-rays. On the other hand, for actual treatment and especially for convalescence, the evidence seems to be that small personalized hospitals are best. And to revive family practice, maybe the right idea is to offer a doctor a splendid suite in a public housing project.

Our contemporary practice makes little sense. We have expensive technology stored in specialists' offices and big hospitals, really unavailable for mass use in the neighborhoods; yet every individual, even if he is quite rich, finds it almost impossible to get attention to himself as an individual whole organism in his setting. He is sent from specialist to specialist and exists as a bag of symptoms and a file of test scores.

In automating there is an analogous dilemma of how to cope with masses of people and get economies of scale, without losing the individual at great consequent human and economic cost. A question of immense importance for the immediate future is, Which functions should be automated or organized to use business machines, and which should not? This question also is not getting asked, and the present disposition is that the sky is the limit for extraction, refining, manufacturing, processing, packaging, transportation, clerical work, ticketing, transactions, information retrieval, recruitment, middle management, evaluation, diagnosis, instruction, and even research and invention. Whether the machines can do all these kinds of jobs and more is partly an empirical question, but it also partly depends on what is meant by doing a job. Very often, e.g., in college admissions, machines are acquired for putative economies (which do not eventuate); but the true reason is that an overgrown and overcentralized organization cannot be administered without them. The technology conceals the essential trouble, e.g., that there is no community of scholars and students are treated like things. The function is badly performed, and finally the system breaks down anyway. I doubt that enterprises in which interpersonal relations are important are suited to much programming.

But worse, what can happen is that the real function of the enterprise is subtly altered so that it is suitable for the mechanical system. (E.g., "information retrieval" is taken as an adequate replacement for critical scholarship.) Incommensurable factors, individual differences, the local context, the weighting of evidence are quietly overlooked though they may be of the essence. The system, with its subtly transformed purposes, seems to run very smoothly; it is productive, and it is more and more out of line with the nature of things and the real problems. Meantime it is geared in with other enterprises of society, e.g., major public policy may depend on welfare or unemployment statistics which, as they are tabulated, are blind to the actual lives of poor families. In such a case, the particular system may not break down, the whole society may explode.

I need hardly point out that American society is peculiarly liable to the corruption of inauthenticity, busily producing phony products. It lives by public relations, abstract ideals, front politics, show-business communications, mandarin credentials. It is preeminently overtechnologized. And computer technologists especially suffer for the euphoria of being in a new and rapidly expanding field. It is so astonishing that the robot can do the job at all or seem to do it, that it is easy to blink at the fact that he is doing it badly or isn't really doing quite that job.

DECENTRALIZATION

The current political assumption is that scientists and inventors, and even social scientists, are "value-neutral," but their discoveries are "applied" by

those who make decisions for the nation. Counter to this, I have been insinu-
ating a kind of Jeffersonian democracy or guild socialism, that scientists and
inventors and other workmen are responsible for the uses of the work they
do, and ought to be competent to judge these uses and have a say in deciding
them. They usually are competent. To give a striking example, Ford assembly
line workers, according to Harvey Swados, who worked with them, are accurately critical of the glut of cars, but they have no way to vent their dissatis-
factions with their useless occupation except to leave nuts and bolts to rattle
in the body.

My bias is also pluralistic. Instead of the few national goals of a few decision-makers, I propose that there are many goods of many activities of life,
and many professions and other interest groups each with its own criteria and
goals that must be taken into account. A society that distributes power
widely is superficially conflictful but fundamentally stable.

Research and development ought to be widely decentralized, the national
fund for them being distributed through thousands of centers of initiative and
decision. This would not be chaotic. We seem to have forgotten that for four
hundred years Western science majestically progressed with no central direction whatever, yet with exquisite international coordination, little duplication, almost nothing getting lost, in constant communication despite slow facilities. The reason was simply that all scientists wanted to get on with the
same enterprise of testing the boundaries of knowledge, and they relied on
one another.

What is as noteworthy is that something similar holds also in invention
and innovation, even in recent decades when there has been such a concentration of funding and apparent concentration of opportunity. The majority of
big advances have still come from independents, partnerships, and tiny companies. (Evidence published by the Senate Sub-Committee on Antitrust and
Monopoly, May 1965.) To name a few, jet engines, xerography, automatic
transmission, cellophane, air-conditioning, quick freeze, antibiotics, and tranquilizers. The big technological teams must have disadvantages that outweigh
their advantages, like lack of singlemindedness, poor communications, awk-
ward scheduling. Naturally, big corporations have taken over the innovations,
but the Senate evidence is that 90 percent of the government subsidy has
gone for last-stage development for production, which they ought to have
paid out of their own pockets.

We now have a theory that we have learned to learn, and that we can program technical progress, directed by a central planning board. But this doesn't
make it so. The essence of the new still seems to be that nobody has thought

of it, and the ones who get ideas are those in direct contact with the work. *Too precise* a preconception of what is wanted discourages creativity more than it channels it; and bureaucratic memoranda from distant directors don't help. This is especially true when, as at present, so much of the preconception of what is wanted comes from desperate political anxiety in emergencies. Solutions that emerge from such an attitude rarely strike out on new paths, but rather repeat traditional thinking with new gimmicks; they tend to compound the problem. A priceless advantage of widespread decentralization is that it engages more minds, and more mind, instead of a few panicky (or greedy) corporate minds.

A homespun advantage of small groups, according to the Senate testimony, is that co-workers can talk to one another, without schedules, reports, clock-watching, and face-saving.

An important hope from decentralizing science is to develop knowledgeable citizens, and provide not only a bigger pool of scientists and inventors but also a public better able to protect itself and know how to judge the enormous budgets asked for. The safety of the environment is too important to be left to scientists, even ecologists. During the last decades of the nineteenth century and the first decade of the twentieth, the heyday of public faith in the beneficent religion of science and invention, say from Pasteur and Huxley to Edison and the Wright Brothers, philosophers of science had a vision of a "scientific way of life," one in which people would be objective, respectful of evidence, accurate, free of superstition and taboo, immune to irrational authority, experimental. All would be well, is the impression one gets from Thomas Huxley, if everybody knew the splendid Ninth Edition of the *Encyclopaedia Britannica* with its articles by Darwin and Clerk Maxwell. Veblen put his faith in the modesty and matter-of-factness of engineers to govern. Sullivan and Frank Lloyd Wright spoke for an austere functionalism and respect for the nature of materials and industrial processes. Patrick Geddes thought that new technology would finally get us out of the horrors of the Industrial Revolution and produce good communities. John Dewey devised a system of education to rear pragmatic and experimental citizens to be at home in the new technological world rather than estranged from it. Now fifty years later, we are in the swamp of a scientific and technological environment and there are more scientists alive, etc., etc. But the mention of the "scientific way of life" seems like black humor.

Many of those who have grown up since 1945 and have never seen any other state of science and technology assume that rationalism itself is totally evil and dehumanizing. It is probably more significant than we like to think that they go in for astrology and the Book of Changes, as well as inducing psychedelic dreams by technological means. Jacques Ellul, a more philosophic critic, tries to show that technology is necessarily over-controlling, standardizing, and voraciously inclusive, so that there is no place for freedom. But I doubt that any of this is intrinsic to science and technology. The crude history has been, rather, that they have fallen willingly under the dominion of money and power. Like Christianity or communism, the scientific way of life has never been tried.

THE NEW REFORMATION

To satisfy the March 4 dissenters, to break the military-industrial corporations and alter the priorities of the budget, would be to restructure the American economy almost to a revolutionary extent. But to meet the historical crisis of science at present, for science and technology to become prudent, ecological, and decentralized requires a change that is even more profound, a kind of religious transformation. Yet there is nothing untraditional in what I have proposed; prudence, ecology, and decentralization are indeed the high tradition of science and technology. Thus the closest analogy I can think of is the Protestant Reformation, a change of moral allegiance, liberation from the Whore of Babylon, return to the pure faith.

Science has long been the chief orthodoxy of modern times and has certainly been badly corrupted, but the deepest flaw of the affluent societies that has alienated the young is not, finally, their imperialism, economic injustice, or racism, bad as these are, but their nauseating phoniness, triviality, and wastefulness, the cultural and moral scandal that Luther found when he went to Rome in 1510. And precisely science, which should have been the wind of truth to clear the air, has polluted the air, helped to brainwash, and provided weapons for war. I doubt that most young people today have even heard of the ideal of the dedicated researcher, truculent and incorruptible, and unrewarded, for instance the "German scientist" that Sinclair Lewis described in *Arrowsmith.* Such a figure is no longer believable. I don't mean, of course, that he doesn't exist; there must be thousands of him, just as there were good priests in 1510.

The analogy to the Reformation is even more exact if we consider the school system, from educational toys and Head Start up through the universities. This system is manned by the biggest horde of monks since the time of Henry VIII. It is the biggest industry in the country. I have heard the estimate that 40 percent of the national product is in the Knowledge Business. It is mostly hocus-pocus. Yet the belief of parents in this institution is quite delusional and school diplomas are in fact the only entry to licensing and hiring in every kind of job. The abbots of this system are the chiefs of science, e.g., the National Science Foundation, who talk about reform but work to expand the school budgets, step up the curriculum, and inspire the endless catechism of tests.

These abuses are international, as the faith is. For instance, there is no essential difference between the military-industrial or the school system, of the Soviet Union and the United States. There are important differences in way of life and standard of living, but the abuses of technology are very similar: pollution, excessive urbanization, destruction of the biosphere, weaponry, and disastrous foreign aid. Our protesters naturally single out our own country, and the United States is the most powerful country, but the corruption we are speaking of is not specifically American nor even capitalist; it is a disease of modern times.

But the analogy is to the Reformation, it is not to primitive Christianity or some other primitivism, the abandonment of technological civilization. There is indeed much talk about the doom of Western civilization, and a few Adamites actually do retire into the hills; but for the great mass of mankind, and myself, that's not where it's at. There is not the slightest interruption to the universalizing of Western civilization, including most of its delusions, into the so-called Third World. (If the atom bombs go off, however?)

Naturally the exquisitely interesting question is whether or not this Reformation will occur, how to make it occur, against the entrenched worldwide system of corrupt power that is continually aggrandizing itself. I don't know. In my analogy I have deliberately been choosing the date 1510, Luther in Rome, rather than 1517 when, in the popular story, he nailed his Theses on the cathedral door. There are everywhere contradictory signs and dilemmas. The new professional and technological class is more and more entangled in the work, statuses, and rewards of the system, and yet this same class, often the very same people, are more and more protestant. On the other hand, the dissident young, who are unequivocally for radical change, are so alienated from occupation, function, knowledge, or even concern, that they often seem to be simply irrelevant to the underlying issues of modern times. The monks keep "improving" the schools and getting bigger budgets to do so, yet it is clear that high schools will be burned down, twelve-year-olds will play truant in droves, and the taxpayers are already asking what goes on and voting down the bonds.

The interlocking of technologies and all other institutions makes it almost impossible to reform policy in any part; yet this very interlocking that renders people powerless, including the decision-makers, creates a remarkable resonance and chain-reaction if any determined group, or even determined individual, exerts force. In the face of overwhelmingly collective operations like the space exploration, the average man must feel that local or grassroots efforts are worthless, there is no science but Big Science, and no administration but the State. And yet there is a powerful surge of localism, populism, and community action, as if people were determined to be free even it it makes no sense. A mighty empire is stood off by a band of peasants, and *neither* can win—this is even more remarkable than if David beats Goliath; it means that neither principle is historically adequate. In my opinion, these dilemmas and impasses show that we are on the eve of a transformation of conscience.

3

Toward Assessment and Control

One need not accept the analysis of John McDermott, nor share the pessimism of Marcuse or Ellul, to be deeply concerned with the negative effects of technology on society. In fact, few contemporary observers, including those who would cheerfully accept the label of "technological optimists," dispute the need for society to develop better ways of controlling the impacts of technology. In recent years, the spread of these concerns has led governments of industrialized nations to begin thinking about new modes of technological planning and decision making.

This final section of *Technology and Man's Future* focuses on one of these new modes, known as "technology assessment" (TA). TA is a process through which the total impact of a technology on society—particularly the secondary and indirect effects that are not immediately apparent—is ascertained. Although TA is certainly not the only approach to controlling technology and in itself does not even assure control of the potential undesirable impacts of technology, the aim of TA is to bring such impacts to public view and thus provide the underpinning for improved long-range planning and policy making.

The term "technology assessment" first gained currency in 1967 through the efforts of Emilio Q. Daddario, at the time a congressman from Connecticut and chairman of the House Subcommittee on Science, Research, and Development. Daddario saw the problem of managing the technology-society relationship as an extremely important one and devoted a major share of his legislative career to this problem. In March 1967 he introduced a bill calling on the federal government to establish a Technology Assessment Board in order "to provide a method for identifying, assessing, publicizing, and dealing with the implications and effects of applied research and technology." Daddario did not regard this bill as a finished piece of legislation, but he hoped that it would be a "stimulant to discussion." Daddario's purpose in initiating his subcommittee's study of technology assessment was "to strengthen the role of the Congress in making judgments among alternatives for putting science to work for human benefit."

The initiative of the Daddario subcommittee resulted, six years later in 1973, in the establishment of the Congressional Office of Technology Assessment (OTA)—a move that has significantly enhanced the capacity of Congress to deal with technological issues. Daddario, who had left Congress in 1970, was appointed the first director of the office.

The establishment of OTA is perhaps the most concrete product of the discussions stimulated by the Daddario subcommittee. However, from the outset of these discussions, it was apparent that TA was a concept that transcended merely enhancing the role of Congress in technological decision making. An early indication of the scope of the TA concept is found in the report of the National Academy of Sciences (NAS), "Technology: Processes of Assessment and Choice," commissioned by the Daddario subcommittee in 1967. The first article in this section is a summary of the academy's report, co-authored by Harvey Brooks, chairman of the panel that prepared it, and Raymond Bowers, one of the panel members. Brooks, professor of technology and public policy at Harvard, and Bowers, head of the Cornell University Program in Science, Technology, and Society, describe the intellectual path followed by the NAS panel and report on its conclusions. Technology assessment processes are constantly in operation, the authors observe, but since costs and benefits are assessed by those primarily concerned with exploiting a given technology, "the frame of reference for the assessment is often quite limited." The problem is one of allocating costs and benefits equitably to different interest groups, and this is fundamentally a political matter. Technology assessment can go only so far; its function is "to clarify the political choices rather than to come up with a final answer." Within this framework, the NAS report discusses those factors, both conceptual and institutional, that inhibit effective technology assessment. Among these are the lack of a method for measuring social costs and benefits, the inability of "diffuse and poorly articulated interests" to inject themselves into the decision-making process, and the absence of adequate assessment methodologies. The authors propose a "constellation of organizations" strategically located within the government that would provide a variety of functions related to technology assessment. On the whole, these institutional reforms are intended to increase the amount of information on the effects of technology and channel this information in such a manner as to ensure its appropriate utilization.

The proposals of the National Academy of Sciences, as well as the approach taken by the National Academy of Engineering in a counterpart study, are subjected to strong criticism in a paper by Hugh Folk, professor of economics and labor and industrial relations at the University of Illinois (Champaign-Urbana). Folk sees the interplay of interests in the policy-making process as an inherently irrational phenomenon and berates the NAS and NAE panels for failing to recognize that simply introducing greater quantities of information into the system, on the assumption that it will be used rationally, will not solve the problem. Folk argues that you cannot separate assessment, no matter how "objective," from the interests it serves. Beyond this, he continues, experts in a given area of technology are generally closely involved with the promotion of that technology and, with all good intentions, tend to accept current institutional arrangements and balances of power ("political feasibility") as given. Folk's answer is "a responsible process of technological debate." Rather than looking for an impossible value-free assessment, he proposes the establishment of a responsible technological opposition, which would perform *counterassessments* of technologies and thus shape the policy-making process through a sort of adversary proceeding.

The Brooks and Bowers paper and the Folk critique date from the early days of the discussions surrounding TA, a period in which this concept was not generally accepted in the science and technology policy community. During the past several years, technology assessment has moved from being the subject of debate—sometimes abstract debate—to the status of a widely known and practiced art. Technology assessments are now being performed in government and nongovernment organizations the world over. Methods of assessment are taught in universities; numerous conferences and symposia have been held on the subject; an International Society for Technology Assessment has been established; and a professional journal has appeared.

The third article in this section consists of a comprehensive, relatively up-to-date overview of the field by one of its most influential practitioners and spokesmen. For several years Joseph Coates led the National Science Foundation's program in technology assessment; later he was appointed assistant to the director of OTA. In this article, reprinted from the *Yearbook of Science and Technology*, Coates describes the differences between technology assessment and traditional modes of technological planning. He explains how technology assessments are done and how they are put to use, and he reviews several recent major assessments on such topics as hurricane seeding, the automobile, and the climatic implications of atmospheric pollution.

Because Coates's survey was prepared when the Congressional Office of Technology Assessment was in its infancy, none of the assessments he describes was performed by that office. Yet an understanding of the role of OTA is obviously important to a well-rounded view of the field. The next article is a product of OTA, which should contribute to such an understanding. "Organization and Operations of the Office of Technology Assessment" is excerpted from OTA's 1976 *Annual Report* and provides a general idea of the activities of the office. As the selection indicates, OTA operates as a service organization for Congress in a manner somewhat similar to the Congressional Research Service, although the scope of OTA's studies is broader and it makes more use of outside contractors. Some—but by no means all—of OTA's work fits the original concept of technology assessment. Other efforts undertaken by OTA include broader excursions into science and technology policy questions. A number of observers have criticized this deviation from the original concept, as well as OTA's performance, its service orientation, and its apparent pattern of steering clear of highly controversial issues. Others have praised its ability to perform valuable, in-depth studies in the often frenzied and politicized congressional environment.

To gain a better sense of the substance of OTA's work, as well as to provide at least a superficial notion of what an actual technology assessment looks like, this part includes a summary of an OTA report, "Coastal Effects of Offshore Energy Systems." Although it is no doubt useful to be exposed to a "real live" technology assessment, readers should be warned that "Coastal Effects of Offshore Energy Systems" is not a *typical* TA. There is, in fact, no such thing as a typical TA. Each assessment is unique in many respects, including the range of impacts it considers, the techniques it employs to study these impacts, and the level of detail at which it operates. The report summarized here is particularly interesting because it involved an innovative program in public participation—an attempt to gage citizen attitudes toward the technologies at issue and accommodate them in the recommendations.

One of the central elements in many technology assessments is the forecast of the technological development whose impacts are to be studied; yet relatively little of the TA literature draws upon the growing field of technological forecasting. The article by David Kiefer, "Technological Forecasting in Technology Assessment," is an attempt to remedy this deficiency. Kiefer reviews various forecasting techniques, including correlation analysis, cross-impact analysis, scenario writing, Delphi, and normative forecasting. He suggests that the best approach is likely to consist of a combination of several of these techniques. He explores the relevance of forecasting to technology assessment and concludes that progress in assessment is likely to be slow and uncertain until there are improvements in technological forecasting.

The next article, "Technology Assessment and Social Control," is by Michael Baram, an MIT professor whose background includes degrees in both law and engineering. In this article, Baram develops a model that describes the means by which citizens whose interests are affected by particular technological developments can participate in decision making relating to these developments and can influence outcomes. Baram sees the present system as an adversarial one pitting beneficiaries of new technologies against those who stand to lose from implementation. What is necessary, he concludes, is "to transform this relationship from an adversarial one to one of joint decision-making and negotiation of differences in good faith among all interested parties."

The involvement of all interested parties in decision-making processes relating to the public development, use, and regulation of technology is also the focus of "Participatory Technology," by James Carroll. Carroll contends that participatory technology is emerging as a "countervailing force to technological alienation in contemporary society." Participatory technology is a broad concept and includes technology assessment as well as litigation— "citizen lawsuit[s] directed toward the control and guidance of technology," and ad hoc activity such as consumer advocacy or political activism related to specific situations and issues. Some forms of participatory technology circumvent the traditional forms of political process, and Carroll foresees a variety of hazards and unanswered questions. Nevertheless, he seems to be cautiously optimistic on the potential of this concept.

Carroll states that technology assessment is only part of a larger process through which people are beginning to assert control over technology. Langdon Winner, in the final selection of part three, declares that this is not enough. Winner, a graduate student at the University of California at Berkeley at the time he wrote this article, reviews a cross section of the recent literature on technology and society and finds it wanting. One major shortcoming in the literature is the focus on technological *change* rather than on the whole range of issues relating to the impact of technology on society. According to Winner, "the bias of the approach is to find opportunities for making judgment and taking action at only those points in which a new development in technology occurs." This is a serious limitation of technology assessment. What is needed, Winner concludes, is not so much technology assessment, but technology criticism: "an intensive and thoroughgoing examination of the role of technology in this culture and its role in our own identifies." To implement technology criticism, Winner prescribes a set of guidelines centering around the willingness of society to say no to a variety of technological developments. Technology criticism begins at home. Each of us must face the problem as an individual.

Technology: Processes
of Assessment and Choice

HARVEY BROOKS AND RAYMOND BOWERS

In recent years concern has mounted over society's apparent inability to channel the application of technology in directions that sufficiently respect the broad range of human needs. Rightly or wrongly, the belief is now widely held that the continuation of certain technological trends poses great danger for the future of man. The unwise or incomplete application of technology has already contributed to some of the most urgent of our contemporary problems: the threat of thermonuclear destruction, the social crisis of our cities, the deterioration of the natural environment, the displacement of workers, and the potential invasion of privacy. There is a growing skepticism toward proposals and projects (for example, the SST) that in an earlier day might have been hailed as symbols of human progress. Influential and thoughtful segments of the public have begun to ask whether technological progress is always for the best—whether we can afford to wait until unforeseen side-effects of technological application reach crisis proportions before we seek means to alleviate them on a piecemeal basis.

There are even some who wish to make modern technology the scapegoat of all our social ills. They perceive technology as having become the master of man and not his servant. This wholly pessimistic attitude rests upon a vast oversimplification, as does the converse notion that technology is the universal solvent of man's problems and needs only to be applied more vigorously to assure an increasing measure of the good life. Between the two extreme positions lies the view that benefit and injury may both result from technology. For those holding this view, it is important and urgent to ask how technological change can be guided by a deeper concern for the interaction between man's tools and the human condition that they modify. This is the concern of "technology assessment." This term is used to describe the examination and evaluation of the likely consequences of technological development and application in order to foster a more constructive evolution for technology. The concept is an extremely broad one embracing the preservation and enhancement of environmental quality, the improvement of the measurement and understanding of social change, and the development of a longer planning horizon in technological development. All these factors also bear on the allocation of public resources.

The growing concern with such problems has brought forth a number of suggestions on how our governmental apparatus should be modified to deal more effectively with them. Proposals have been made for a council of ecological or environmental advisors, an interagency council on environmental quality, a select Senate committee on technology and human environment, and a council of social advisors. Proposals exist for amendments to the Constitution asserting the right to a pure environment and for the creation of a fourth branch of government, an "evaluation branch."

This article describes an examination of the problem of technology assessment by a group convened by the Committee on Science and Public Policy of the National Academy of Sciences; the study was carried out at the request of the Subcommittee on Science, Research and Development of the House Committee on Science and Astronautics.[1]

The origin of the study can be traced to Representative Emilio Q. Daddario's bill to establish a technology assessment board, "to provide a method for identifying, assessing, publicizing and dealing with the implications and effects of applied research and technology." The original bill was introduced not as a piece of perfected legislation but rather as a stimulant to discussion. Representative Daddario and his subcommittee sponsored not only the study described in this article but also a parallel study, carried out quite independently, by the National Academy of Engineering.

To make our task manageable, the study group was forced to delineate boundaries. We set aside as beyond our scope the ultimate philosophical issues posed by technical civilization. Nor did we discuss the value implications of theoretical discoveries in the sciences. Our focus was on technology—what

1. This is a summary of *Technology: Process of Assessment and Choice,* Report of the National Academy of Sciences, Committee on Science and Astronautics, U.S. House of Representatives, and is available from the Superintendent of Documents. The members of this panel were, apart from the two authors of this article, Laurence H. Tribe, Hendrik W. Bode, Gordon McKay, Harvard University; Edward C. Creutz, Gulf General Atomic, Inc.; A. Hunter Dupree, Brown University; Ralph W. Gerard, University of California, Irvine; Norman Kaplan, George Washington University; Milton Katz, Harvard University; Melvin Kranzberg, Case Western Reserve University; Hans H. Landsberg, Resources for the Future, Inc.; Gene M. Lyons, Dartmouth College; Louis H. Mayo, George Washington University; Gerard Piel, Scientific American; Herbert A. Simon, Carnegie-Mellon University; Cyril S. Smith, Massachusetts Institute of Technology; Morris Tanenbaum, Western Electric; Dael Wolfle, American Association for the Advancement of Science.

man can do and what he chooses to do with what he knows. We did not attempt to assess in detail the specific consequences or implications of any particular technological development. (In this sense our study is complementary to that carried out by the National Academy of Engineering, which did consider some specific cases in detail.) We recognized at the outset that the assessment of technological prospects and hazards is already a pervasive activity in both industry and government, as well as among many private associations such as conservation groups. Thus we undertook to identify what seem to be the most serious deficiencies in existing processes of assessment and decision making. The critical question is how broad are the criteria on which these assessments are made. Do present assessment processes deal with a wide enough sphere of effects, both social and environmental? Since we concluded that they do not, we then asked how we could begin the extremely difficult task of altering present evaluative and decision-making processes so that private and public choices would reflect a greater sensitivity of the total effects of technology on the human environment. We sought mechanisms for achieving this without denying ourselves the benefits of continuing technological progress.

It was necessary to concentrate frequently on the detrimental effects of technology. This was an almost inevitable consequence of our assignment to identify the deficiencies in present procedures; it is not to be construed as an antitechnology bias. Indeed, it was not our function to set up a net balance sheet on technology, but rather to deal with the institutions that govern the rate and direction of technological change.

It was the belief of our panel that, although current political attention appears to be focused on the negative effects of technology, an effective system of technology assessment would as often stimulate the development and application of under-utilized technologies and identify new opportunities for beneficial use of technology as it would alert us to possible deleterious side effects. Many of the problems currently identified as products of technological development—overpopulation, congested cities, deteriorated housing, crowded airways, polluted air—can also be seen as having resulted from the failure to develop and disseminate parallel technologies which would have mitigated the undesired effects—methods of fertility control, cheaper industrially produced housing, air traffic control systems, better design of fixed and mobile power plants. Thus, it is not technology itself but the unequal and unplanned relative speeds of development and application of different technologies that has partly created our problems.

In the 1930's the Great Depression showed us that we could no longer afford the waste of productive resources involved in permitting individual economic decisions to proceed without social control. Yet, in many ways the controls that were instituted strengthened the market system and increased the options of the entrepreneur and the consumer, while protecting them from some of the risks of economic disaster. We believe that the current years are presenting an environmental and social crisis, resulting from unguided technology, that bears a close resemblance to the economic crisis of forty years ago. We also believe that the control measures that are necessary can strengthen rather than weaken technological innovation, and can shield it from the unreasoning and capricious political reaction that will surely result as we move from one environmental and social crisis to another in the absence of adequate foresight and planning. Already we see that much of our technological planning—in highways, airports, power plant location, aircraft development, for example—is being increasingly disrupted by unanticipated public resistance, at great costs not only to technology itself, but also in postponement of benefits to the public. Furthermore, the progress of science in recent years has greatly increased the menu of technological options available to us. We are in a position to choose among many feasible technological paths to the same objective, sometimes at an increased economic cost, which, however, society will be increasingly willing to pay if an equitable way of assessing it can be found. Thus an important aspect of technology assessment is the evaluation of alternate means to the same end and a comparison of their social and economic costs. Choices between alternative technologies are partly economic and political decisions. In our opinion, it is neither feasible nor desirable to develop an assessment mechanism that would circumvent market and political modes of accommodating the conflicts of interests and values that must arise; rather, we view assessment as one of many inputs into the complex network of public and private decision-making processes that together mold the growth of technology and its integration into society.

The earliest form of technology assessment in the U.S., and the one which is still dominant, emerged with the development of capitalism and the system of markets and prices to assess needs and priorities. In this country, the federal government has also long played a significant role in affecting the direction of technological development. Federal involvement through interstate commerce regulation, the patent system, and participation in technological ventures has roots that go back to the early days of the republic. However, the involvement of the federal government on a massive scale did not occur until World War II. Today the government finances nearly 50 percent of industrial research and development, and virtually every government agency is deeply involved in technological programs. The influence of the federal government is now critical in highway planning and construction, water resource development, housing, the development of nuclear power, agriculture, the extraction of natural resources, aviation, the exploitation of the oceans, and many other areas. Numerous agencies have been created either to regulate technological activities or to perform specialized functions related to the impact of technology on particular facets of the environment or on the consumer. These include the Federal Communications Commission, the Federal Power Commission, the Food and Drug Administration, the Atomic Energy Commission, and many others. Government involvement in technology development is now pervasive and has in many cases significantly modified and even replaced the forces of the market in determining the rates and directions of technological change.

Within this set of governmental and market processes, the initial assessment of the costs and benefits of alternative technologies is normally undertaken by those who seek to exploit them. Thus, the frame of reference for the assessment is often quite limited. While diverse groups such as professional societies and conservation organizations may have inputs to the evaluation, the assessment is usually based on the contending interests of those who already recognize their stake in the technology and are prepared to enter the public arena to defend their position. In all but a few special situations, usually when Congress takes a special interest, no other assessment occurs. The regulatory agencies when involved are often restricted to narrow assessments because of specified limits in their jurisdictions and mandates; these limits are sometimes arbitrary and sometimes appropriate. While technological decisions are made within a framework of social and legal restraints, the central question asked in contemporary technology assessment is what the technology will do to the economic and institutional interests of those who wish to exploit it or what it will do to the interests of those having a stake in competing technologies. The recognition and analysis of broader impacts usually occurs only later in ad hoc assessments of the problems after they have reached serious proportions and have generated acute public concern. No mechanism exists to trigger such studies in a systematic way at the early stages of the process of technology development and diffusion. The vacuum that is left is partially filled by the activities of articulate individuals such as Ralph Nader and Rachel Carson as well as by conservation organizations which attempt to represent the "public interest." Their efforts, which excite both admiration and criticism, are a consequence of a deficiency in our present evaluation and decision system.

The important problems of technology assessment must inevitably involve conflicts of interests, values, and goals. Technological development will necessarily affect some people adversely and others beneficially. There is no agreed quantitative method by which the costs and benefits may be evaluated. We seriously doubt that concepts such as the "general welfare" or "the public interest" can be aggregated like the final figure on the balance sheet showing net profit or net loss. The assigning of costs and benefits to different groups is fundamentally political, and the purpose of technology assessment is to clarify the political choices rather than to come up with a final answer.

The difficulties of computing all costs and benefits should not prevent us from formulating general principles. For example, the preservation of future options must be a key factor. Other things being equal, those alternatives that leave maximum room for maneuver in the future should be favored. For example, policy should reflect the fact that the pollution of a lake is more difficult to reverse than the pollution of a river. The reduction of future options ought to be counted as a cost incurred in a particular undertaking; yet this is rarely done in current assessments. In less affluent societies than ours, it may be necessary to discount the future for short-term gains, but in the United States this policy becomes harder and harder to justify.

Technology assessment by its very nature deals with uncertainties. In the past, the benefit of the doubt was most frequently given to the developer. The working assumption was that a technological trend should be permitted to continue so long as it yielded a profit to those who exploit it. However, our experience in the last few years with such events as the Santa Barbara incident and the accumulation of pesticide residues suggests a reconsideration of this assumption.

It is clear that some of our present difficulties can be attributed to the lack of effective constituencies informed and influential enough to inject diffuse and poorly articulated interests into the decision-making process. There is often an absence of influential spokesman within this process whose task it is to see the impact on segments of society beyond those that perceive themselves to be directly and immediately affected. This certainly does not mean that the advantages lie always with those who are proposing technological innovations; often the antitechnological forces are very strong. New technology that promises to upset power relations, employment patterns, or traditional procedures in an industry usually excites vigorous and sometimes successful opposition; think, for example, of the building industry, shipping, and even education. The difficulty lies not with the representation of those groups that directly perceive their interests to be affected either positively or negatively, but in the fact that those groups for which the consequences are less obvious or more remote in time have little voice in the decision-making process. Slight effects on many people over long periods of time are likely to be neglected in comparison with more dramatic damages or benefits.

Another problem is the lack of consistency in the criteria of assessment or regulation of alternate technologies that serve the same social purpose. For example, are safety standards or environmental pollution standards with respect to the extraction and transportation of oil more or less stringent than the safety standards for the location and construction of nuclear power plants? To the extent that these standards are not treated consistently, an arbitrary bias may be generated with respect to one type of power plant over the other.

The achievement of a more rational and effective system of technology assessment faces some major obstacles; a satisfactory methodology of assessment is far away. We do not know how to balance conflicting interests. We do not know how to value in a quantitative manner goals such as clean environment or preservation of future choice. There is an absence of analytical tools. Projections of the impact of technology are limited by failure of imagination, especially when it comes to foreseeing the cumulative effects of scale. For example, in 1948 there were 100,000 television sets in use; one year later there were a million; a decade later there were fifty million. The social and psychological consequences of such phenomenal growth are hard to contemplate, let alone predict. Our failures to imagine all the possible uses of new technologies can often preclude adequate perception of social and environmental consequences. As late as 1958, an authoritative report on the consequences of the automobile failed to mention atmospheric pollution. Nor can we imagine all the consequences for the supporting system that a new technology will require. For example, the current crisis in air transport arises in part from failure to develop an air traffic control system adequate for the technology of modern aircraft, and also from failure to develop airports and ground transportation adequate for the volume of traffic. Perhaps the greatest difficulty is that of forecasting changes in technology itself that can both ameliorate and aggravate consequences perceived at the beginning of the development period. Our understanding of the interaction of technology with society is not well founded; much remains to be learned about how pollutants disperse in the environment and how children react to various kinds of television programs. Nor is the data base on which general theories might be constructed at all adequate. Our monitoring of secondary effects of technology is in a primitive state. And the obstacles go beyond inadequate analytical methods and insufficient theoretical understanding. In large measure, the problems are institutional: economic, legal, or political constraints upon the interests and authority of the decision makers. These necessarily result in distortion. Institutional constraints must affect technological decisions when an institution feels that it only has the mandate to consider those consequences directly affecting its own constituents or clients. For example, public utility commissions have no authority to consider investments that improve the environment in establishing the rate base for power plants. Moreover, some institutional structures result in a very strong vested interest in the stimulation or prevention of a particular technology. In government, there are jurisdictional boundaries which frequently bear no relationship to the technological problem under examination. This problem is probably most acute in environmental questions.

Technology assessment is so complex, that it is not surprising that during our study we frequently had doubts that anything significant could come from viewing it on the all-inclusive basis that seemed to be required. The processes we seek to improve are too bound up with the very fabric of our society to admit of sudden and sweeping alteration. But the rejection of instant solutions does not mean that we cannot begin in an evolutionary manner the extremely difficult task of altering present evaluative and decision-making processes in a way that would remove some of the obvious defects of our present procedures. Our study concluded that improvements are feasible. We believe there is a need for additional mechanisms of technology assessment beyond those currently operating because these are inadequate to deal with the scale of application of technology expected in the future. New mechanisms are necessary to supplement and coordinate existing mechanisms rather than to supersede them. Existing procedures, whether they involve government agencies, private industries, or professional groups have intrinsic limitations both by design and because of unconscious biases. There is a need for a program of technology assessment that is broader in fundamental conception and scope and better designed to take into account the interests of groups which, at the inception of a technological development, are unorganized or do not yet perceive their interests potentially affected. We need evaluations that are more responsive to changes in the values, sensitivities, and priorities of society. Neither the evaluation nor the original formulation of relevant questions should be too limited by the interests and biases of direct interest groups. While one will never be able to devise procedures that totally avoid such distortions, much can be done to improve the current situation.

Technology assessments are carried on at many locations in our society, but they are too fragmented and uncoordinated to provide an institutional basis for the support of research, analysis, education, and monitoring that is necessary for a national technology assessment capability. No group at present has the responsibility for standards and criteria and for the development of coherent principles of assessment that can be applied consistently in many different situations. There is no system of precedents, analagous to case law, which can be transferred from one assessment problem to another.

While we see a need for new procedures and institutions to strengthen the quality of technology assessment, we also acknowledge that the present multiplicity of processes is essential because technology pervades almost every aspect of our social organization. Our study did not contemplate a highly centralized process of technology assessment as a solution. Even if practical, centralization would be unwise, politically unacceptable, and even dangerous. Pluralism in this matter is essential in the context of our society, not only because it is the only principle consistent with our political values, but also because it insures a healthy competition of ideas and avoids at least some of the negative impact of innovation which could be as dangerous as the side effects of technology.

We thus envision a constellation of organizations, with components located strategically within both political branches, that can provide a focus and a forum for technology assessment activities throughout the government and the private sector. We see the following functions for the new technology assessment mechanisms: (1) examine particular areas of technology using both in-house personnel and contracts with outside organizations to undertake comprehensive assessments of social and environmental effects of technology; (2) sponsor basic research on theoretical problems and issues related to technology assessment by extending grants for studies to be conducted by government agencies, universities, and not-for-profit organizations; (3) review specific assessments performed by other agencies, confining this review to an evaluation of the criteria and procedures employed in the assessment processes, the nature and reliability of the evidence relied upon, and the adequacy of the representation of potentially affected interests; (4) develop an information center on technology assessment and carry out research to identify gaps in the existing body of data; (5) issue an annual technology assessment report reviewing governmental work in this area, describing new methods and new problems that have emerged, and suggesting future priorities; (6) provide an effective forum for responsible assessment activities of individuals and groups currently operating outside the present governmental and industrial technology assessment institutions. We include in this last activity the sponsorship of conferences, symposia, and the holding of public hearings; (7) prepare policy papers recommending specific actions to Congress, the President, and executive or administrative bodies bearing on the sponsorship or regulation of technology.

An important goal is to achieve greater consistency in assessment principles; these could be used to improve the quality of assessments carried out by private organizations and specialized government agencies. Such principles could result from a conscious attempt to formulate general policy, but they could also evolve from the experience gained from dealing with individual cases selected in part for their potential in setting precedents.

Before discussing specific organizational arrangements, we wish to make some general comments concerning the limitations of the scope and powers of the new institutions we shall propose. Any new technology assessment mechanism must maintain as detached and neutral a stance as possible toward each issue that comes before it. For this reason, it should be insulated from direct policy-making authority. It should have neither the responsibility for promotion of any particular technology nor regulatory powers. Above all, it must be given no authority to screen or clear new technological undertakings, though obviously its evaluations and recommendations should carry weight with those agencies which have such authority. Unlike the Federal Aviation Agency it must not itself be entrusted with the realization of a supersonic transport or even an operational air traffic control system. Unlike the Atomic Energy Commission it should not be held accountable for the avoidance of excessive radiation. To give it responsibilities of this kind would deprive it of its unique perspective as an entity with no ax to grind. Given the current popularity of proposals to entrust some environmental agency with the power to censor all technological developments and forbid the introduction of those deemed excessively injurious, a further word on this subject seems in order. Our study concluded that one could not vest such authority in any agency without subjecting it to external political pressures that it could not resist. That is, the allocation of such sweeping powers to a new assessment entity would rob it of any special claim to objectivity and render its judgments at least as suspect as those of any other regulatory or technology-promoting agency.

At the outset of the creation of this technology assessment mechanism, its activities should be restricted to those areas of technology that are strongly and directly influenced by federal policy. We believe that the federal government ought to put its own house in order before it seeks to impose new requirements for state or local action or new standards for the private sector. The involvement of the federal government in technology is so broad that this restriction still leaves an enormous sphere of activity.

In the design of a new governmental institution, it is important to be sensitive to the dangers of technology assessment, especially its possible secondary consequences. The most serious problem lies in its effect on the delicate process of industrial and technological innovation. There is a very real risk that new assessment institutions could stultify progress by magnifying risks or difficulties and ignoring the possibility of finding solutions as problems arise. New assessment mechanisms could create sufficient new uncertainties in the prospects for innovation that private and public investment in new areas of technology would be discouraged. If the technology assessment mechanism is not sensitive to the need to encourage innovation, the cure may be worse than the disease. It must be recognized that new technology has unanticipated or secondary benefits as well as undesirable side effects. When the development of nuclear power was started, it was not anticipated that this power might alleviate the problem of atmospheric pollution.

Another danger is one that is inherent in every attempt to improve rationality in politically charged areas of discourse. Just as systems analysis has occasionally been used to provide a spurious mantle of objectivity for essentially predetermined value preferences, so, too, there is a risk that technology assessment, without independent criticism, may become a weapon of individuals and groups in defense of their own interests or narrow ideological aims.

In trying to design a governmental organization that is likely to be effective in this area, one can specify a number of desirable characteristics. However, these characteristics are likely to be mutually contradictory, at least to some degree. For example, any effective assessment organization needs to be close to the center of important political decisions in order that it may be influential; yet it needs to maintain a degree of political neutrality in order to ensure the integrity, objectivity, and credibility of its evaluations and assessments. It needs to address politically pressing and urgent issues; yet its time perspective should be longer than that of most political decisions. It must provide critical analysis of private sector plans affected by federal policies and programs; yet it must be an organization that will obtain the confidence and cooperation of industry. It must provide a forum for public representation and open hearings; yet it must be able to respect the privacy of individuals and the legitimate proprietary interests of industrial organizations. Clearly compromises will have to be made in designing new mechanisms. Any new system should be able to modify its procedures, assumptions, and even its location within government as it learns from experience. Perhaps, if new mechanisms and institutions are created by statute, their organization, procedures, and accomplishments should be subject to formal review after a specified term of existence.

Our study group concluded that it was necessary to have important components of the new technology assessment mechanism associated with both the executive and congressional branches of government. The executive component should be closely linked to the President. Having considered many alternative means of achieving this, we concluded that the best location would be within an expanded Office of Science and Technology (OST), possibly under a deputy director, since it is difficult to separate technology assessment from many of the functions currently performed by OST. Furthermore, a wholly separate office would be likely to lead to a situation in which the new office became the rallying point for antitechnology forces while OST took on an increasingly protechnology bias. The responsibilities of this part of the mechanism would include the direction of an information management system for technology assessment, the preparation of an annual report, the initiation of conferences and symposia, and the preparation of in-house policy papers. We hope that such activities would strongly influence the political and budgetary decisions carried out in the office of the President. Since we cannot foresee the expansion of the OST component to the scale necessary to support related extramural activities, we believe that there should be a new Technology Assessment Division within the National Science Foundation to complement the activities of the Office of Science and Technology. This division would administer the substantial program involving work to be performed outside of the executive office on contracts and grants, especially in universities and other private organizations. The executive component could be expected to review specific assessments performed by other government agencies or departments either on its own initiative or by requests from other agencies. Such a review would be limited to an evaluation of the criteria and procedures employed in the assessment process, the nature and scientific adequacy of the evidence relied upon, and the representation of potentially affected interests. We would guess that the total annual budget of the new operation in the executive branch might ultimately reach the order of $50 million with about 20 percent being spent "in-house" and 80 percent in the contract or grant program with external organizations. Some idea of the scale of this operation can be given by noting that the following government organizations had budgets of approximately this magnitude in fiscal 1969:

General Accounting Office	$58 million
Library of Congress	$50 million
Civil Aeronautics Board	$63 million
Food and Drug Administration	$70 million

We do not believe that a viable technology assessment mechanism can be built if it is restricted to the executive branch. There are many arguments for this point of view, but most of them ultimately center on undue influence of the President and his executive agencies on the course of the assessment process. Complementary organizations more directly accessible to the Congress are needed. We need to provide within Congress or close to Congress an effective public forum for responsible assessment activities of individuals or groups operating outside present governmental and industrial institutions. Congress needs direct access to more sophisticated and professional judgments relating to the technology assessments it considers. Such judgments cannot be obtained entirely from existing substantive and appropriations committees, though they will surely play a role. They do not provide adequate focus because of internal rivalries and fragmentation by jurisdictional divisions. We have considered two possibilities. One is a joint congressional committee on technology assessment. This committee's relationship to the proposed executive technology assessment entities would be analogous to the relationship of the joint committee on internal revenue and taxation to the Department of the Treasury or the joint economic committee to the Council of Economic Advisors. Using these as a model, we believe that the high standard of professional competence required in the staff of the committee can be achieved. We do not propose that this joint committee have any jurisdiction over specific legislation or appropriations. While it will obviously wish to develop its own independent sources of information, we assume that it would have access with appropriate safeguards to the information system developed in the executive branch.

An alternative congressional component could be centered in a separate technology assessment office serving the Congress as a whole. Such an office would carry out assignments given to it by the Vice-President, the Speaker or the chairman of any interested committee of Congress. Unlike the Legislative Reference Service and the Legislative Drafting Service, it would not be expected to accept assignments from individual members of Congress. Its functions would be similar to those suggested for the joint committee. The director of such an office might be appointed by the President with the advice and consent of the Senate, but his term of office should be sufficiently long to provide a measure of insulation from presidential politics, perhaps analogous to the comptroller general, who is removable only by a concurrent resolution of both houses of Congress.

While developing these recommendations we did consider a quasi-independent commission separated from both of the political branches. While this kind of separation has obvious advantages in terms of freedom from political interference, the separation of the assessment process from the center of political decisions seems a very heavy price to pay. In any case we believe that a totally apolitical assessment mechanism is a myth. It cannot be totally apolitical and relevant simultaneously.

One question of great importance that did not receive much attention in the panel's deliberations was the assessment of military technology. While many will think it is absurd in a discussion of the impact of technology on our society to exclude consideration of the military, there are features of military technology that made it difficult to include in our evaluation. Military technology is frequently not visible to the public and a considerable proportion of the technological data is either classified or proprietary. The control over the flow of this information is effectively in the hands of the proponents of technological innovation who assess technology only in terms of national security conceived in the narrowest sense. Furthermore, military technology is strongly conditioned by the interpretation of intelligence and information which can be of a highly sensitive character. While our discussions did not encompass military technology, we nevertheless were convinced of the importance of having some mechanism for independent assessment of proposed military technology by a group of fully cleared experts not directly responsible for national security and sensitive to broader social, political, and environmental implications.

Our study concluded with the conviction that however our specific recommendations be viewed, *some* form of constructive action is imperative and cannot be long delayed without increasing the difficulty of implementation and diminishing the prospects of success. The future of technology holds great promise for mankind. However, if society persists in its present course, the future holds great peril whether from the uncontrolled effects of technology itself or from an unreasoned political reaction against all technological innovation, which could condemn man to poverty, frustration, and the loss of freedom.

The Role
of Technology Assessment
in Public Policy

HUGH FOLK

Recent discussions of technology assessment suggest that additional information will improve policy making in technology and science. It is premised that the government wants to make good technological policy, has the power to make good policy, and would recognize a good policy if one were proposed. These premises are at least questionable, if we interpret "good" as meaning in the interest of the survival, prosperity, and liberty of the mass of the population. Many powerful politicians (such as appropriations subcommittee chairmen) have no concern for the national interest at all, but serve the parochial interests that permit their political survival. The government is often powerless to deal with significant problems because of the domination of significant parts of the regulatory apparatus by those who are subject to regulation and because authority is fragmented. Few politicians either possess the scientific sophistication necessary to make good judgments on technological questions or trust persons with the capacity of judgment. If viewed as a part of the policy making process, and not merely another sterile academic exercise, technology assessment must be adapted to the existing political process in which special interests, restricted and fragmented governmental jurisdiction, and untrustworthy advice flourish.

Technology assessment may be viewed as part of a rational process of policy making with four steps: (1) identifying possible outcomes of policy alternatives; (2) estimating the valency or probability of each of the possible outcomes; (3) estimating the utility or disutility of each of the outcomes to the interested parties; and (4) weighing the utilities and disutilities to the interested parties and deciding if the policy alternative is better than other alternatives.

Policy for technology may be treated in this framework and differs in no interesting formal way from any other kind of policy. Technology assessment is merely a special type of policy assessment. Policy assessment encompasses the first three steps of the policy-making process. It generates data for the decision maker, who carries out the fourth step.

WHY POLICY MAKING IS NOT RATIONAL

As a consequence of the technical complexity of the decisions, the vast number of decisions they must make, and the shortage of time, neither the Administration nor the Congress is capable of developing sound policy assessments on which decisions could be based. At the same time, they do not often identify and employ trustworthy experts to perform policy assessments for them. Even worse, they do not always believe technology assessments if they are made.

This lack of procedure for utilizing trustworthy experts has created the debate over technology assessment which has led the Science Policy Research Division, Legislative Reference Service, Library of Congress,[1] National Academy of Sciences,[2] and National Academy of Engineering [3] to produce reports on the subject.

Why was not such a procedure constructed years ago? The funds are at the command of the government. The NAS and NAE panels believe the desirability is obvious. I can only conclude that neither the Administration nor the Congress want a rational system of policy assessment. Politicians are elected at vast expense because they serve powerful interests not all of which are compatible with the public interest. Many of them are honest men, at least intellectually honest, and make the decisions they believe are best.[4] But they understand that sound policy assessment might limit their freedom of action and their ability to serve their masters in good conscience

1. *Technical Information for Congress,* Report to the Subcommittee on Science, Research and Development of the Committee on Science and Astronautics, U.S. House of Representatives, 91st Congress, 1st Session. Prepared by the Science Policy Research Division, Legislative Reference Service, Library of Congress. Washington, D.C.: U.S. Government Printing Office, 1969.

2. *Technology: Processes of Assessment and Choice,* Report of the National Academy of Sciences. Washington, D.C., Committee on Science and Astronautics, U.S. House of Representatives, July 1969.

3. *A Study of Technology Assessment,* Report of the Committee on Public Engineering Policy, National Academy of Engineering. Washington, D.C., Committee on Science and Astronautics, U.S. House of Representatives, July 1969.

4. Policy decisions nearly always hinge on questions of judgment, such as the probability of various outcomes. No responsible politician is willing to abdicate his power to experts, especially those whose good judgment is not beyond question. Technology assessment, as conceived of in the current model involves a division of political responsibility that few politicians are willing to accept.

and political safety. Agency bureaucrats also recognize that external assessment may make serving their clientele more difficult.

Under the present procedure for gathering "expert advice," agencies and interests produce expert testimony. Anyone with the ability to pay $300 a day can find a qualified expert who will testify to anything. Thus, expert advice conflicts if interests conflict. In this situation the politician can decide the issue the way he wishes, defending himself by selecting favorable expert testimony. By making the decision on technical grounds he can conceal his personal social welfare function by which he reduces conflicting interests to a single decision. Thus a servant of the military-industrial complex can masquerade as a moderate on war questions, a servant of domestic oil producers can masquerade as a defender of the consumer, or a servant of the American Medical Association can masquerade as a promoter of public health. If the policy assessment were distinct from the decision making, these masquerades would be impossible. Many politicians who seek to conceal their real values perceive intuitively that good advice would threaten their survival.

Not that they get much of it, for there isn't a great deal of it around. There are not enough "experts" who are very expert.[5] No one seemed capable of determining whether a battery additive was any good, or identifying the hangups in foreign aid in a fashion generally acceptable to the scientific community. The judgment of scientists on questions of war has frequently been as wrong as that of politicians or generals.

Few scientists know anything that is interesting to policy makers. They are extraordinarily unscientific when they are justifying a grant or criticizing some other specialty of which they are ignorant. Only a few possess any capacity to foretell the future, and who can say which ones they are? Politicians apparently believe that scientists are irrelevant, and scientists believe that politicians have their minds made up. I suspect both are correct more often than not. The distrust of politicians for scientists' judgment, and of scientists for politicians' honesty and intelligence is the critical political problem in technology assessment. No matter how objective an assessment might be, it will become embroiled in political controversy if the matter is important.

Neither the NAS or NAE reports want anything to do with politics or politicians. All they want is for the politicians to pay attention to the advice

5. The key problem is that good advice hinges on a thorough grasp of the technical background on the problem and an understanding of and tolerance for the political issues. On military and foreign policy questions, at least, this background often depends on access to official and classified information. On most policy questions much of the political information needed is not generally available or known.

they get and "to raise the level of political discourse."[6] They want to be close to the President or Congress but free of political influence. They want the impossible. Even the President's dog is political. Neither the NAS or NAE panelists face up to the fact that politicians would appoint or at least influence the composition of the assessment panels.[7] Most politicians know what kind of advice they want, and will make sure that they get it. The President knows what kind of NSF Director, Assistant Secretary of HEW for Health, or Council of Economic Advisors he wants, and he tries to get them. The Department of Defense knows what kind of advice it wants on ABM and it gets it. To scientific outsiders, at least, the kinds of technology assessment prescribed by the NAE and NAS Reports would be more of the same preselected conclusions politicians already get. The selection of outside reputable scientists who might appear to the public to have some expertise merely make foregone conclusions more difficult to attack.

There are two major problems in the use of outside experts for technology assessment. The first is that outside experts are either inexperienced in the area under study or are unlikely to be very good at technology assessment. It is at present a nonexistent art for which there are no artists. The combination of technologist and social scientist with appreciation for the relevant technology and the political considerations is rare, perhaps nonexistent. The intuitive understanding which scientists often believe they have may not stand up when subjected to sophisticated technological and methodological criticism, and this is the second problem. A technology assessment is a target and it will be shot at by those who disagree with the results. In many instances the critics will be the "scientific outsiders" not entirely ignorant of the technological and scientific questions involved, but typically ignorant of political reality, prone to oversimplify, and profoundly mistrustful of the small self-selected scientific elite.

Despite the rather unworldly air of the NAS Report, it is a sound piece of

6. The public is seldom concerned, never informed, and scientists have neither the interest nor the competence in either alerting or informing them. This makes many scientists political outsiders.

7. Most of the panelists know of the system of co-optation (having themselves been co-opted) by which expertise is brought into government, but they cling to the view that the President's Science Advisory Committee and his Special Assistant for Science and Technology are "not political." But they would not have got into those roles unless they were useful to politicians and at the same time acceptable to the scientific community. To be a politician one need not smoke cigars and kiss babies. Nevertheless, many scientists cling to the belief that scientists (sometimes "only scientists") are "objective" while politicians are not.

analysis, well thought out, intelligent, and well researched. Except for its confidence that an assessment panel can deal with the needs of diverse interests in advance, it is a useful analysis. The NAS Report discusses in considerable detail the organizational location of technology assessment activities, but it does not in fact deal with the important political problem of what happens to the assessment once it is done. But the NAS is only talking about assessment, the NAE tried to do it.

SOME BAD EXAMPLES

The NAE assessment studies are themselves subject to these criticisms. The panel believes good assessment depends on experienced assessors and narrow definition of problems, but narrowness is itself a problem.

The Aeronautics and Space Engineering Board of the National Academy of Engineering, which prepared an assessment of subsonic aircraft noise, is made up largely of experts whose experience and economic interests are related to the airline and aircraft industries. It is inevitable that experienced experts will usually be drawn from the interests involved in a problem. In many instances the experts will have created the problem. The ASEB appears to be incapable of entertaining an idea injurious to air transport. Just as automotive executives and engineers could not generate any interest in automotive safety, so these men cannot generate any interest in quiet. They perceive the problem in terms of "tolerable noise," as does the Federal Aviation Agency (which is well represented on the panel) which establishes standards at levels slightly below that at which people complain vigorously, and thus keeps the public sullen but not mutinous. Even so, the FAA has never taken any serious action to enforce its standards even after it was coerced into establishing them.

Turning to the assessment itself, we read "Abatement will be costly and will occur only when public pressure fosters regulation from federal and local authorities and when the airline and manufacturing industries work out feasible alternatives together (p. 76)." That is to say, when they are finally forced to, the industry and the FAA will serve the public welfare. They will resist as long as they can, but as long as court relief is refused they will punish the public without restraint or compensation. This is a bald admission that the public cannot expect protection from the Administration or Congress without political action.

The assessment itself is not very useful for it says nothing about the costs and benefits of the various strategies. As a result, no politician has the uncomfortable data which might influence his decision. He can continue to do what he has done. Because there are no quantitative results, there is no real policy assessment. The Board is quite casual about the inadequacy of their report. Consider (p. 95) ". . . technology assessment of subsonic aircraft noise must deal first with the question of whether the public pressures directed at airlines, airport operators, or the Congress are sufficient to force heavy economic investment needed to solve the problems by any of the strategies available. It would be a waste of time to study other alternative strategies if it is found that the problem does not warrant high-priority public action beyond the status quo strategy."

Well, there it is. Squeaky-wheel politics at its most cynical. No grease until a Ralph Nader is awakened by a low-flying jet.

But this is what you get from technology assessment as the NAE conceives it. Similarly, when one turns to the other bad example, one finds even the exiguous "assessment" of Multiphasic Health Screening is castrated in advance. "The center must be sufficiently flexible in operation to permit each physician to dictate the specific tests that are to be given his patients. . ." (p. 102). The major problem in medical technology is the individual physician, his incompetence, his technical backwardness, his unwillingness to be part of a medical system. There is no technical difficulty in MHS. The Kaiser Foundation has used it for years. They find it useful in their integrated medical care delivery system. The individual physician dominates medical politics and economics. He impedes the use of MHS, and it is his self-interest to which this whole assessment is subordinated. The panel clearly wants to retard MHS because they foresee widespread screening will produce knowledge of unknown illness which the present system cannot handle, and they subordinate their assessment to the dominant political power in medicine.

All of the NAE assessments are "politically realistic" in that they consider alternatives which the panelists view as attainable. But in doing this they prejudge the political questions. Why should a body of experts take institutional arrangements, pressures, and power as given? If they will not consider bold new technical alternatives, who will? Besides, technical experts are seldom competent to judge political feasibility, and when they examine only "realistic alternatives" they are acting as politicians. It is not for technology assessment to play at politics, but to say what all alternatives are, and whom they will affect. Politicians will provide a sufficiency of attention for political considerations.

A RESPONSIBLE PROCESS OF TECHNOLOGICAL DEBATE

Both the NAS and NAE panels admit that a single best policy is unlikely to exist, and if it exists it is unlikely to be found. Even so they believe that suitable objective panels can be selected, conduct their deliberations quickly, and provide essentially value-free advice to Congress and the Administration. If done with sufficient care, the advice will assist the decision makers in making policy. It won't be this easy. The panels will be made up of experts, and these experts will have interests that will consciously or unconsciously smuggle values and implicit policy into the technology analysis itself. Even if through divine intervention the panel produces a value-free assessment, those whose interests are adversely influenced by the tendency of the report are unlikely to accept the results as value free. The integrity, probity and intelligence of the panelists will be examined in detail. It is not inconceivable, as Ralph Nader and Judge Haynsworth discovered, that political opponents will develop a sudden interest in the sex life and investment activities of those who offer themselves to do good things for their country. We may deplore such inquisitions, but is it not foolish to deny that they are commonplaces in the political process. What aegis will protect the assessment panels from attack? Dedication to the pursuit of science is no longer a certain shield and sure protection against criticism, as anyone who has visited a university campus in recent years should be aware. Nor should we dismiss the criticism that campus activists direct against scientific research as trivial, for an increasing amount of it comes from our best students and even some of our most awe-inspiring fellow scientists.

It would seem to me wise to accept as a political fact that any assessment of an interesting problem is likely to be embroiled in controversy. Those who wish to engage in such exciting activities should look to their flanks. When they prepare assessments they should employ "no men," devil's advocates, and experts on "the intentions of the enemy." Even forearmed, they should be ready for criticism.

For criticism and debate is an essential part of the democratic political process. It is only through adversary proceedings that that part of policy assessment which is sound may be identified, and that part which is insupportable may be shown up for what it is. If we are careful, and also very fortunate, it may be possible to construct a responsible process of technological debate to which government-sponsored technology assessment will be subjected. But it takes two responsible parties to produce a responsible debate. If the government assessments are not fair and open, if they rely on information too confidential to be shown the public, if they generate only information that supports positions acceptable to the government, then who would expect the opposition to act responsibly. But let us assume, if only for the sake of argument, that the Administration and Congress tried to generate reasonably responsible technology assessments. The remaining need is for a responsible technological opposition. This would require a marked change in behavior for the opponents of government. They would have to produce respectable counter-assessments, and to do this they would need to generate experts on the questions under consideration. Those who would pursue counter-assessment as a profession cannot expect government to employ them or grants to support their studies and researches. I would expect most of the counter-assessors would have to generate their competence in social technology as a hobby or sideline to a reasonably straight scientific career. It is to be hoped that the sideline would not draw retaliation on them.

It has taken centuries for European governments to discover that oppositions are essential to stable government, and the Soviet Union has not yet made this discovery. There was often an irreversible tendency for those who opposed Louis XIV or Henry VIII to lose stature, frequently by a head's length. Since the McCarthy era opposition has been somewhat safer for American scientists, but opposition must be responsible if it is to survive for very long. Responsible opposition involves a fundamental acceptance of the legitimacy of the process, an acceptance of the rules of procedure, and a readiness to assume political responsibility if the occasion arises. Not all of the opponents of governmental technology policy meet these criteria. But if technology policy is to be forged in the fire of political controversy, then a responsible technological opposition must constitute itself. These counter assessors must separate themselves from the closed, co-opted, scientific and technological elite that pretends to be above or beyond politics and ally with those political interests and politicians whose objectives are consonant with survival, prosperity, and liberty as the counter-assessors perceive these goals. They must train themselves in the skills, the arts, and even the wiles of the assessment process.

The university can make essential contributions to the creation of responsible technological debate, just as it has to debate on social and economic policy in the past. Responding to the demands for "relevance" emanating even from places so unlikely as schools of medicine and engineering, the university can organize itself to educate both the assessors and the counter assessors in the values, goals, and aims of a human society, in the tools of social analysis, in the technological and scientific possibilities which both motivate and constrain human action. In so doing, the university will both relieve the stresses that threaten to tear it apart and instill in science the human goals that were once its impulse and its recompense.

Technology Assessment

JOSEPH F. COATES

Within the last two generations, virtually everything that people use, touch, feel, live with, live on, work with, or play with has been dramatically transformed by technology—not always in positive ways. Modern communications and agricultural, chemical, and biomedical developments have certainly brought society to an unprecedented level of comfort and prosperity, but they have also often brought unanticipated and undesirable consequences. Indeed, there are few major problems of society that are not strongly influenced by modern technology. Urban congestion, environmental pollution, war, international trade unbalance, crime, changing mores, and the institutional crises in education, religion, and the family are clearly and predominately driven by technological changes.

PUBLIC CONCERN

Americans have always been enthusiastic for technology, but the recent shift in public attitude from one of positive expectations of new achievements to one of deepening concern over negative effects is unmistakably apparent. The concern derives from the unique nature of technology in American society: the scale and the scope of technology, the integration of technology across the continent, the large budgets in both private and public sectors now committed to technological developments and projects, and the irreversibility of much of what is done.

These unique characteristics are well illustrated by the Federal Highway Program, which spreads a network across the country to bring people together both personally and commercially with ease and speed. Like it or not, good or bad, what has been done is set in concrete, and it is unlikely that anything dramatic can be done to significantly modify the situation in less than a generation. Another example is telecommunications technology, including the telephone, radio, television, satellite communications, and—more recently—national computer information networks. This technology represents enormous aggregate investment: about $500 per capita for the telephone system alone, with comparable investments for radio and television. Yet when one examines the technology against obvious and widely celebrated promise, one finds that the lowest-common-denominator taste determines the menu on television, as reported in "Television and Growing Up: The Impact of Televised Violence," the result of an intense study by the Department of Health, Education, and Welfare. The tale is as melancholy as the evidence is strong. Telecommunications technology has a corrupting effect on young people. Perhaps this happens because the technology is managed predominately for private gain, not the public good, without adequate incentives for high quality and diversity.

EFFORTS TO CONTROL TECHNOLOGY

In this background of pervasive concern over the negative effects of technology, people must seek ways of controlling the effects of technology on their lives. Three mutually complementary lines of action are open. First, the political system—through elected officials, legislatures, and regulatory agencies—must exert new, more effective control over the technology. Second, new and better means must be found to anticipate the consequences of technology beyond those immediately and usually accounted for in engineering design and economic analyses. Third, citizens at large and in various organized interest groups need deeper and more reliable information and analyses about impending technological developments, while exercising the political process more vigorously to reflect their needs and wishes. As a corollary, the large bureaucracies in the business sector and in government which plan, implement, and regulate technology must become more open in revealing their plans and more sagacious in looking forward to consequences and actions in both the long run and short run.

SST and the Pipeline

The interrelations of these courses of action are illustrated by two recent major technological projects, the supersonic transport (SST) and the trans-Alaska pipeline. The failure of the advocates of the SST to satisfy Congress that they adequately understood its implications led to the shelving of that project, at least for the time being. Similarly, the failure of bureaucratic advocates of the trans-Alaska pipeline to adequately deal with the risks as well as the benefits, and to examine in depth the needs and alternatives in getting oil from the Alaska North Slope, led concerned citizens to take their uncertainties and misgivings to court and to delay the project until certain questions were examined.

Technological Imperative

The celebrated and feared "technological imperative"—the view that technology has a force of its own which demands its continual development and fulfillment—no longer seems to have the vitality of a decade ago. Projects like the SST and the trans-Alaska pipeline, involving many billions of dollars and important national issues of business, commerce, and trade, have at least been stalled while the advocates of technology are forced to examine more closely the implications of what they would do. This is where technology assessment comes in.

DEFINITION

Technology assessment may be defined as policy studies examining the fullest range of impact of the introduction of a new technology or the expansion of a present technology in new or different ways. One might look at it as an analysis of the total impact of a technology on society. Technology assessment, therefore, is much broader than the traditional technological planning, which is usually based on meeting some sort of potential need, or satisfying or creating some new market. In traditional technological planning, the feasibility, cost, profit, and elementary considerations of safety are the dominant considerations.

Technology assessment should be made with the knowledge that:

1. Decisions will be made, including in many cases the decision not to go ahead with a particular technology or project.

2. The organization, structure, and output of an assessment study should be directed at informing decision makers about alternative actions and the probable consequences.

3. New knowledge, of necessity, generates new ignorance. Consequently the historical models of a technological development do not necessarily provide full and sound guidance for new technology. The automobile is not well modeled by the horse and buggy. The airplane is not well modeled by the railroad, nor is the airplane a good model for space flight. Radio is not a good model for television, and television is not a good model for the expanded capabilities of cable television or computer networking. Historical experience, while too often neglected, is only a partial guide to the effects of a new technology.

4. In approaching the problems of management of new technologies, one must bring into the analysis both certainty and uncertainty and establish a set of sound policies and actions based upon the interplay of not only what is known with some certitude, but also what is not known. In the past, decision makers have generally attempted to operate on the basis of firm knowledge and certitude.

5. The long-range indirect and unanticipated effects of a technology are often more significant than the immediate planned consequences. For example, the disease control programs in the underdeveloped world, in achieving their objectives, have created a more intractable problem of a continually growing population.

To be useful therefore, a technology assessment must go far beyond conventional engineering and cost studies to look at what else may happen in achieving an immediate goal, to the total range of social costs, the impacts on the family, on legal, political, and social institutions, on the environment, on international relations, on land-use planning, on the structure of cities, and on the makeup of populations.

OUTCOME OF A TECHNOLOGY ASSESSMENT

Imagine that a good technology assessment has been conducted and is put in the hands of the decision makers and the concerned public. What kinds of decisions and actions might be expected to result?

Fear of Assessment

Two broad fears have been expressed about the results of technology assessment. On the one hand, the large bureaucracies tend to see technology assessment as an almost conspiratorial attempt to thwart economic development and retard the growth of the nation. Those bureaucracies see only a crippling arrest of technology from the attempt to anticipate secondary effects. On the other hand, many concerned citizens have too often found themselves misled by government and industry with regard to the implications of technology. In the past many large bureaucracies have been negligent in demonstrating due caution and care about the implications of technology. Consequently, such citizens tend to see technology assessment as another administrative whitewash.

Variety of Results

Although it is undoubtedly true that any tool or technique will be misused sometime, the extremists' pessimism results in part from seeing technology assessment as resulting only in go or no-go recommendations. There are many other, more likely outcomes of an assessment.

Modifications in the Project. For example, suppose it is discovered that a manufacturing process will release a unique pollutant into a river. Action can be taken to modify the process to reduce or eliminate the pollutant. Such a provision is usually more effective and certainly cheaper when designed into a facility than when it is added on later.

Specifications for Monitoring. A program for focused environmental or social monitoring may result when there is uncertainty about the effects of technology. A weather modification program, for example, may possibly have adverse effects on the animal and plant life of a region. In assessing the risk, one may quickly reach the limits of empirical and theoretical biological knowledge. The only sensible action may be a program of monitoring the effects as the technology unfolds. Similarly, in the social area, effects of a welfare program or an innovation in education or the introduction of a new contraceptive cannot be fully anticipated. An assessment may focus and structure a program of social monitoring to lead to timely and appropriate feedback. (One cannot help feeling that if people had looked more closely at what television, fossil-fuel plants, the auto, or housing subsidies were doing to them over the years, they would be better off now.)

Stimulation of Research and Development. An assessment may suggest that a particular effect of a technology might be adverse, but evaluators may not know enough to be sure. Specific focused research may be required to provide an answer. In other cases a project may be so negative in its consequences that the assessment will direct research toward alternative ways of achieving the same goals. The alternatives may, in turn, require specific focused research on the questions associated with them. An assessment may also define corrective research. For example, toxic effluents coming out of a particular manufacturing process may direct research to scrubbing and recovery techniques to deal with the undesirable material.

New Benefits.   Federal water projects provide a classic example of how unexpected benefits can be derived from major technology. It was recognized early that the lakes formed behind large dams were used spontaneously for recreation. Such benefits have now become a standard consideration in all major water projects. One may anticipate that the search for benefits in other technological projects may be fruitful and lead to their earlier, more successful exploitation.

Regulatory Gaps.   The regulatory apparatus is, by and large, set up to deal with yesterday's problems. Yet the issues of most concern are the risks or opportunities from new technology. It is reasonable to expect that an assessment would reveal inadequacies in the present regulatory setup, and corrective measures could then be recommended.

Legislative Needs.   Often, basic legislation may be required to deal with a new technology. For example, in the study of a proposed snow enhancement project in Colorado the analysts judged the means of regulation and control over snow enhancement and over the mechanisms of distributing costs and benefits to be inadequate. They then suggested new legislation to set up new regulatory arrangements.

New Institutions.   Managing the space information satellite, for example, has led to Comsat, and the problem of radio and television programming has led to the Corporation for Public Broadcasting. Similar new institutions needed as a result of technological developments will be indicated by technology assessments.

Intervention Experiments.   An assessment may reveal an irreducible uncertainty about the effects of a particular technology. It might make sense in such cases to start off with a small facility or implement the technology partially in a certain area or place. For example, public housing would be better today if a more experimental approach had been taken to design, occupancy, maintenance, and organization, instead of allowing virtually the same kinds of high-rise multiple slums to proliferate across the country. Intervention experimentation does not mean infinite delay; it does mean that diverse concepts can be tried and closely and carefully examined. The intervention experiment is a conscious effort to do something on an experimental basis to systematically modify and study a facet of society as affected by technology. This approach undoubtedly will grow in importance in the future. Already, there are income maintenance experiments to determine if poverty can be eased without creating a class of permanently poor, and educational voucher programs to evaluate a major new means of bringing schooling to young people. One can see the growing importance of experimentation in community development. One can see it in a variety of technological applications such as using telecommunications to provide new ways of delivering health care. In an age in which technology is so dominant it seems only natural that an experimental approach should permeate the introduction and adoption of technology.

Delay of the Project. Postponing new projects can be expected to be a fairly common outcome of technology assessment, at least in the near future. However, as public and private managers of technology become more attuned to anticipating the future, and as technology assessment becomes a more common management decision-making aid, delays will become less severe and less common, because technology assessment will be introduced earlier and more effectively in the planning cycle.

Basic Information. Raw material, for all parties at interest, is a major product of any good technology assessment. In the American political system, based as it is on adversary and advocacy processes, various parties to a discussion often find themselves with inadequate knowledge about a technology and its implications. A sound technology assessment provides illumination and guidance to all adversaries, and so makes for a more sophisticated analysis and discussion.

TECHNOLOGY ASSESSMENT ACT

Technology assessment had its origins in the U. S. House of Representatives, in the Subcommittee on Science, Research, and Development of the Committee on Science and Astronautics, then headed by Emilio Q. Daddario, Representative from the State of Connecticut. Beginning in 1965, Daddario started work on the concept of technology assessment and initiated a series of hearings and studies over the next few years on various means and approaches to dealing with and managing technology. Concern with technology did not originate with the Daddario committee, but the work of the committee did give sharp focus to the need for new approaches to establishing a base of knowledge to anticipate the consequences of technology.

Initial Efforts

In the early years several bills were put forward, and papers were commissioned from the National Academy of Engineering, the National Academy of Sciences, and the National Academy of Public Administration. The papers addressed the question of whether it is feasible, practical, and useful to promote the studies implicit in the goals of technology assessment. In each case, the academies came forward with results which affirmed not only the desirability but the urgency and practicality of such activity. Years of work came to legislative fruition with the passage of the Technology Assessment Act of 1972 (Public Law 92–484), which set up the Office of Technology Assessment to serve Congress. In the words of the bill, Congress should "equip itself with new and effective means for securing competent, unbiased information concerning the physical, biological, economic, social, and political effects of such [technological] applications; and utilize this information, whenever appropriate, as one factor in the legislative assessment of matters pending before the Congress, particularly in those instances where the Federal Government may be called upon to consider support for, or management or regulation of, technological applications."

PIONEERING ASSESSMENTS

During the several years of deliberations over the Office of Technology Assessment, numerous studies were made of the feasibility, methods, techniques, and the desirability of assessment. Several executive agencies of the Federal government launched numerous technology assessment projects of their own.

Partial Assessments

In addition, there is a long and continuing history of partial assessments of the effects of technology. These assessments have usually been limited to economic consequences, although there are some quite early ones touching on the social consequences of technological developments. Perhaps the most significant of these was a U.S. Department of Agriculture study in 1938 of mechanization of cotton agriculture, which forecast the mass displacement of southern agricultural workers. Unfortunately, the recommendations resulting from that study were ignored.

Work at NASA

More recently, the National Aeronautics and Space Administration initiated three major intellectual ventures. Under NASA sponsorship, Raymond Bauer examined the need for better measures of social effects, and suggested a comprehensive system of social indicators of the impact of technological ventures as a means of guiding social policy. The result of Bauer's activities was his ground-breaking book *Social Indicators* (1966). At roughly the same time, NASA supported a study of the history of the technological development of railroads and their social effects as a potential model for anticipating the effects of the NASA space program. And as a third venture, NASA launched a program of policy studies in science and technology at George Washington University in Washington, an institution with a particular interest in technology assessment. NASA , jointly with the Department of Transportation, also funded a recently completed technology assessment under the title "Civil Aviation Research and Development," one part of which took a particularly close look at short takeoff and landing (STOL) aircraft and airports close to or in cities. The assessment raised grave doubts as to the economic, environmental, and social feasibility of a STOL program.

TECHNIQUES

Anticipating that the technology assessment movement, when institutionalized and reduced to general practice, could have a major effect on the management of Federal technology programs, the Office of Science and Technology in the Executive Office of the President initiated a pilot study to systematically explore techniques for assessment.

Common Steps

Out of this study, conducted under Martin Jones of the Mitre Corporation, came an analysis in which seven steps were identified as common to five technology studies (of automotive emissions, computers and communications, industrial enzymes, mariculture, and water pollution by domestic wastes). However, these steps (Fig. 1) should not be regarded as a detailed prescription or methodology but rather as seven "supercategories" that ought to be considered in any policy-related assessment of technology. The selection of study methods is, of course, largely determined by the particular technology under assessment.

step 1	define the assessment task discuss relevant issues and any major problems establish scope (breadth and depth) of inquiry develop project ground rules
step 2	describe relevant technologies describe major technology being assessed describe other technologies supporting the major technology describe technologies competitive to the major and supporting technologies
step 3	develop state-of-society assumptions identify and describe major nontechnological factors influencing the application of the relevant technologies
step 4	identify impact areas ascertain those societal characteristics that will be most influenced by the application of the assessed technology
step 5	make preliminary impact analysis trace and integrate the process by which the assessed technology makes its societal influence felt
step 6	identify possible action options develop and analyze various programs for obtaining maximum public advantage from the assessed technologies
step 7	complete impact analysis analyze the degree to which each action option would alter the specific societal impacts of the assessed technology discussed in step 5

Fig. 1   SEVEN MAJOR STEPS IN TECHNOLOGY ASSESSMENT

Environmental Impact Statement

An independent examination of methods and techniques for assessing the
impacts of technology has resulted from requirements of the National
Environmental Policy Act of 1969 for the preparation of environmental

impact statements. In the words of Section 102 of the act, each agency must "include in every recommendation or report on proposals for legislation and other major Federal actions significantly affecting the quality of the human environment, a detailed statement by the responsible official on: (i) the environmental impact of the proposed action, (ii) any adverse environmental effects which cannot be avoided should the proposal be implemented, (iii) alternatives to the proposed action, (iv) the relationship between local short-term use of man's environment and the maintenance and enhancement of long-term productivity, and (v) any irreversible and irretrievable commitments of resources which would be involved if the proposed action should be implemented."

The obligation to prepare environmental impact statements has created a general demand throughout the Federal system for systematic exploration of the secondary impacts of projects, and a consequent demand for the development of methodology, techniques, approaches, and procedures.

In the first 3 years the act was in existence—that is, until January 1973—some 3500 impact statements have been prepared at an aggregate cost of about $65,000,000. From that massive effort much has been learned about the methods and techniques appropriate for anticipating effects of technology on the physical and biological environments. At the same time, however, the effort has highlighted the need to go much further in developing more systematic, focused, decision-related analytical methods to discover and examine options.

RECENT MAJOR ASSESSMENTS

A number of major technology assessments have been accomplished in the last 5 years. For example, two different groups at the Stanford Research Institute, working under different sponsors, have completed interesting assessments of weather modification.

Increasing Snowfall

The first of the Stanford studies was an assessment of a Department of the Interior project to routinely increase snowfall in the San Juan Mountains of Colorado as a means of increasing the fresh-water runoff in the Colorado River. The need for that study was suggested by the Interagency Committee on Atmospheric Sciences (the group which monitors and coordinates the Federal weather programs). It was financed by the National Science Foundation.

The conclusions of the study involve almost all the possible outcomes of a technology assessment. The study confirms the validity of the anticipated increases in the snowfall and fresh-water runoff. It predicts large numbers of small effects on the biota, none of which seem likely to be of major short-term consequences, but many of which may be candidates for a focused environmental surveillance program. On an annual basis, the increased snow enhancement will be undetectable because the random variations in annual snowfall exceed the average increase. However, the overall effect over many years will be to drop the tree line by several hundred feet.

Costs and Benefits. The study also looked at the costs and benefits— not only in direct economic terms, but also in social costs to the community. It concludes that increasing snowfall is the cheapest of several alternative ways of bringing fresh water to Colorado. However, the benefits and cost of the project are so intimately tied in with a variety of continuing subsidy programs in water and agriculture that it was difficult to come to an unequivocal estimate of the benefits of the program in relation to the costs. Field surveys in the Colorado area revealed divergent opinions and attitudes toward the project, varying from support to outright hostility.

Sidelights. The study team was able to identify some potentially important consequences of the snow enhancement project which are of no importance to any of the antagonists or advocates of the project, but objectively could be significant. The study also identified difficulties and gaps in the regulatory responsibility of controlling the snow enhancement and made systematic recommendations for institutional and legislative change.

Seeding Hurricanes

In an unrelated effort, the Stanford Research Institute conducted a study of seeding hurricanes as a means of reducing damage from these storms. Relying largely on decision theory analysis, the study group plotted "decision trees" (Fig. 2) in which the decision to seed or not to seed can be analyzed in terms of probability of various outcomes and the associated property damage. The study concludes:

"The decision to seed a hurricane imposes a great responsibility on public officials. This decision cannot be avoided because inaction is equivalent to a decision not to permit seeding. Either the government must accept the responsibility of a seeding that may be perceived by the public

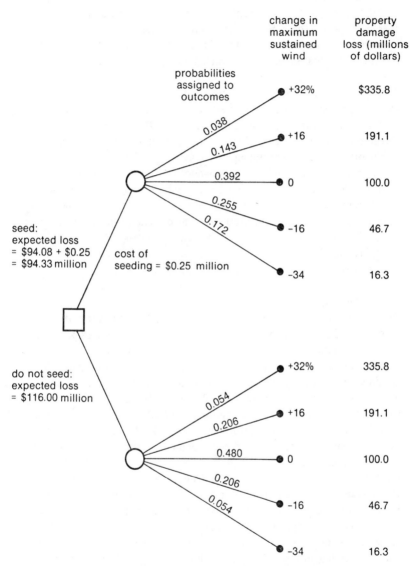

Fig. 2 A DECISION TREE FOR SEEDING A HURRICANE. (FROM R.A.

(From R.A. Howard, H.E. Matheson, and D.W. North, "Decision to Seed Hurricanes," *Science*, 196:1191-1202, June 16, 1972)

as deleterious, or it must accept the responsibility for not seeding and thereby exposing the public to higher probabilities of severe storm damage.

"Our report to the National Oceanic and Atmospheric Administration recommended that seeding be permitted on an emergency basis. We hope that further experimental results and a formal analysis of the tactical decision to seed a particular hurricane will precede the emergency. However, a decision may be required before additional experimental or analytical results are available. A hurricane with the intensity of Camille threatening a populous coastal area of the United States would confront public officials with an agonizing but unavoidable choice.

"The decision to seed hurricanes cannot be resolved on strictly scientific grounds. It is a complex decision whose uncertain consequences affect many people. Appropriate legal and political institutions should be designated for making the hurricane-seeding decision, and further analysis should be conducted to support these institutions in carrying out their work." (From R. A. Howard, H. E. Matheson, and D. W. North, Decision to seed hurricanes, *Science*, 196:1191 - 1202, June 16, 1972).

The Automobile

The automobile is a nearly universal concern. One study by the International Research and Technology Corporation for the Department of Transportation examines the macroeconomic effects on industry, energy, and raw materials of a possible mass conversion of present internal combustion engines to one of three alternative power systems. A somewhat more comprehensive study conducted by Hittman Associates in Columbia, Md., under the sponsorship of the National Science Foundation examines the effects of a transition to some 14 alternate automotive power systems in terms of energy, environment, raw materials, pollution, macro- and microeconomic effects, and social consequences. Meanwhile, a joint university venture involving the Columbia University Law School, the Harvard University Department of Economics, and the Massachusetts Institute of Technology Engineering Department has examined the consequences of implementing legislation on pollution standards for automobiles due to go into effect in 1976. This study raises questions about enforcing the legislation, as well as the technical and economic feasibility of the dual catalyst system (the principal method of exhaust control now under consideration).

Problems of the automobile have also spread to Europe. In a multinational funded study, the Organization for Economic Cooperation and

Development is examining the future role of the automobile in European society and is studying in detail alternative methods and strategies for regulating its consequences. One might anticipate that the status of the automobile in Europe is perhaps a decade—if not a generation—behind what it is in the United States. Thus a well-structured policy study, with the alert support of several national governments, would have a profound and beneficial effect on the development of that technology in Europe.

Aviation

Airplanes and jetports are a continuing technological concern. The National Academy of Sciences has conducted two major assessments of proposed jetports. One conducted in 1970 examined the consequences of a major jetport in Florida to serve the Miami area. The conclusion was that the geophysical and biological effects would be so severe as to make the proposed airport totally undesirable.

Kennedy Airport Expansion. Much more interesting from the point of view of its impact, complexity, and methodological elegance is a study conducted 2 years later by the same organization for the Port of New York Authority in which a proposed extension of the Kennedy Airport into Jamaica Bay is examined. Jamaica Bay is a large (35,000-acre) marsh within the confines of New York City. The study concludes not only that the extension of the jetport is physically unnecessary but that the alternative development of the bay as a major recreational resource is far more valuable to the citizens and the commerce of New York City. The study also makes recommendations for the development of high-speed ground transportation from the center city to the existing jetport and comes up with a package of constructive proposals quite different from that originally anticipated.

This result illustrates a major consequence of any technology assessment, that it is likely to reveal the unexpected, likely to draw conclusions which fly in the face of the preconceptions of sponsors and advocates of a technology. Such conclusions, of course, are to be fully expected since people are as unaccustomed to examining presuppositions as they are to systematically looking to future impacts. It is almost inevitable that the first wave of technology assessments be distressing news for many people. One might anticipate, however, that the early revelation of potential bad news will be heralded as a benefit rather than a bane.

Atmospheric Pollution. Because the advocates of the supersonic transport failed to put convincing studies before Congress, the SST was denied legislative support. As a consequence, the Department of Transportation has launched what is perhaps the most generously planned, lavishly funded technology assessment to date. The Climatic Implications of Atmospheric Pollution program (CIAP) concerns a comprehensive study of the upper atmosphere as well as the surface of the Earth, and living things on Earth as affected by SST (Fig. 3). One of CIAP's most formidable tasks is to develop a mathematical model for the behavior of the atmosphere (Fig. 4). If successful, the model will make it possible to predict the impact on climate of high-altitude aircraft, and from this, to specify engine requirements. Whatever the outcome of the assessment may be, it will undoubtedly give strong direction to future assessments of major technological ventures.

NSF Assessments. In 1973 the National Science Foundation (NSF) launched a series of eight major technology assessments, including the assessments of geothermal energy, solar energy, electronic banking and the checkless-cashless society, the shift from chemical to biological pesticides, the movement to integrated hog farming, alternative work schedules, and strategies and techniques for conserving energy. NSF already has underway assessments of remote sensing from satellites,

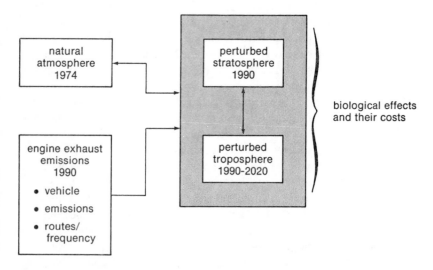

Fig. 3 STRUCTURE OF THE CLIMATIC IMPLICATIONS OF ATMOSPHERIC POLLUTION PROGRAM (CIAP). THE PROGRAM WILL STUDY CLIMATE OVER THE NEXT HALF CENTURY.

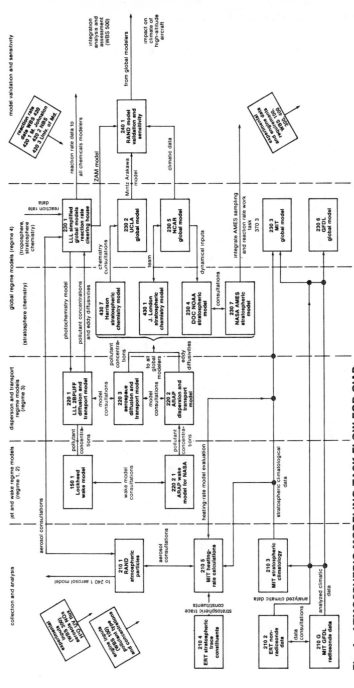

Fig. 4 ATMOSPHERIC MODELING TASK FLOW FOR CIAP

biomedical technologies, and outer-continental-shelf oil and gas resource development.

SOCIAL TECHNOLOGY

If one defines technology as the application of arts and sciences to the achievement of human goals, there is no difficulty in classifying automobiles, electric lights, highways, dams, pacemakers, contraceptive pills, nylons, and hybrid corn as "technologies." However, the definition is also capable of embracing changes in institutions and organizations—changes such as the invention of mass armies and the subsidiary invention of the military draft, the land grant act establishing the state college system in the United States, the invention of pay-as-you-go income tax, and many others. In general, one might regard legislation as a major means of institutionalizing such social inventions and therefore clearly in need of continuing assessment. Justice Warren E. Burger in his 1972 State of the Judiciary address suggested that legislation should be subject to an assessment for impacts on the judicial system. It is only a small step to generalize Burger's concept to examination of the impacts of legislation on society at large. In fact, some assessments of this sort have been conducted, notably two studies of the impacts of marijuana on society, one by an American commission and the other by a Canadian commission. Both studies draw substantially the same conclusions about the effects and make recommendations for changing legislation (a social technology). The famous study by the Obscenity and Pornography Commission is another example of the assessment of social technology, in which the implicit social technology is modification in the laws regulating and controlling pornographic material; and, as mentioned earlier in this article, the Department of Health, Education, and Welfare assessment of violence on television is a major—albeit partial—assessment of television technology.

RESPONSIBILITY AND FUNDING

Technology assessments usually have been funded by the Federal government, although they may have been conducted by university groups, ad hoc groups, or commissions. One may expect a growing trend toward assessments by state governments of those technological issues specifically within their jurisdiction. More effective assessment of technology in the business community is much to be hoped for. The need for business involvement is emphasized by the near-fiasco of several years ago, during the intense concern over the effects of phosphate and synthetic detergents on water supplies. The chemical industry seriously planned some hundred million dollars in plant facilities to manufacture an alternative material, nitrilotriacetic acid, only to discover well down the road that its reported toxic effects could be far worse than those it was intended to correct. Business will probably move into the broader examination of the incidental effects of technology, if for no other reason than to be better prepared to deal with the increasingly questioning climate of concern. It is ever more expensive to lack prescience.

Efforts by Citizens

Citizens and citizens' groups, although intensely concerned about the effects of technology, are at serious disadvantage because they are unable to marshal technological data, much less to analyze the data. The growing experience with assessment may encourage citizens' groups to undertake these relatively expensive enterprises and thereby effect a shift in the quality and sophistication of the public discussion over the management of technology.

International Assessment

Many technologies have multinational and transnational effects. Some topics, for example, that the European community might find attractive to assess are the development of North Sea oil resources, the English Channel tunnel, a unified monetary system, and a bridge across the Straits of Massina.

One would hope that assessments conducted under government funds, by being public, will illuminate discussions over the management of technology and provide the useful raw materials to all sides in a particular dispute. Such "public" assessments are subject to intensive scrutiny, and their quality should therefore steadily rise and thus improve the overall decision process.

Expense

Technology assessments are relatively expensive. By their nature, they generally call for multidisciplinary teams working over fairly long periods of time in close contact. Most of the assessments mentioned in this article cost in the range of $100,000 to $300,000. However, some major projects calling for new research, field investigations, or follow-on studies to closely define risks may cost several million dollars. The costs of preparing the environmental impact statements on the trans-Alaska pipeline are alleged to have run about $8,000,000. The CIAP study is expected to run to $9,000,000. "Violence and Television" (Department of Health, Education, and Welfare) over a period of 2 1/2 years—involving new research as well as analysis—cost $1,500,000. However, preliminary assessments of the video telephone conducted at Cornell University cost about $30,000.

CONCLUSION

Technology assessment is an inevitable culmination in modern society of a number of trends that make the management of technology urgent and crucial. The wide recognition of a problem has always spawned new approaches to its solution. In this case the ubiquitous problems of management of technology will inevitably yield new foresight, imagination, analysis, and wisdom in guiding society.

Organization and Operations of the Office of Technology Assessment

from THE 1976 OTA ANNUAL REPORT

The Office of Technology Assessment (OTA) was created by the Technology Assessment Act of 1972 (86 Stat. 797) to help the Congress anticipate, and plan for, the consequences of uses of technology. OTA received funding in November 1973, and commenced operations with the convening of the 93rd Congress, 2d Session, in January 1974.

The statute specifies that OTA shall consist of a bipartisan Congressional policy Board, an OTA Director, a Deputy Director, and such other employees and consultants as may be necessary in the conduct of the Office's work. In addition, the Board is assisted by a Technology Assessment Advisory Council comprised of 10 public members eminent in technological or educational fields, the Comptroller General of the United States and the Director of the Congressional Research Service of the Library of Congress.

The Congressional Board sets the policies of the Office and is the sole oversight body governing OTA. The OTA Director is the chief executive officer and is responsible solely to the Board, of which he is a member. The function of the Advisory Council is to advise the Congressional Board on such technology assessment matters as may be requested.

Six Senators and six Representatives, evenly divided by party, serve on the OTA Congressional Board. They are appointed respectively by the President Pro Tempore of the Senate and Speaker of the House. The current [1976] Board Chairman is Congressman Olin E. Teague, D.-Texas, and the Vice Chairman is Senator Clifford P. Case, R.-New Jersey. The two posts rotate between the Senate and the House in alternate Congresses. The Board members from each House select their own Chairman or Vice Chairman, as the case may be.

In providing assistance to the Congress, OTA is to: identify existing or probable impacts of technology or technological programs; where possible, ascertain cause-and-effect relationships; identify alternative technological methods of implementing specific programs; identify alternative programs for achieving requisite goals; make estimates and comparisons of the impacts of alternative methods and programs; present findings of completed analyses to the appropriate legislative authorities; identify areas where additional research or data collection is required to provide support for assessments, and undertake such additional associated activities as may be directed.

Initiation, Processing, and Flow of Assessments.—The Office of Technology Assessment, by statute, is located within and is responsible to the legislative branch of Government. Accordingly, its basic mission is to provide Congressional committees with assessments or studies which identify the range of probable consequences, social as well as physical, of policy alternatives affecting the uses of technology. Requests for OTA assessments may be initiated by:

(1) The chairman of any standing, special, select, or joint committee of the Congress, acting for himself or at the request of the ranking minority member or a majority of the committee members;

(2) the OTA Board; or

(3) the OTA Director, in consultation with the Board.

The authorization of specific assessment projects and the allocation of funds for their performance is a policy responsibility of the OTA Board. The Board has established priority areas of study, and has approved individual assessment projects within those areas. In arriving at these decisions, the Board considers recommendations and plans developed by OTA staff, and applies the following general selection criteria, developed in consultation with the Advisory Council:

• Is this now or likely to become a major national issue?

• Can OTA make a unique contribution, or could the requested technology assessment be done effectively by the requesting committee?

• How significant are the costs and benefits to society of the various policy options involved and how will they be distributed among various impacted groups?

• Is the technological impact irreversible?

• How imminent is the impact?

• Is there sufficient available knowledge to assess the technology and its consequences?

• Is the assessment of manageable scope—can it be bounded within reasonable limits?

• What will be the cost of the assessment?

• How much time will be required to do the assessment?

• What is the likelihood of Congressional action in response to the assessment?

• Would this assessment complement or aid other OTA projects?

The development and performance of each OTA assessment is supervised by a program manager, assisted by other staff professionals with expertise in the subject under study, and by a citizens advisory committee or panel, comprised of persons directly involved with major aspects of the study. Assessments are conducted by OTA program managers and staff with assistance, as appropriate, from panels of experts, consultants, contractors, and other Congressional information agencies. The approach to a given assessment project can be determined in a variety of ways and may involve exploratory meetings or workshops of advisory panels, staff analyses, and consultant studies.

In most instances, assessments are directed by OTA personnel and utilize a task force approach or a series of workshop panel meetings, augmented by contract studies of specific aspects of the overall project.

For assessments which include the resources of an outside contractor, the OTA staff, working closely with its multi-disciplinary advisory group and representatives of the Congressional Committees requesting the study, develops a detailed request for proposals which includes "a statement of work" defining the task or tasks covered by the contract. Qualified parties are invited to submit competitive bids. All proposals received by OTA are considered in the Office's contractor-selection process.

As the assessment or study proceeds, responsibility for its management remains solely a function of OTA. The resources of the associated advisory committee or panel are utilized throughout the entire project. Members and staffs of the interested Congressional Committees also are kept informed on a regular basis of the progress and, as appropriate, the preliminary findings of the study. In many instances, such preliminary information assists Committee staffs in their legislative analyses and preparations for public hearings.

Completed assessments and studies are transmitted by the OTA Congressional Board to the Committee which requested the project, as well as to other interested Committees, and are printed for public dissemination. The Committees of the Congress have first access to OTA assessment results and findings. At the direction of the Board, printing and public dissemination of final OTA reports takes place at the earliest possible date in accordance with arrangements worked out with the requesting Committee(s).

Staffing and Organizational Structure. The OTA professional staff has been recruited from the academic community, from industry, and from government scientific and technical agencies. With the exception of those officers with overall administrative responsibilities, professional staff members are assigned to specific program areas according to their experience and training. Staff professionals have been drawn from a wide variety of disciplines and backgrounds, including the physical sciences and engineering, the social sciences, the law, and general administration. Skilled professionals from Executive Branch agencies, detailed to OTA on a temporary basis, have made major contributions, as have participants in several Congressional fellowship programs. A chart detailing OTA's organizational structure accompanies this [report].

Financial and Budgeting Activities. —Administrative and financial aspects of OTA operations are overseen by an Administrative Officer who reports to the Director. Support functions provided by the Office of Administration include procurement and contracting, budget and financial

OFFICE OF TECHNOLOGY ASSESSMENT

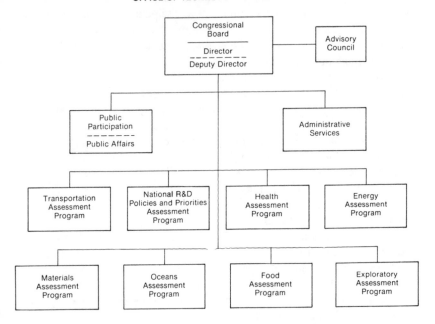

accounting and control, office management and scheduling, payroll, personnel, travel, office space, security, accounts payable and receivable, reproduction and printing, and other miscellaneous administrative support services.

In response to the growth in demand for OTA assessments, the Technology Assessment Board approved submission of a budget request totalling $8.5 million for fiscal year 1977. Estimated OTA expenditures during fiscal year 1976, which includes an added quarter to provide transition to an October 1-September 30 fiscal period, total $8.1 million. A table providing details of OTA's budgetary growth, by program, since the inception of funding in November 1974, accompanies this section.

Public Participation.—Public participation in the technology assessment process is an important OTA objective. In addition to the wide use of citizen advisory groups and consultants, the Office seeks to disseminate information to the various parties at interest in the subject being assessed so they may become more effectively involved in public decision-making processes. In keeping with this objective, meetings of OTA's Congressional Board and Advisory Council are open to the public. Also, the OTA

| | Fiscal Year | | | |
BUDGETARY HISTORY	1974 actual	1975 actual	1976 estimate[1]	1977 request
[Dollar amounts in thousands]				
By program:				
Energy	$322	$433	$1,233	$1,046
Food	16	268	979	1,099
Health	162	69	1,200	1,040
Materials		1,257	1,083	1,150
Oceans	12	710	904	1,102
Transportation	472	402	1,076	1,119
International trade		56	180	155
R. & D. policies and priorities			253	629
Exploratory	32	177	252	287
General and administrative	331	650	961	873
Total	1,347	4,022	[1]8,121	8,500

[1] 15-month period, including transitional quarter.

Director is advised by an officer of public participation as well as a public affairs officer.

The Officer of Public Participation, reporting directly to the Director, coordinates an overall program of activities to facilitate citizen involvement in the technology assessment process, including the establishment of improved communications with business, industry, citizen/ consumer, labor, public interest, professional societies and impacted groups; the creation of out-reach mechanisms; and the instituting of public education programs.

OTA's first full-scale public participation experiment has been conducted as an integral part of the OTA Oceans Assessment Program's regional assessment of the impacts of coastal effects of offshore energy systems for New Jersey and Delaware. Information has been gathered through citizen workshops and through responses to a widely-distributed informational brochure and questionnaire. These inputs are proving beneficial to the overall project by providing valuable insights into public perceptions of the technologies under assessment, while simultaneously increasing public understanding of those technologies. The end result of this activity will be to ensure that citizen viewpoints are considered in the final assessment report.

Exploratory Assessment Program.—OTA screening procedures for evaluating assessment requests include smaller scale, exploratory assessments undertaken to provide a better basis for decisions by the OTA Board as to whether certain major study projects are warranted.

The OTA program of Exploratory Assessments is established to involve senior staff personnel and consultants in a systematic mechanism for defining and evaluating specific assessment proposals submitted to OTA which do not fall into other program areas. During 1975, preliminary evaluation of the feasibility and value of broadband communications in rural areas was conducted at the request of the Senate Committee on Agriculture and Forestry.

The Exploratory Assessments Program has begun an examination of the requirements and opportunities which science and technology present to the U. S. educational system. Following a three-month planning effort, begun in November 1975, a proposal was developed for a study of long-range trends and shifts in American society which may underlie changes needed in education, including both formal institutional and non-institutional learning, along with their public, private, and commercial aspects.

A third exploratory study was made during the year to design an assessment of the role of U.S. advanced technology as it influences the nation's position in international trade. Comprising a survey of literature and documents, a review of governmental activities, and interviews with public and corporate officials, the survey provided a foundation for structuring a proposed incremental assessment. As a result of this preliminary effort, and building upon the resultant comprehensive information base, plans have been made for specific assessments of the state of U. S. technological competitiveness and U.S. productivity, and the public policy options associated with these issues.

Information Services.—OTA technology assessment activities are supported by an Information Services staff, which maintains an in-house library containing basic background materials and current data resources. In addition, this staff maintains liaison with the Library of Congress to facilitate OTA use of its extensive facilities and services.

The Information Services staff also provides on-line access to several computerized data-retrieval networks including: SCORPIO, a Library of Congress system which provides information on current policy-oriented literature and the status of bills introduced in Congress; TRIS (Transportation Research Information Service), a file operated by Battelle Memorial Institute which yields document citations on transportation-related materials; ATS (Administrative Terminal Service), an IBM program available on the Library of Congress Computer which is used for text editing and report generation; and INFONET, a commercial network through which OTA can generate and operate its own computational and analytical programs.

Other Activities.—Evaluation of the technology assessment process, as it is being evolved within OTA and elsewhere, is an important concern of the Office. Toward this end, plans were set in motion for two complementary OTA activities to be carried out during 1976. First, an in-house review will be conducted of the various assessment methods and approaches employed by OTA during its first two years. Emphasis will be placed on identifying lessons to be learned from OTA's assessment experiences. Second, national hearings will be held by the OTA Board to develop information on technology assessment activities in the private sector and in other governmental agencies. This activity will build upon the record initiated by the Board during its 1974 hearings to ensure close liaison between OTA and the National Science Foundation.

Along with the Congressional Budget Office (CBO), the Congressional Research Service (CRS), and the General Accounting Office (GAO), OTA is a formal participant in an interagency research notification system, designed to facilitate the coordination of activities and exchange of information among the four organizations, and to avoid duplication of effort. Representatives of the four agencies meet regularly and each of the offices submits bi-weekly status reports on program activity for publication in a central directory of Congressional research activity.

Coastal Effects of Offshore Energy Systems

UNITED STATES CONGRESS
OFFICE OF TECHNOLOGY ASSESSMENT

INTRODUCTION

BACKGROUND

About half of all Americans live and work within 50 miles of a coastline—along the Atlantic or Pacific Oceans, the Gulf of Mexico, or the Great Lakes. According to a Senate Commerce Committee study, that figure may grow to 80 percent of the total population by the turn of the century. With any such concentration of people in less than 10 percent of the Nation's land area will come intense development and competition for land for housing, industry, commerce, energy facilities, resort communities, and transportation networks.

The consequences of 25 years of accelerated dredging, filling, and construction in coastal areas are not understood at this time. So far, the growth of population in the coastal areas has proceeded with little research into the long-range implications of increased activities in those areas. It is known that marshes, estuaries, and tidal flats along the coasts of the United States are crucial to sustaining marine life, directly or indirectly. It is not known how much more development and what kinds of development can take place in coastal areas before the complex relationships between land and sea and between human life and marine life may be irreversibly disrupted. In fact, it is only since the enactment of the Coastal Zone Management Act of 1972, the principal legislation dealing with problems of the coastal zone, that these questions have been addressed in an organized fashion.

This assessment is an attempt to add to the understanding of the effects of coastal development by focusing on three energy systems which have been proposed for the waters off New Jersey and Delaware.

The objective of the study has been to trace the likely consequences of three energy systems for the ocean environment, the coastal environment, and the economics and patterns of life in both States during the next two decades.

The three systems are:

1. Oil and natural gas development on the Mid-Atlantic Outer Continental Shelf;

2. Installation of a deepwater port to accommodate supertankers in the Mid-Atlantic area; and

3. Construction of at least two floating nuclear powerplants.

The study was requested by Senator Ernest F. Hollings, chairman of the National Ocean Policy Study and sponsor of the Coastal Zone Management Act. The request was approved by the Technology Assessment Board on July 23, 1974.

This report has been prepared by the Oceans Program of OTA with the assistance of an advisory panel of 11 members from industry, Government, and academia, who have reviewed draft material for each section of the report and met periodically to comment on the course of the study and to provide guidance to the staff. The Advisory Panel provided advice and critique throughout the assessment, but does not necessarily approve, disapprove, or endorse the report, for which OTA assumes full responsibility.

The Technology Assessment Board approves the release of this report, which identifies a range of viewpoints on a significant issue facing the U.S. Congress. The views expressed in this report are not necessarily those of the Board nor of individual members thereof.

STUDY AREA AND APPROACH

This study concentrated on proposed developments off the coast of New Jersey and Delaware for several reasons, one being that plans to deploy energy facilities off the coasts of those States are actual rather than hypothetical proposals.

The Department of the Interior accepted bids in August 1976 for leases on 154 tracts on the Outer Continental Shelf off the New Jersey and Delaware coasts and it was expected that oil companies could begin exploratory drilling within 6 months after the sale of leases.

In the summer of 1976, the Nuclear Regulatory Commission (NRC) was well along in its technical evaluation of, and hearings on, proposals to moor two floating nuclear powerplants inside a breakwater off the New Jersey coast.

Plans to build a deepwater port in the area have been in suspension since the early 1970's, when changes in the world oil situation reduced the economic incentives for such a port. But the Delaware Bay area would be a logical candidate for siting a deepwater port if future changes in the oil distribution system revived interest in a port.

In addition, New Jersey and Delaware share some characteristics with other coastal States. Both depend on expanded industrial activity to create new jobs and sustain economic growth. Expanded industry means expanded energy resources and both States depend on other regions of the United States or on foreign suppliers for all of their oil and natural gas. Both States also depend heavily on tourist income which, in turn, depends on the attractiveness of beach areas which would be vulnerable to damage from accidents during the operation of any of the three energy systems.

Finally, planning for the offshore energy systems has been proceeding faster than planning for effective management of coastal areas under the Coastal Zone Management Act.

Because many States share these characteristics to some degree, the findings of this study can be applied to other States if adjustments for differing conditions and levels of resources are made that might be anticipated in other areas.

The study approach was basically the same for each energy system. A foundation of data was developed to provide a framework for analyzing issues for Congressional consideration.

The first step in assessing each system involved a detailed examination of each technology and how it most likely would be deployed. This phase of the study considered only those technologies and systems in their most likely configurations in waters off New Jersey and Delaware and drew largely on published reports. The reports were supplemented by analysis in areas where published data did not provide enough detailed information for full development of issues and options.

The next step in the study was to identify and evaluate the probable impacts of the energy systems on the ocean and coastal environments either as a result of routine operations or as a result of malfunctions which experience with similar technology in other areas has shown are likely to occur. In the case of floating nuclear powerplants, which have not been installed anywhere, the projections of impact were based on land-based nuclear-plant experience adjusted to reflect operation in an ocean environment.

Finally, the study produced estimates of the effect that each energy system would have on New Jersey and Delaware. These included changes in employment in the region, in the cost and reliability of energy supply, the impact on air and water quality, on road and rail networks, on land that would be diverted from other possible uses to support the proposed systems, and on general patterns of life within each State.

SELECTION OF ISSUES

In the course of the study, areas of possible conflict emerged between technology and the environment or among institutions that would share responsibility for the systems. Potential or actual conflicts which appeared to be amenable to policy consideration by Congress or by State governments or private groups were identified. These conflicts are discussed in the report as issues with options for congressional consideration. In most cases, the issues evolved from analysis of the likely consequences of deployment of a technology under existing legal and institutional frameworks and comparison of those consequences with changes in law or custom.

The nature of the issues differs from system to system.

In the case of oil and natural gas development, the major issues are concerned less with individual technology than with the system as a whole and particularly with the institutional framework in which the system operates. In the case of deepwater ports and floating nuclear powerplants, the issues stem largely from the technology, from questions about its reliability, and from avenues that offer promise of reducing risk by changing design or by more careful analysis of risks inherent in the technology.

The changing events that are natural with technologies in active planning required flexibility in the execution of this assessment. Pertinent new or revised information became available to the study team at every stage. Some of the analysis required for the overall assessment had timely congressional utility and was published in special documents or released in draft form by the Technology Assessment Board.

These publications include the following reports:

- Oil Transportation by Tankers: An Analysis of Marine Pollution and Safety Measures.
- An Analysis of the Feasibility of Separating Exploration From Production of Oil and Gas on the Outer Continental Shelf.
- An Analysis of the Department of the Interior's Proposed Acceleration of Development of Oil and Gas on the Outer Continental Shelf.
- Coastal Effects of Offshore Energy Development: Oil and Gas Systems.

These documents and drafts were of particular help to congressional committees responsible for developing amendments to the Coastal Zone Management Act and amendments to the Outer Continental Shelf Lands Act of 1953.

PUBLIC PARTICIPATION

To broaden the information base for this study and to make certain that public attitudes toward the three energy systems were taken fully into account, OTA conducted a public participation program as part of the assessment.

Workshops were held in New Jersey and informal meetings with groups of private citizens as well as representatives of interest groups were held in Delaware to explore citizen attitudes. About 15,000 brochures explaining the technology assessment process and asking for views on all three technologies were distributed in both States. About 1,000 persons responded to a questionnaire that was included in the brochure and an analysis of the responses is included as an integral part of this report.

MAJOR FINDINGS AND SUMMARY

The following are the major findings of this assessment of the three energy systems which have been proposed for deployment off the coast of New Jersey and Delaware. A summary of the assessment of each of the technologies is included after the findings.

● No significant damage to the environment or changes in patterns of life in either New Jersey or Delaware is anticipated during operation of the three systems at presently projected levels. However, careful planning, engineering, and strict operational monitoring are required for each of these complex systems. To a large extent, such planning and monitoring will depend on the quality of oversight by the responsible Federal agency.

● Future deployment of ocean technologies on a scale larger than that anticipated at the present time could create serious conflicts among users and impose excessive burdens on ocean and coastal environments. No formal mechanism exists or is planned for resolving conflicts or directing research to discover the cumulative social and environmental consequences of vastly expanded uses of the oceans.

● Changes in Federal practices are necessary to reduce delays in determining offshore oil and gas resources, to provide full attention to State and local needs and potential impacts, and to assure strict enforcement of operating standards to minimize ocean and coastal pollution. Consolidation of authority within the Department of the Interior is essential to supervision of offshore development and the coordination of operations with State and local governments.

● While floating nuclear powerplants may offer economic and environmental advantages over land-based nuclear plants, the siting of nuclear plants on water may present unique accident risks which have not yet been comprehensively assessed by the Nuclear Regulatory Commission.

● Tankers that would use deepwater ports off New Jersey and Delaware pose a greater pollution and safety threat than the ports themselves. Confining tanker operations to a port several miles from the coast may offer environmental and safety advantages, provided that the tankers using the facility are strictly regulated.

● There are specific alternatives which, if substituted for each of the proposed offshore projects, could supply equivalent amounts of energy to the Mid-Atlantic region. None, however, offers clear social, environmental, or economic advantages. Increased imports are an alternative to offshore oil and gas development. Onshore nuclear plants and coal-fired plants are alternatives to floating nuclear powerplants. Greater reliance on small tankers is an alternative to deepwater ports. Reduction of energy consumption could offer long-term advantages, but there are no specific plans at the State or national level for an energy conservation program that might eliminate the need for the energy supplies which would come from one or more of the proposed offshore systems.

A principal product of this assessment is the development of public policy issues associated with the deployment of each offshore technology and the identification of congressional options for addressing those issues.

OFFSHORE OIL AND GAS SYSTEMS—SUMMARY

The submerged Outer Continental Shelf (OCS) lands of the Mid-Atlantic were classified by geologists as a potential source of oil and natural gas in the late 1950's, but they did not become a priority target for development until the 1970's.

Following the oil embargo imposed by the Organization of Petroleum Exporting Countries in October 1973, accelerated leasing and development of the Mid-Atlantic OCS was made a high priority item in the Administration's plan for lessening U.S. dependence on foreign sources of oil.

In 1974, studies by the U.S. Geological Survey estimated that as much as one-third of the U.S. oil reserves for the future were most likely to be discovered in the OCS regions. In the Mid-Atlantic, estimates were that oil production could be as much as 7 percent of the 1973 national production level and gas production could be as much as 8 percent of the 1975 national production level.

As first announced, accelerated OCS development called for leasing a total of 10 million acres in a single year, an amount equal to what had been leased during the previous 21 years.

Although the Bureau of Land Management (BLM), Interior's lead agency in leasing, had been examining the possibility of an accelerated program for 2 years before the 1973 decision was made, it was not prepared for a sudden change of this magnitude. In the period since the acceleration program was announced, BLM has been chronically short of staff, particularly the specialists required for analyzing coastal and onshore impacts in frontier States. BLM was also unprepared for the adverse reaction of Atlantic Coastal States to the 1973 accelerated leasing decision.

The Governors of both New Jersey and Delaware publicly favor early exploration of the Mid-Atlantic OCS for oil and natural gas, but their support is qualified. Both have argued for changes in Federal OCS policy as a condition of their full support.

The desire for change stems from several factors. One involves basic uncertainties about environmental and economic impacts of a technology which is alien to the Mid-Atlantic even though it is familiar to the Gulf of Mexico. Another involves a series of lapses in communication and coordination between the States and the Interior Department which have raised doubts among State officials about the capability of the Federal Government in planning for operation of offshore oil and gas systems.

The Mid-Atlantic OCS program intensified pressure on the State governments, particularly from residents along the coast, to protect their beaches. Because existing law restricts major decisions about OCS development to the Federal Government, State officials have argued for a role as active participants, rather than observers, in three general areas. They are:

● Drafting of oil and gas regulations and enforcement plans which could affect the quantities of oil that may be spilled during offshore development;

● Selection of areas to be leased which will affect locations of such facilities as onshore staging areas, pipeline landfalls, tank farms, and gas processing plants; and

● Approval of development plans which set a pattern of deployment of technology that would prevail in the area during the life of a Mid-Atlantic oil and gas field.

State officials also desire more centralization of responsibilities and authority within the Interior Department to facilitate the flow of information to the States.

This report contains detailed descriptions of each of the component elements in a typical offshore oil and gas system, starting with geophysical survey ships which are used to gather preliminary data on resources and continuing through technology used for exploration drilling, production drilling, transportation, storage, and processing. Deployment of technology is traced over time for two assumptions—one in which 1.8 billion barrels of oil and 5.3 trillion cubic feet of gas are discovered and recovered and another for 4.6 billion barrels of oil and 14.2 trillion cubic feet of natural gas.

It is estimated that 25 platforms could be installed offshore, each with 24 producing wells, within 14 years after the initial lease sale to produce the 1.8 billion barrels of oil at an average peak rate of 313,000 barrels per day. Under the 4.6 billion barrel assumption, there could be 52 platforms, each with 24 producing wells within 15 years after a lease sale. Peak daily rate for this assumption would be 650,000 barrels.

Onshore, the oil and gas distribution network, averaging both assumptions, would cover about 3-square miles with pipeline rights-of-way, staging areas (of up to 170 acres), tank farms (covering 50 to 75 acres each), and gas processing plants (on sites of about 100 acres each). If drilling platforms were fabricated in either State, land needs would increase by about 1,000 acres.

Five areas in the New Jersey—Delaware region could serve as staging areas for offshore development, three coastal sites and the port complexes of New York City and Philadelphia—Camden. All three coastal sites—Atlantic City and Cape May, N.J., and Lewes, Del.—would meet such staging area requirements as availability of harbors for supply boats, accessibility by rail, proximity to lease sites, and availability of land for storage and service facilities. Service firms under contract to oil companies would choose staging areas on the basis of lowest overall operating costs.

Earlier studies by the Council on Environmental Quality, the American Petroleum Institute, and the Department of the Interior have produced varying projections of the physical, biological, and social changes that would result from offshore development in the Mid-Atlantic OCS. The earlier studies used different assumptions about the amounts of oil and gas that may be recovered and different State and/or regional boundaries for consideration. When these projections are adjusted to a common base, however, they fall within the same general range of effects that are estimated in the OTA study.

It is concluded that, if a major spill occurred at a drilling or production platform 50 miles at sea, the odds are one in ten that an oil slick would reach the beaches of New Jersey and Delaware.

The danger of oil striking a beach would increase if a spill occurred as a result of a pipeline rupture nearer to shore. The danger would decrease if a spill occurred at structures farther than 50 miles from shore. The platforms expected as a result of the first Mid-Atlantic lease sale will be located approximately 54 to 100 miles from shore. The distance lowers the risk of oil striking the beach and also makes the structures invisible from shore.

One element of the offshore oil system that would require particularly careful planning is the placement of pipelines in coastal areas. There is general agreement that pipelines should be routed to avoid marshlands, a design that would be difficult to achieve along the New Jersey or Delaware coast, virtually all of which is backed by marshlands.

Direct employment in New Jersey and Delaware would peak at about 9,000 workers if the high estimate of 4.6 billion barrels of recoverable oil is correct and at about 4,500 workers if the median estimate of 1.8 billion barrels is correct. Capital expenditures would total between $2 billion and $4 billion. Peak land requirements for the high estimate would be about 1,645 acres in the New Jersey–Delaware region. Of that, 320 acres could be coastal land around coastal harbors and the remainder would be inland. Seven hundred acres would be required for pipeline rights-of-way that probably would parallel existing railroad lines or highways.

Analysis of the tax systems of a variety of coastal States, including New Jersey and Delaware, indicates that per capita tax revenue from OCS-related installations onshore would be significantly higher than the statewide average per capita revenues from other sources, except during the first 2 or 3 years of development. The principal reason is that the major onshore installations, such as tank farms and pipelines, are capital intensive, and therefore produce substantial sales and property tax revenues. However, this estimate is for statewide revenues only. It is quite possible that particular localities within a State will experience net adverse budgetary impacts during the course of OCS development, since there is little reason to expect that the tax revenue-producing onshore facilities would be located in the tax jurisdiction of the communities that must provide public services and facilities for the population supporting offshore exploration and development. This problem may also occur between States if the oil and gas are not landed in the same State in which the main support bases are located. It is also possible that a locality could experience a net negative fiscal impact if extraordinary expenditures for public facilities such as roads are required to support OCS development.

The major source of potential impacts on air and water quality onshore would be any new refinery capacity that might result from OCS development. Ambient air quality standards, particularly those related to oxidant levels, could be a significant constraint on new or expanded refinery capacity. Concentrations of waterborne pollutants in refinery effluent are relatively small and probably would not significantly affect the quality of a receiving stream. Refinery cooling, however, could produce thermal pollution problems in Delaware Bay or Newark Bay, both of which are already very close to the maximum permissible load.

Dramatic changes in regional energy prices should not be expected to follow OCS development. Lower transportation costs might give New Jersey and Delaware a price advantage compared with some other regions of the country. But future prices would depend, in part, on oil and gas price control policies.

As a result of its study, OTA has identified the Federal-State conflicts as the major issues. Eight specific OCS issues are treated in this report. They are:

Federal Management System.—Federal management of the offshore oil and gas program is fragmented within the Department of the Interior and coordination with other Federal agencies which share jurisdiction is ineffective.

Regulation and Enforcement.—Inadequate regulation and enforcement of offshore oil and gas technology could result in more accidents and more oil spills than would occur if a more effective system were implemented.

Oil Spill Liability and Compensation.—Existing laws are not adequate either to assign liability or compensate individuals or institutions for damages from oil spills resulting from exploration, development, or production in the Baltimore Canyon Trough area.

Oil Spill Containment and Cleanup.—There is no assurance that the technology utilized in the Baltimore Canyon Trough or in any other OCS frontier region would be adequate for oil spill surveillance, containment, and cleanup.

Environmental Studies.—Environmental research and baseline studies are not formally coordinated with the Interior Department's leasing schedule and there is no requirement that information gathered be used in the decision-making process for sale of offshore lands and subsequent operation.

State Role.—The limited role of State governments in the decisionmaking process for OCS development under existing laws and practices may lead to unnecessary delays and improper planning for such development.

Pollution Research.—The effects of pollutants which may be discharged during OCS operations cannot presently be determined with any accuracy and recent research efforts have not clarified conflicting claims by oil companies and environmental groups regarding the amount and consequences of marine pollution.

Conflicting Ocean Uses.—There are potential conflicts between OCS oil and gas activities and vessel traffic engaged in commercial shipping and fishing activities. However, there has been no comprehensive study and analysis to identify all conflicts and to find ways of resolving them.

OFFSHORE OIL AND GAS SYSTEMS—FINDINGS

Effects of OCS Development

● Oil and natural gas can be produced in the amounts presently projected off the Mid-Atlantic coast without significant damage to the environment or disruption of patterns of life in New Jersey or Delaware if operations are carefully designed, planned, and monitored. However, careful planning, engineering, and strict operational monitoring are required for each of these complex systems. To a large extent, such planning and monitoring will depend on the quality of oversight by the responsible Federal agencies.

● Changes in lines of authority within the Department of the Interior would improve the Department's ability to supervise offshore development and to coordinate operations with State and local governments.

Federal-State Relations

● States cannot participate in a meaningful way in the process that leads to major leasing and OCS decisions under present policies. The State role at present is little more than that of commentator.

● Existing laws and regulations do not clearly specify the information about OCS activities to which States are entitled, a lapse that encourages disputes over rights to data between State and Federal officials.

● Federal efforts to deal with State concerns are fragmented among many departments and agencies and seldom reflect a sense of need for coordination, clear lines of communication, and close working ties.

● The Interior Department's relations with State governments are improving but relations still depend more on individual judgments by Interior Department officials than on formal administrative procedures on which the States can rely.

● Changes in Federal OCS policies and practices have lagged behind changes in the social and political climate in the Mid-Atlantic in which offshore development will occur. The lag is particularly important with respect to environmental concerns and a desire among States for greater access to Federal information and decisionmaking.

● As of mid-1976, the Office of Coastal Zone Management had not asserted itself as coordinator of State and Federal activities involving the effects of offshore development on the coastal zone.

● Concerns of New Jersey and Delaware officials over environmental and social impacts of offshore development are compounded by their doubts about the quality of Federal management of the leasing program and doubts about the effectiveness of the enforcement of OCS regulations.

● Neither Delaware or New Jersey wants to delay offshore development unnecessarily, but both are prepared to seek legal remedies if development in the Mid-Atlantic proceeds without what they consider adequate State participation in decisions.

Planning

● Federal requirements under the Coastal Zone Management Act that Federal activities be consistent with a State's coastal zone management plan have played no role as yet in Mid-Atlantic OCS activities because neither New Jersey or Delaware has completed coastal zone management plans.

● The exact location of OCS facilities and the magnitude of development impacts will not be known until Outer Continental Shelf "frontier areas" have been explored and the size and location of petroleum resources have been determined.

Regulation, Safety, and Pollution

● The regulation of offshore technology by the U.S. Geological Survey (USGS) is based on general guidelines to the industry with minimal inspection and enforcement. USGS regulations are more concerned with specific pieces of equipment than with the total oil and gas production system.

● Techniques exist, but are not always used, for setting design standards and installation practices and for testing all major items of equipment involved in OCS operations.

● Federal regulations are not sufficiently precise with regard to standards for construction of offshore platforms or pipelines.

● The purpose of the Interior Department's OCS environmental studies program and its role in the management of OCS activities is not clearly defined. In their present form, environmental surveys conducted under the auspices of this program are not useful either in writing environmental impact statements or in making OCS leasing decisions.

● Federal pollution research efforts are not as well coordinated as are those sponsored by private industry.

Oil Spills

- Under some weather conditions, oil spills from a platform as far as 50 miles at sea could reach the New Jersey and Delaware coasts but it is not possible to predict the point of impact.

- Weather, wind, and ocean currents will affect the dispersion, trajectory, chemical composition, and ultimate disposition of oil spills. These conditions vary from season to season, and even from day to day, but research on ocean conditions in OCS areas has a low budget priority.

- The Federal Government does not set definitive standards for the industry to follow in carrying out its responsibility to provide cleanup equipment in the event of a major oil spill. USGS does not inspect cleanup equipment but relies on industry to make its own inspections.

- USGS procedures for monitoring discharges of oil and other pollutants during OCS operations are inadequate and the agency does not use monitoring equipment that is available and in use by other Government agencies.

- Under existing Federal practices there are no standards that cleanup and containment equipment, which would be available in the Mid-Atlantic, must meet, and no assurance that a major oil spill actually could be confined and removed from the water even if the best equipment is available.

- At the present time, the laws of an adjacent State would be used to determine a lessee's liability for oil spill damages but neither New Jersey or Delaware laws provide for compensation to injured parties.

Impacts

- Drastic changes in regional energy prices will not result from offshore development in the Mid-Atlantic.

- A net fiscal benefit to Mid-Atlantic State governments probably will result from onshore facilities related to offshore development but there may be localized fiscal problems and the advantage would not occur until after the first 3 years of offshore activity.

- Discovery of offshore oil would not necessarily lead to construction of new refineries in the Mid-Atlantic. In fact, existing air quality regulations might prevent construction of new refineries in New Jersey and Delaware.

- The major impacts on air and water quality in the region would result from expanded refineries and from gas processing plants.

- There is no formal mechanism for resolving conflicts among the many users of the ocean or for directing research to discover the cumulative environmental consequences of expanding the use of the ocean for energy development and other purposes.

DEEPWATER PORTS—SUMMARY

In the late 1960's, energy supply patterns and environmental concerns seemed to justify construction of at least one deepwater port for supertankers off the coast of New Jersey and Delaware.

By 1976, that was no longer the case. A series of changes in State laws and Federal policies, capped by the inflation and uncertainty of supplies that followed sharp increases in world oil prices, had changed the region's petroleum distribution system dramatically.

Plans for expanding old refineries and building new ones were on the shelf. Increases in demand for petroleum products were being met by Gulf Coast and Caribbean refineries. Inflation had doubled original estimates of the cost of a deepwater port.

Extensive interviews with industry officials and analysis of feasibility studies disclose that—barring future changes as drastic as those of the early 1970's—the oil industry will not revive Mid-Atlantic deepwater port plans for at least 10 years.

New tax policies, changes in environmental laws, changes in oil prices or sharp increases in Mid-Atlantic demand for imports could change the picture again. It also is possible that environmental or political goals could prompt States to build a deepwater port even if it were not attractive on purely economic grounds.

In the meantime, the oil industry is moving ahead with plans to build two deepwater ports off the shores of Texas and Louisiana that eventually can handle 10 million barrels of oil a day. A program of refinery construction and expansion is underway in both Texas and Louisiana to handle imports of crude oil.

During the period of strong Government and industry interest in Mid-Atlantic deepwater ports, several sites and types of terminals were studied, including a sea pier located inside Delaware Bay. Of these, the technology most likely to be placed in waters under Federal jurisdiction is a large monobuoy complex located far enough from the coast to serve the largest supertankers in the world fleet. These are 480,000 deadweight ton (dtw) ships, a quarter-of-a-mile long, that carry up to 3.7 million barrels of oil and require 110 feet of water depth for maneuvering. One site that could accommodate the largest tankers is 32 miles off southern New Jersey where waters are 110 to 115 feet deep.

Oil could be pumped from the site through underwater and overland pipelines to the Delaware River refinery complex which includes seven refineries with a total capacity of 890,000 barrels of petroleum product per day. The capacity of the refineries could be nearly doubled without acquiring additional land.

During the course of this study, several bulk-oil terminal designs were analyzed. The monobuoy was selected for detailed study because it is a proven technology, already in operation in more than 100 deepwater ports around the world, and because it is less expensive, safer, and more accessible in rough weather than other designs.

A monobuoy is a floating steel drum, 30 feet to 50 feet in diameter, which is anchored over a buried pipeline leading to shore. Tankers tie up to the buoy, connect the buoy's floating rubber hoses to their cargo compartments and pump oil through the hoses and into the pipeline.

Under 1976 conditions, the cost of building and operating a monobuoy complex off Delaware Bay would make the price of transferring oil through the deepwater port higher than the existing system, which uses lightering barges. Another barrier is Delaware's Coastal Zone Act which prohibits pipeline landfalls in that State. New Jersey's Coastal Area Facilities Review Act does not prohibit pipeline landfalls outright but both the present and immediate past Governors of New Jersey are on record in opposition to deepwater port development in their State.

Thus, the descriptions of technology and the likely consequences of its deployment which are discussed in this study are purely hypothetical. Basic changes in policy and the economics of oil distribution will be necessary before a deepwater port can be deployed in the region.

Given the lack of interest in a Mid-Atlantic deepwater port on the part of Government officials and the oil industry, the matter is not a major public issue at this time. The passage of the Federal Deepwater Port Act of 1974 also has reduced the number of issues of Federal concern.

However, this study has identified several potential issues. They include:

Tanker Design and Operations. —Tanker spills are the source of five to fifteen times as much oil as all offshore drilling and port operations combined; yet pollution control regulations are far less stringent for tankers than for either deepwater ports or offshore oil and gas operations.

Oil Spill Containment and Cleanup at Deepwater Ports. —The use of offshore deepwater ports may reduce the risk of certain oil spills and environmental damage below that of transporting crude oil by smaller tankers into the congested New York Harbor and Delaware Bay. Even the very small risk of a catastrophic spill from a supertanker, however, dictates that stringent pollution control and cleanup systems be used.

Standards in State Waters.—Under existing Federal law, operators of deepwater ports in State waters could ignore the safety and environmental pollution standards that apply to ports outside the 3-mile limit.

Adjacent Coastal State Status.—Differing interpretations of statutory criteria for determining adjacent coastal State status make it difficult to predict which States could qualify for that status in the future and whether some States may be deprived of the benefits of such status.

DEEPWATER PORTS—FINDINGS

Construction

• A deepwater port is not likely to be built to serve the Mid-Atlantic during the next 10 years.

• Industry is not likely to abandon its existing marine transportation system for supplying the Mid-Atlantic with oil products as long as there is no clear cost advantage.

• Expanded or new refinery capacity would be necessary to make a deepwater port economically feasible. But existing Federal and State air quality regulations make construction of new refineries along the Delaware River and Bay unlikely in the foreseeable future, although existing refineries may be expanded without exceeding pollution standards.

Environment

• Because a decision to build a deepwater port would logically follow—not force—a decision to build new refineries, a port is likely to be postponed at least until, and if, refinery capacity in the Mid-Atlantic expands significantly.

• A deepwater port system would offer environmental advantages over small tankers operating in existing ports. Presently, small tankers spill twice as much oil that can damage the coastal zone as would be spilled in a deepwater port system.

• The most serious threat of oil spills as a result of a deepwater port system comes from the tankers using the port. Yet, tanker regulations are less strict than port regulations.

• Because of the serious design limitations of containment and cleanup equipment, even the most advanced equipment will be effective only about 55 percent of the time in winter seas off the Mid-Atlantic coast. These facts emphasize the importance of preventing spills rather than regulating cleanup equipment.

Planning and Procedures

• Coast Guard Vessel Traffic Surveillance Systems are not required for deepwater ports in State waters and budget priorities in the Coast Guard could delay installation of these systems for the ports.

• There is disagreement among Federal officials, State governments, and other interested parties as to statutory criteria for determining which States near a deepwater port are eligible for economic assistance and regulatory powers of the Deepwater Port Act.

• Applications for the construction and operation of deepwater ports in State or territorial waters are not under the jurisdiction of the Deepwater Port Act and there is minimal coordination between the two agencies which do have jurisdiction—the Army Corps of Engineers and the Department of Transportation.

FLOATING NUCLEAR POWERPLANTS—SUMMARY

Late in 1972, New Jersey's largest public utility company concluded that floating nuclear powerplants moored off the coast would solve a major problem faced with all large-scale generators—access to cooling water. The company, Public Service Electric & Gas Co., which generates more than 60 percent of the State's power, also concluded they could be built for less money and be less environmentally damaging than land-based plants. Access to cooling water was crucial to the company's future plans. At the time its customers were using electricity at rates that meant doubling Public Service's generating capacity every 8 years—a rate of growth well above the national average—and the number of sites for new plants that could be built without cooling towers was severely limited.

During the period of steep growth in demand in the late 1960's and early 1970's, the offshore plant was a critical element in Public Service's long-range plans for providing new generation facilities. Its construction schedule called for having large amounts of new generating capacity in place by the early 1980's. Two land-based nuclear plants near Salem, N.J., were running 5 years behind schedule. Construction of two more nuclear units was delayed when objections to the use of Newbold Island in the Delaware River forced Public Service to relocate the project to Hope Creek, just north of the Salem plants. Lead times for land-based plants elsewhere in the State, were running between 8 and 12 years.

In September 1972, after conducting its own site surveys off the New Jersey coast, Public Service contracted to buy the first two floating plants to be produced by Offshore Power Systems, Inc. In 1973, Public Service signed a contract for two more floating plants.

Today, after 3 years of analyzing the offshore power concept, staff members of the Nuclear Regulatory Commission (NRC), and some other Federal agencies have come to the same general conclusion about the cost and environmental impact of floating nuclear powerplants. These staff judgments are tentative and are not in any sense formal endorsements of the concept or the construction plans. The Public Service proposal still must work its way through a series of reviews, public hearings, and decisions by Federal and State agencies and meet challenges from environmental groups, New Jersey beach communities, and some nuclear scientists and engineers who say that the systems are unnecessary, and may be unworkable or unsafe. Before an off-shore nuclear plant can start generating power it must clear three separate stages of licensing. The first of these probably will not be completed before 1977.

The preliminary NRC staff reviews nevertheless have provided enough encouragement to the companies involved in the floating nuclear power-plants—the Atlantic Generating Station Units 1 and 2—that they have spent more than $120 million thus far for plans, environmental studies, and in tooling up for production.

Public Service plans to have the first plant operational in 1985 and the second in 1987.

Each plant is designed to generate 1,150 megawatts (MWe) of power, a supply that Public Service estimates will provide about one-third of the additional power it plans to be generating by 1987. The plants are designed to generate power for 40 years, after which they will be shut down and decommissioned.

Several advantages of supplying electricity from offshore stations have been advanced in recent years by supporters and some analysts of the concept. Promoters of offshore plants take the position that:

● Unlimited supplies of cooling water are available at ocean sites and the environmental consequences of discharging heated water into the ocean will be minimal compared with the consequences of discharging heated water into rivers, lakes and bays.

● Offshore construction eliminates the disruption of coastal marshlands and estuaries to a great extent.

● The floating power concept moves in the direction of standardized nuclear plant designs, a goal the Nuclear Regulatory Commission (then the Atomic Energy Commission) set in 1972.

● Shipyard construction of plants will shorten the time required to put a nuclear plant in operation after a decision is made to build it.

● Volume production can cut costs and improve quality control.

Federal and State agencies have been reviewing the offshore powerplant proposal informally since late 1971 and formally since July 1973, when the Atomic Energy Commission docketed an Offshore Power Systems application for a permit to build eight floating nuclear powerplants.

During that time, the Atlantic Generating Station has received encouragement from the staff of the Council on Environmental Quality, which views the proposal with "guarded optimism." The Nuclear Regulatory Commission's Office of Nuclear Reactor Regulation has declared the project "generally acceptable" as to environmental impact and risk. The same office concluded in a Safety Evaluation Report published in September 1975 that with some modifications in design "there is reasonable assurance that . . . [the reactors could be installed] without undue risk to the health and safety of the public."

During prehearing conferences on the Offshore Power Systems application for a manufacturing permit, intervenors have challenged many of these claims, questioned design features, raised doubts about the need for any new generating capacity in the area, and argued that the technology is unproven and should not be tested near New Jersey communities.

The State of New Jersey, which has not sought official intervenor status, has complained to the Nuclear Regulatory Commission that neither of two environmental impact statements NRC has published "faces up fully to all the risks [of floating plants] about which you owe the public your professional advice."

In a May 4, 1976 letter to NRC, David J. Bardin, New Jersey Commissioner of Environmental Protection, wrote that the most important lapse was in not addressing the possible consequences of a major accident "on the ground that such failures were unlikely to occur."

Some of the major points that intervenors have argued in prehearing conferences since 1974 are:

● The plant will be vulnerable to external hazards such as ship collisions, airplane crashes, and severe storms. Damage to the plant could result in dispersal of radioactive materials injurious to human health and aquatic life.

● Transportation and handling of radioactive fuel and wastes involve risks to human safety and health and to the marine and coastal environment.

● Evacuation in case of an accident will be difficult, especially in summer months, and there are no adequate plans or procedures for such emergencies.

• Fear of nuclear accidents will reduce the appeal of the area for recreational uses and have a detrimental effect on the region's tourist-based economy.

• Other impacts that could be adverse include industrialization of the ocean around the site, onshore support facilities, dredging, and defects in underwater electrical transmission lines.

• NRC should prepare a comprehensive, programmatic EIS on the construction of floating nuclear powerplants located offshore.

More than 15,000 New Jersey and Delaware residents were contacted by OTA as part of the public participation program of this study. From these participants, more than 1,000 responses dealing specifically with the floating nuclear plant were selected for analysis. The analysis showed that the public was generally well aware that advantages and disadvantages must be weighed in deciding whether to build a floating nuclear plant. The analysis, along with press reports and statements at public hearings, also showed that the public sees the disadvantages as involving questions of safety, environmental degradation and high construction costs. The advantages include increased energy supplies with resulting economic expansion and cheaper power than would be possible with continued use of oil-fired generating plants.

Specific concerns about safety involve possibilities of accidents, leakage of radioactive waste and unresolved questions about the permanent disposal of nuclear waste. There was a perception among those who answered the OTA questionnaire that floating nuclear powerplants are experimental and that there is no experience on which to base estimates of risk and reliability.

One of the advantages cited in questionnaires and workshops is that nuclear powerplants are less polluting generally than fossil-fueled plants. In turn, participants saw advantages in floating plants over land-based plants in their distance from shore and the elimination of pressures on New Jersey water supplies for cooling water.

In this study, OTA has analyzed available information on costs, benefits, environmental impact, safety, waste disposal systems, transportation, transmission cables, and decommissioning activities associated with the floating plants. The study does not attempt to evaluate controversies about the safety and performance of nuclear plants in general; these are beyond the scope of the coastal effects analysis. It concentrates, instead, on exploring differences between the designs of floating and land-based plants and comparing the advantages and disadvantages of each.

The major issues identified by OTA in its study of the floating nuclear plant are:

Risks From Major Accidents.—The Nuclear Regulatory Commission

(NRC) is not evaluating the risks from accidents in floating nuclear plants comprehensively enough to permit either a generic comparison of the relative risks from land based and floating nuclear plants, or an assessment of the specific risks from deploying floating plants off New Jersey.

Deployment in Volume.—As many as 59 floating nuclear powerplants could be built by a single manufacturer by the year 2000 but no policy analysis of the impacts of deploying that many plants in U.S. coastal waters has been done or is contemplated.

Technical Uncertainties.—Several technical aspects of the deployment, operation, and decommissioning of floating nuclear powerplants have not been analyzed thoroughly enough to permit judgments about the relative risks of the overall system.

Siting of Floating Powerplants Outside U.S. Territorial Limits.—Because there is no physical barrier to location floating nuclear powerplants more than 3 miles offshore, proposals for siting plants outside territorial limits are possible. However, U.S. authority to regulate floating nuclear powerplants outside U.S. territory is not clear under existing international law.

FLOATING NUCLEAR POWERPLANTS—FINDINGS

Energy Supply

● The two 1150 megawatt floating nuclear plants proposed to be located offshore New Jersey could produce about 10 percent of the State's electrical needs projected for 1990.

Planning and Procedures

● No detailed procedure or design standards have been developed for transporting fuel to a floating plant or for carrying irradiated fuel and other radioactive wastes to shore.

● Offshore sites for nuclear powerplants offer advantages over shore-based sites in terms of impacts on the marine environment.

● The floating nuclear powerplant concept of standardizing design may provide a method for controlling escalating costs of nuclear powerplants.

● There are several decommissioning options for the floating nuclear plant, but only the one of dismantling the radioactive internals at the plant site and disposing of them appears to be technically and economically feasible.

● Existing international law does not specifically settle the question of jurisdiction over a floating nuclear powerplant located beyond national territorial limits, and the Nuclear Regulatory Commission appears not to have authority under present law to approve siting of a U.S. nuclear power-plant in waters outside of U.S. jurisdiction.

● Federal licensing of floating nuclear plants is confined to rather narrow technical and administrative questions related to building eight plants and deploying two of those plants off the coast of New Jersey. It does not consider the implications of approving the larger scale deployment of floating nuclear powerplants.

● The one U.S. company now developing a capacity to build floating nuclear powerplants intends to build and market four such plants a year after 1985. Operating at peak capacity beginning in 1977, this company could produce 59 floating nuclear plants by the year 2000.

Safety

● The nuclear reactor and floating barge are proven technologies but the combination of the two as a system is not.

● A critical review of completed studies discloses little foundation for concluding that either construction or routine operations of the two plants at the Atlantic Generating Station would endanger public health or environment.

● In the unlikely event of a core-melt accident in a floating plant, the molten core eventually would melt through the bottom of any barge and release radioactive materials directly into the ocean where they could contaminate beaches and be absorbed in the food chain.

● The probability of a core-meltdown accident in a floating nuclear powerplant is comparable to the probability calculated in WASH–1400, commonly known as the Rasmussen Report, for land-based plants. However, the expected consequences of releases of radioactive materials as a result of a core-melt at a floating plant could be significantly different.

● The probability of an atmospheric release of radioactive materials may be as much as seven times greater for a core-melt at a floating plant than for a core-melt at the land-based plant, as calculated in WASH–1400. However, the amount and consequences of the release may be reduced by design features and offshore siting of the plant.

● The Liquid Pathways Generic Study being prepared by the Nuclear Regulatory Commission and Offshore Power Systems comparing the radiological consequences of accidental release of radioactive materials into water at floating plants and land-based plants is not as comprehensive as WASH–1400's analysis of the consequences of accidents, partly because it does not consider economic impacts.

ALTERNATIVES TO OFFSHORE TECHNOLOGIES—SUMMARY

New Jersey and Delaware would have a limited number of alternatives over at least the next two decades if any or all of the proposed offshore energy systems were not deployed.

Without strong national leadership in conservation and energy supply programs, the most likely course for the Mid-Atlantic region during the next 20 years is to extend the energy system that already is planned or in place.

ALTERNATIVES TO OFFSHORE TECHNOLOGIES—FINDINGS

● There are specific alternatives which, if substituted for each of the proposed offshore energy projects, could supply equivalent amounts of energy. Increased imports are an alternative to offshore oil and gas development. Onshore nuclear plants and coal-fired plants are alternatives to floating nuclear plants. Greater reliance on small tankers is an alternative to deep-water ports. None of the specific near-term alternatives offer clear social, economic, or environmental advantages.

● Reduction of energy consumption could offer longer term advantages but there are no specific plans at the State or national level for an energy conservation program that might eliminate the need for energy supplies that would come from one or more of the proposed offshore systems.

● Utility managers will choose existing and tested technologies that are most apt to match the consumption levels in their forecasts and will assign reliability of power supply a higher priority than cost.

● The most promising alternatives for stretching out supplies of fossil fuels are programs to improve insulation of homes and offices, changes in automobile design to increase mileage, and use of existing technologies to increase the amount of power generated per unit of fuel.

● Coal is a potential substitute for every basic fuel in the United States and supplies could last for more than a century even if consumption were to quadruple. However, massive conversion to use of coal would entail major changes in transportation networks, in air quality standards, new mining techniques, and new miner-training and safety programs.

● Utility companies and other energy suppliers in Mid-Atlantic States will not factor supplies of oil and natural gas from the Baltimore Canyon Trough into their future plans until exploration establishes likely production levels.

● No single new technology or change in the way existing technologies are used is likely to provide more than a small percentage of total energy requirements before the end of the century. Solutions to energy problems will be found in putting together many relatively small conservation and supply programs.

● Given existing laws, regulations, fuel supplies, and technologies, New Jersey utilities report that they would replace floating nuclear powerplants with shoreline floating plants, land-based nuclear plants, and coal-fired plants, in that order of preference.

● Solar energy will not contribute much to energy supplies before the end of the century unless Federal programs to cut solar installation costs and private plans to market solar products are given higher priorities than they now enjoy.

Technological Forecasting in Technology Assessment

DAVID M. KIEFER

The link between technological forecasting and technology assessment is both clear and strong. The tie is so close, in fact that as the concept of technology assessment wins wider acceptance, technological forecasting and planning studies are not infrequently equated with assessments, despite the latters' focus on secondary and indirect impacts of technology on the environment and society at large as well as on technology itself. Yet much as the formulation of economic programs would be hamstrung without some understanding of likely future economic trends, so the development of policy for controlling technological change— and that is what technology assessment is all about— would be much more difficult lacking a sense of future trends in technology.

Forecasting is important not only to provide insight into new technologies that are emerging, to outline the probable future course (or courses) of their development, and to sketch the range of potential costs and benefits, but also to indicate when and where they might first appear. It provides a guide to possible future achievement against which technological progress may be judged. It is needed, no less, as a means for identifying technologies which may be useful in the future but remain undetected or undercultivated in the present. "Technological forecasting," as former U.S. Congressman Emilio Q. Daddario has pointed out, "means predicting the results of the competition among technically feasible goals for political acceptance."

Yet the bulk of the rapidly expanding literature dealing with technology assessment to date seems often to focus in a philosophical manner, more on how the process might be institutionalized, where it should be undertaken, by whom, and for whose use, rather than on what tools and techniques (of which technological forecasting is but one) will be required to successfully carry out the assessment process. One of the deficiencies in such limited attempts at technology assessment as have been made so far is that they generally have been retrospective and restricted in scope. And for the most part they have been undertaken in response to a specific problem created by the introduction of new technology into society, rather than in anticipation of innovation. Ours tends to be a crisis-oriented society in a world where policy that is initiated only as a reaction to real and present threats is proving increasingly inadequate for coping with those threats. Assessment in the past has often been on a trial-and-error, hit-or-miss basis, with little perspective beyond short-term hazards, opportunities, and alternatives. It has viewed the future narrowly—if at all— as no more than an extension of the immediate past. Technological forecasting must come into play, therefore, to lengthen the time horizon in which technology assessment and planning can take place.

It is possible for an established or emerging technology to be assessed, in a limited manner at least, without a forecast. Much of the information needed for assessment may be already in existence; it remains only to be uncovered by a diligent search of the pertinent scientific and technical literature, reinforced perhaps by a limited amount of original, independent laboratory or field research and testing. This is especially the case when the assessment is restricted to a relatively narrow innovation or advance, such as a specific new drug, pesticide, or food additive or a modification of an established device or technique.

Until assessment becomes more accepted and widely used, therefore, many proponents of the concept see it based to a considerable extent on a careful and thorough documentation and evaluation (as to relevancy, authenticity, acceptability, and like criteria) of data presently available. The intent will not be just to supply a greater amount of information to policy-makers, to be sure, but rather to improve the quality, pertinence, and completeness of the information on which they must base their decisions. In many cases, a painstaking analysis of existing information sources would be adequate for spelling out incipient dangers and drawbacks posed by emerging technological developments.

But it is nevertheless also clear that if technology assessment is to probe the future in order to fulfill many of the wider objectives that its backers envision—if it is to act not just as a screening device for eliminating potential hazards but also as an early warning system and as a means for systematically evaluating secondary and indirect consequences and allocating limited technological resources with minimum waste—then the act of assessment demands more than just a documentation of existing information dealing only with present technology. A study is required also, of where emerging technological developments are likely to lead and of their possible impact on other areas of technology, as well as on society as a whole and its environment. Hence the forecasting of technology is essential, both to uncover otherwise unexpected or unforeseen problems and to disclose unappreciated or unexpected opportunities, options, and alternatives. This is especially true because assessment, if it is to be effective, should be triggered as early as possible, before a new technology has become well entrenched or developed a momentum of its own.

But can technological forecasting meet this challenge? Economic forecasting is largely a post-World War I development. Over the past 50 years it has evolved a rather formidable methodology involving econometric models, input-output analysis, the study of leading indicators, and the like. Despite these refinements, its shortcomings are clear. It remains an imprecise and uncertain, if nonetheless unavoidable, tool for policymakers in business and government.

In contrast, technological forecasting, although much in vogue now, is still in its infancy. Its antecedents lie in the writings of science-fiction authors and the speculations of science popularizers during the first half of the 20th century. But its development as a formal endeavor stems largely from the need, following World War II, for organizing and planning huge military and aerospace research programs. It has come into its own only within the past decade. Its reliability is still largely untested and its worth must still be accepted with a considerable degree of faith.

Yet even within this relatively short time many interesting techniques have been developed for predicting technological change in an organized, logical, and systematic manner. The literature on the subject has burgeoned. The current state of the art is well surveyed in several recent books.[1]

In general, there are two broad approaches to technological forecasting. One of these, often termed *exploratory* forecasting, seeks to hang the future on the framework of the past and present. It attempts to delineate what alternative opportunities for the future lie within the capabilities of the present. Its rationale rests on the assumption that the technology that will be put in use tomorrow is foreshadowed by the science of today or is a direct outgrowth of current technological knowledge. Hence an important aspect of forecasting is a careful monitoring of the present.

One of the earliest—and still one of the most widely used—methods for forecasting consists of extrapolating historic data into the future, a technique which also has long been used for economic, business, and demographic forecasting. Many series of data (the maximum speed of aircraft, for example), when plotted as a function of time, form a pattern to which a curve can be fitted and then projected. A refinement of curve-fitting techniques involves the use of an envelope curve to superimpose a single general line to a number of more specific ones. Thus a single attribute (such as the maximum speed of transportation) can be forecast without stipulating the means (horse and buggy, automobile, jet plane) by which it is attained.

Correlation analysis, based on precursor events, can be used to forecast related technologies when the attainment of one specific characteristic (such as the speed of commercial aircraft) is found to normally lag in time behind another (the speed of military aircraft). Somewhat similar is the use of analogy: Technological development may be analogous to biological growth rates, for instance, or generalizations regarding the appearance of technological events of the past may be used to suggest what might happen under similar circumstances in the future.

Quantitative forecasts are also possible through the use of network analysis and decision tree techniques, although these probably are more strictly applicable to planning than for forecasting as such. A decision or relevance tree

1. Erich Jantsch, *Technological Forecasting in Perspective* (Paris: Organization for Economic Cooperation and Development, 1967); James R. Bright, ed., *Technological Forecasting for Industry and Government* (Englewood Cliffs, N.J.: Prentice-Hall, Inc., 1968); Marvin J. Cetron, *Technological Forecasting: A Practical Approach* (New York: Gordon & Breach, 1969); Robert U. Ayres, *Technological Forecasting and Long-Range Planning* (New York: McGraw-Hill Book Company, 1969); Marvin J. Cetron and Christine A. Ralph, *Industrial Applications of Technological Forecasting* (New York: John Wiley, 1971).

essentially is a graphical array of possible pathways toward a desired objective which displays (in a quantitative manner insofar as possible) the relationships between actions and events. It is designed to provide an orderly way for looking at the manner in which one event influences or leads to another, with emphasis placed on the points of branching where decisions regarding alternative courses must be made.

Cross-impact analysis, developed at the Institute for the Future, and its related techniques make use of a matrix which arrays and evaluates, in terms of probabilities, the influences and interactions within a set of possible parameters or future events and attempts to identify chains of causal linkages. Cross impacts stemming from one possible development or alternative course of action may change the probability of occurrence for other events within the set. Statistical analysis of changes in the likelihood of occurrence of some events as a result of changes for others permits the most important chains of events to be singled out.

Intuitive forecasting methods also have gained prominence. One such technique is scenario writing, popularized by Herman Kahn and the Hudson Institute but used more widely for sociological and political forecasting. A scenario attempts to describe, in systematic but hypothetical and largely qualitative terms, the future sequence of events that would appear logically to evolve, step by step through cause-and-effect relationships, from any given set of conditions or recognized trends. Emphasis is placed on those critical decision points from which alternative chains or events might arise and on the simultaneous interactions between events and their environment. A single set of assumed initial circumstances can generate an entire family of related scenarios (or alternative futures), any one of which may be plausible.

The widely publicized Delphi technique, originated at Rand Corp., is designed to apply the collective expertise and intuition of a panel of anonymous experts by developing a consensus through several steps of systematic questioning and polling about future events. The polling process is carefully organized so as to minimize the biases that might otherwise arise from interacting personalities or other psychological influences within the expert panel. A feedback system is used to sharpen or narrow the forecast through successive rounds of polling which are designed to call the attention of the panelists to factors that they might have initially overlooked or dismissed and to force them to rethink or defend responses which differ markedly from the panel's overall views. Personal factors presumably cancel out one another in the process. The outcome typically is an approximate schedule of future occurrences. Delphi exercises can be particularly useful for exploring the future when adequate historic data are unavailable or when future developments are likely to be strongly influenced by such nontechnical considerations as changing social values or political feasibility.

In contrast to all these methods of forecasting from the past and present into the future, *normative* forecasting reverses the process. It starts with some future need, mission, or objective and attempts to work backwards in time toward present capabilities so as to define the technological pathways and means by which a goal might be reached and to identify the technological barriers which must be overcome in the process. The aim is less to prophesy than to "invent" the future, with the focus not on that which might happen but on that which should happen. Since such goal-oriented forecasting by intent is designed to be self-fulfilling, normative techniques tend to be more suitable for planning than for forecasting alone. (Of course, any forecast will tend to be self-fulfilling, when it is optimistic, or self-defeating, when it is pessimistic, if it is sufficiently credible to encourage steps toward attaining a promised benefit or toward avoiding a disagreeable or unwanted outcome).

Many other techniques for technological forecasting have been formulated. As a whole, however, they are mostly modifications, combinations, expansions, or refinements of those summarized above. In their attempts to map the future, forecasters in a few short years have constructed a surprisingly complex (and often jargon-ridden) methodology.

It would be unreasonable to single out any one or more of these techniques as most appropriate for technology assessment. Each assessment must be designed to fit the specific requirements and characteristics of the particular problem under investigation.

At first glance, normative approaches might seem best in the light of technology assessment's fundamental concern with goals and priorities. Unfortunately, the establishment of national goals that are concrete and well-defined, rather than merely statements of broad generalities or platitudes, has met with scant success. And even more difficult than the identification of publicly acceptable goals is the definition of explicit priorities for attaining those goals.

Perhaps the best approach would be an eclectic one integrating several techniques of forecasting in order to sharpen the reliability of the overall forecast while minimizing the shortcomings to be found in any one method. Intuitive Delphi forecasting, for example, might be used in conjunction with more quantitative methods, such as curve fitting, that would provide a statistical link with the past. Or a carefully prepared scenario could be used to provide a broad perspective for the deliberations of a Delphi panel. The use of cross-impact matrices has increasingly proved useful in conjunction with Delphi exercises.

The difficulty in combining techniques, of course, lies in the cost and complexity that ensues. Forecasting is but one step in the overall assessment process, and most often a relatively early one at that. A forecast that requires several months to prepare would only unduly postpone the completion of the final assessment. It is possible to conceive of very elegant and exhaustive forecasting procedures. But in practical terms, decisions must be made within a time frame that does not allow unlimited delay in order to generate new information or sharpen techniques. Assessments must be timely, therefore, if they are to serve as early warning devices and be of practical rather than merely academic interest. Of course, the earlier they are done the fewer hard facts and figures will be available. Nevertheless, while forecasting is designed to reduce uncertainty in the assessment process, it cannot be expected to totally eliminate it.

For all its apparent sophistication, moreover, technological forecasting is still in its formative years and must be viewed with skepticism and caution. It is easy—perhaps all too easy— to be overly critical of what has been accomplished so far, however.

Quantitative techniques for fitting curves or correlating related trends can be criticized for being naive or simplistic. (One of the advantages of such methods, on the other hand, is their intrinsic simplicity and the ease with which they can be applied, given an adequate array of historic data, and understood.) Extrapolations and correlations are meaningful only if it is clear that past trends will continue unchanged and that present patterns are likely to repeat themselves. These methods are most suitable for relatively short-term forecasts dealing with rather limited technologies. They cannot be used to forecast beyond the range of what is currently known. They tend, too, to focus on developments that can be described statistically to the exclusion of that which can be stated only qualitatively, although the latter may be no less significant or real.

Analogy, meanwhile, can only suggest possible courses for future occurrences. Cross-impact techniques are limited to interactions between pairs of events or dichotomous situations and are dependent on the ability to assign reasonable probabilities to future events.

The Delphi method hinges heavily on how well the panel of experts is organized and how well informed it is, as well as on the formulation of the questions put to the panel. Emphasis on consensus tends to stifle minority opinions, no matter how intelligent, for the sake of general agreement. And the Delphi procedure also is likely to be cumbersome, time consuming, and comparatively expensive. Wide-ranging scenarios may also be time consuming, and their validity is difficult to evaluate.

No technique of technological forecasting, moreover, can really envison the flashes of innovation or the unpredictable discoveries which bring about much technological change. Nor can the social, political, economic, and other external pressures and constraints which significantly influence technological development readily be taken into account. Forecasting that is purely technological tends to see innovation as something that will happen regardless of social change and policies and to assume a steady-state society and a steady-growth-rate economy. Even when social factors are brought into play, they generally are done so in terms of the impact of technology on society rather than the other way round. Yet it is clear that social values can affect technological priorities or the allocation of resources; technological innovation often results as a response to social or economic demand and takes place only if a willingness exists on the part of society to put a new technology to use. It is rather ironic that aerospace industry, which probably has done more than any other to apply technological forecasting to practical needs has had the greatest problems in coping with changes in technological priorities and political policy during the past couple of years. The fundamental difficulty in foretelling social and political change—or of even devising meaningful social indicators for measuring such changes statistically—remains a serious obstacle not only for technological forecasting but for technology assessment as well.

Any forecast for use in technology assessment, of course, probably must include a large component of subjective-judgment, for much of the insight needed can be acquired in no other way. Quantitative statements about the future may appear more scientific (especially if they are presented in the form of a computer readout), but qualitative forecasts are not necessarily less realistic or objective. Quantitative measures should be included where they can. But judgment is often the only source of information concerning future social, political, and environmental effects. To exclude it from the forecast would only unduly restrict the forecaster's perspective.

It is important, too, that the forecast be presented in terms of alternative futures. By identifying possible alternatives or options, together with the probability of their attainment (especially in the light of reinforcing or conflicting events), the forecaster provides an array of possible actions from which the decision-maker can select a course of action.

Questions of reliability can be resolved, at least to some degree, once it is recognized that any forecast of more than the near-term future must be continuously reviewed and revised if it is to remain useful. Any technological forecast has a limited shelf-life, especially when it embraces areas where technological change is most rapid. All long-range forecasts are certain to become obsolete before their terminal date is reached. Hence, both forecasting and assessment must be ongoing processes subject to periodic updating and modification. And any forecast should have continuity designed into it in the form of interim milestones that permit its reliability to be tested periodically prior to its completion.

In any event, to judge the worth of a forecast by stressing its "accuracy" (which can only be verified by hindsight) is a mistake, although a common one. A technological forecast, after all, is less a prediction of what is likely to happen than a statement of potential technological capabilities and opportunities which will be realized only after rational choice is made to implement the forecast.

Forecasters must not lose sight of the present while they engage in the intellectually stimulating task of weighing the future. Their task usually lies less in foretelling what will be at some time to come than in providing a frame of reference for current policy making, in reducing at least some of the uncertainty that befogs the critical decisions that must be reached here and now, and in minimizing the technological surprises that thwart systematic planning. The greatest value of a forecast may well be its ability to stretch the imagination or catalyze fresh thinking. It is worthwhile, as well, if it just serves to pose previously unconsidered questions, leads to a searching review of established assumptions and interpretations, or points to unexplored opportunities. Raising new questions may be more important in the long run than merely devising better answers to questions that have gone stale. The very act of forecasting, if it leads to a disciplined, logical evaluation of current conditions and spotlights problems and deficiencies, is in itself of value.

Nevertheless, the user of a forecast must be wary that the forecast, whatever its intended purpose, is not biased or self-serving or nothing more than a projection of the forecaster's own personal beliefs, commitments, and prejudices. Forecasts have been made merely to enhance the prestige of the forecaster or to win for him an audience. They may be undertaken, also, to gain support for a pet project or program or acceptance for a decision already reached. Thus it is important to know not just how a forecast was made, but why it has done as well, in evaluating its worth.

The point is that if a forecast is to prove useful, either for technology assessment or for any other purpose, it must be credible. And it must be communicated to decision-makers in terms that they can relate and react to. Plausibility is more important than accuracy or sophisticated techniques and tools. Only when a forecast is believable and captures attention will anyone take serious action on it. But despite the increasing vogue of futures research, the acceptance of technological forecasting for policy making and long-term planning has been far from unanimous.

In part, the blame may rest with the forecasters themselves. Their focus on the mechanics and methodology of forecasting and their interest in turning what had heretofore been a rather arcane and obscure art form into something more of a scientific discipline is readily understandable. Yet they seem to be doing all too little to win converts or credibility. The rapidly expanding literature of technological forecasting and long-range planning is especially opaque, if not impenetrable, to the uninitiated, muddied as it is by an unfortunate tendency toward coining obscure words and acronyms.

Forecasters frequently seem more enthralled with the entertaining tasks of model building, manipulating and massaging series of data, and imposing some sort of formal, stylized structure on the seemingly random process of scientific discovery and technological innovation than they are with the more mundane chore of explaining to the world outside what their studies and speculations are all about or how they might find practical application. Increasingly sophisticated and complex methodology may appear designed, as a result, less to make forecasting more reliable and rational than to conceal its shortcomings and veil its relevance to the world at large. At the same time, excess concern with methodology may only stultify the imagination and intuition that must be an important part of even the most quantitatively based technique. Technological forecasting, in short, is in need of plainer language and of writing unencumbered by dense and tangled jargon.

The importance of forecasting, and futures research is clear if we are to see meaningful national goals and priorities, to allocate our finite resources of money and technology over an increasingly widening range of national needs, and to assess the direct and indirect consequences and benefits of accelerating technological change. The advent of technology assessment as formal, institutionalized endeavor presents forecasting with both a challenge and perhaps its greatest opportunity.

Until we learn to forecast better, progress in technology assessment will be slow and uncertain. Nevertheless, we must apply whatever methodological tools are now available as best we can, meanwhile honing them through wider use.

Economic forecasting has advanced largely because of a growing government commitment in the past quarter of a century to promoting economic growth and dampening the fluctuations of business cycles. Technological forecasting should benefit similarly once technology assessment becomes an accepted process for guiding technological growth.

Technology Assessment and Social Control

MICHAEL S. BARAM

The emerging concepts of corporate responsibility and technology assessment are, to a considerable extent, responses to problems arising from technological developments and their applications by industry and government. These problems appear in the relatively discrete sectors of consumer protection and occupational safety and in the diffuse sectors of community quality of life and the national and international environments.

CONSUMER PROTECTION

As products have become more sophisticated and defects in them less easily detected by the consumer, the common-law principle of caveat emptor, "let the buyer beware" has been largely abandoned by the courts, and the principle of strict corporate liability has been frequently adopted *(1)*. Federal and state legislation and regulatory agencies for consumer protection have multiplied with this shifting of responsibility. Nevertheless, common law, legislation, and regulation pertaining to product safety have been largely ineffective (*1*, p. 2):

1. *Final Report of National Commission on Product Safety* (Government Printing Office, Washington, D.C., 1970), pp. 73-79.

... federal authority to curb hazards in consumer products is virtually non-existent. . . legislation consists of a series of isolated acts treating specific harzards in narrow product categories. . . . Despite its humanitarian adaptations to meet the challenge of product-caused injuries, the common law puts no reliable restraint upon product hazards.

As a result, Ralph Nader and other crusaders have mobilized citizens against specific technological developments embodied in hazardous products and processes—such as the Corvair and various food additives.

The 92nd Congress enacted the Consumer Product Safety Act, thereby creating an independent commission with the authority to develop mandatory safety standards for many product categories and to carry out related functions to protect consumers (2). However, regulation of automobiles, drugs, boats, foods, and other product categories is excluded and left to existing programs. The commission is expected to maintain the regulatory agency tradition of reliance on industrial testing and reports; and "Except for the availability of [commission] information and the opportunity for litigants to argue the fact of compliance or noncompliance with mandatory Government standards, the law is expected to have little effect on products liability litigation" (3). It is too early to determine whether or not the law will bring about an effective regulatory program.

OCCUPATIONAL HEALTH AND SAFETY

The incidence of harm to workers, the difficulties of employee recovery under the common law, and the inability of the judicial system to internalize such "costs" sufficiently to bring about a preventive approach by corporate management are among the factors that led to workmen's compensation laws and insurance programs (4), and agency standards for occupational hazards. The National Labor Relations Act (5), and most recently the Occupational Safety and Health Act (6) have provided frameworks for decision-making on automation and hazardous technological developments. Nevertheless, high injury rates persist in several industrial sectors (7) as old and new technology continues to create lethal environments for employees—for example, "The

2. Public Law 92-573 (1972).

3. *U.S. Law Week*, 41 (No. 16), p. 1061 (1972).

4. See, for example, J. Sweet, in *Legal Aspects of Architecture, Engineering and the Construction Process* (West, St. Paul, Minn., 1970), sect. 30.07, pp. 634-637.

5. 29 U.S. Code 151.

6. 29 U.S. Code 651, See *Job Safety and Health Act of 1970* (Bureau of National Affairs, Washington, D.C., 1971) for collection of relevant materials.

7. D. Cordtz, *Fortune* (November 1972), p. 112.

National Academy of Sciences reports a study showing that the life-span of radiologists is five years shorter than the national average . . ." (8, p. 1,3).

The introduction of new automation technology has traditionally brought about strong union opposition because of impacts on job security (9). Now, impacts on employee health provide new bases for opposition. As a result, some new, highly automated plants have been shut down—Rio Tinto's lead processing plant in the United Kingdom and General Motors' Vega plant in Lordstown, Ohio, have recently suspended operations until the economic and the physical and mental health effects of new automation technology on employees could be determined and diminished (10).

COMMUNITY QUALITY OF LIFE

The impacts of industrial and government technology on health, land use, esthetics, and other aspects of community quality of life (11) have finally aroused organized citizen opposition. Government transportation and energy programs are now persistently opposed by local communities. Corporations that have traditionally provided the economic base for communities are now increasingly confronted by litigants seeking compensatory damages, restraining orders, and injunctions; by newly aggressive local officials responding to citizen complaints and invoking long-dormant police powers against noise, smoke, and other nuisances; and by state and federal officials enforcing air and water quality programs. Despite judicial reluctance to enjoin ongoing industrial activity that concurrently provides local economic benefits and environmental degradation (12), the expanding enforcement of public nuisance and pollution control laws has recently brought about a number of plant closures (13).

Nevertheless, the economic objectives of states and local communities and

8. As discussed by F. Grad, in *Environmental Law* (Bender, New York, 1971), pp. 1-115.

9. *Harv. Law Rev.* 84, 1822 (1971).

10. Coverage in the media has been extensive. See the 1971 and 1972 issues of *London Observer* and *New York Times*—for example, *New York Times* (7 March 1972), p. 17.

11. *Man's Health and the Environment* (Department of Health, Education, and Welfare, Washington, D.C.: 1970), pp. 97–125.

12. Boomer v. Atlantic Cement Co., 26 New York 2nd ser. 219, 257 New Eng. 2nd ser. 870 (1970) provides a classic example of judicial caution.

13. See "Economic dislocation early warning system reports" Environmental Protection Agency, Washington, D.C. (mimeographed).

the fear of job losses and other dislocations that would arise from project or plant shutdowns will continue to determine the pace at which community quality of life is rehabilitated and environmental degradation controlled (*14*). The complex task of resource management must be undertaken by state and local governments. How else to reconcile the objectives of economic and social opportunity— housing, economic development, transportation, and so on—with enhanced community quality of life—open space, recreation, esthetically pleasing surroundings, population stability? The reconciliation of such diverse objectives will not be possible until the consequences of technology can be systematically assessed, until rational siting and land use guidelines have been established, and until state and regional planning find a viable political structure.

NATIONAL ENVIRONMENTAL QUALITY

Ehrlich, Commoner, and other early crusaders may have been critically received, but nations are now embarking on serious, more effective pollution control programs. In the United States, the new water pollution control program has been designed to achieve use of the "best practicable" pollution control technology by 1977, the "best available" technology by 1983, and a national "no pollution discharge" goal by 1985 (*15*). The air quality program provides authority for federal control over new stationary sources of air pollution, over automotive emissions, and over all sources of air pollutants hazardous to human health (*16*). New legislation has established federal authority to limit the noise emissions of numerous corporate products (*17*); and laws to tighten up control over pesticides and hazardous materials have again been enacted (*18*).

The national commitment now authorizes control over most forms of pollution caused by technological processes, ensuring more rigorous analysis, regulation, enforcement, and citizen participation. Nevertheless, many tech-

---

14. Note, for example, the numerous requests for variances from air pollution control requirements by industry and chambers of commerce that are now being processed and granted.

15. Public Law 92-500 (1972).

16. 42 U.S. Code 1857, as amended by Public Law 90-148 (1967), Public Law 91-604 (1970), and Public Law 92-157 (1971).

17. Public Law 92-574 (1972).

18. Public Law 92-516 (1972).

nology-created pollution problems remain—the management and disposal of radioactive waste, toxic materials, sludge, and solid waste. In addition, new technologies such as weather modification and marine resource extraction are now being developed and experimentally applied, and they will undoubtedly create new problems and new legislation in our already "law-ridden society" (*19*, p. 32). The pattern is obvious and disturbing: the development of a technological advance, insistence upon its application by interest groups in industry and government, utilization, the appearance of environmental problems, legislation, regulation, and extensive litigation to control environmental impacts (*20*).

ASSUMPTIONS

These problems of consumers, employees, communities, and nations are the results of the processes we use to develop, apply, and regulate our technology—of our methods of social control. Social control is, in turn, the result of complex interactions of underlying political, economic, and cultural forces.

What is to be done? We can continue to grapple with the problems as they crystallize, using the established and ineffective patterns of post hoc legislation, regulation, and litigation. On the other hand, we can boldly attempt to alter the underlying forces or causes, and their interactions, but this calls for information we do not have and demands an acknowledgement that the forces at work in different political systems are yielding substantially similar problems (*21*).

The most feasible strategy appears to be one of intervening in those decision-making processes of the public and private sectors that bring about technological applications; such intervention would take the form of introducing new frameworks for planning and decision-making. The development and use of coherent frameworks for technology assessment and utilization could meet many of the demands for corporate and governmental responsibility. Clearly, the use of such frameworks will affect the underlying social

19. *Legal Systems for Environment Protection,* legislative study No. 4 (U.N. Food and Agriculture Organization, Rome, 1972), pp. 23–32.

20. Congressional recognition of the relationship between technological advance and environmental deterioration is expressed in Title I, Section 101(a) of Public Law 91-190 (1970).

21. C. S. Russell and H. H. Landsberg, *Science* 172, 1307 (1971); M. I. Goldman, *Science* 170, 37 (1970).

forces not directly confronted and will entail considerable reliance on established legal and regulatory procedures (22, 23).

The task of developing frameworks for technology assessment and utilization must be undertaken in full recognition of several realities.

1) Application of any such framework to a particular technological advance will yield differences in opinion and information from professionals, as well as from concerned citizens.

2) Continuing research, monitoring experiments, and changing designs will not necessarily resolve such differences, but will generally reveal the trans-scientific nature of decisions to be made about the further development and utilization of a specific technological advance: for example, the decisions will ultimately involve value-based consideration of the probable harm of the advance and the scope, magnitude, and acceptability of that harm (24).

3) Receptors—consumers, employees, and citizens generally—will find elitist decision-making and compensatory solutions to possible harmful effects inadequate, and they will actively seek to participate in the planning, design, and implementation stages of the technology application process.

4) A multiplicity of inadequate decision frameworks for technology assessment and utilization already exist and are employed by, for example, Congress, regulatory agency officials, corporate management, insurance rate-setters, courts, and organized citizen's groups.

Given this statement of the problem and these assumptions, it appears that the task is to somehow "get it all together"—to develop an understanding of how technology interacts with society and its institutions of social control; to demonstrate that citizens, corporations, and public institutions are all inter-

22. The council on Environmental Quality has partially defined the task (23, p. 343): "The contemporary world is to a great extent determined by technology . . . . The scale and speed of technological change may well have outstripped the ability of our institutions to control and shape the human environment . . . . It is important to understand the emerging technologies of the future and their implications for the environment and our way of life . . . . Predicting what and how new technologies will shape the future is a difficult task . . . . Even more difficult than predicting future technological developments is assessing what the full impact of any particular technology will be . . . . Despite the difficulties of assessing technology, it is essential that it be done . . . . We must develop the institutional mechanisms capable of making technology assessments . . . . " Implicit in the council's proposal is the need for new methods to be employed in the development of assessments and the need for assurance that such assessments will indeed be used in decision-making in relevant public and private institutions.

23. Council on Environmental Quality, *Environmental Quality: Third Annual Report* (Government Printing Office, Washington, D.C., 1972).

24. A. Weinberg, *Science* 177, 27 (1972).

related in specific patterns and thereby share responsibility for rational planning and decision-making; and to shape a common conceptual framework that can be readily applied by each decision-maker, in order that the different results can be compared meaningfully and used to choose knowledgeably among alternatives.

DEVELOPING A COHERENT FRAMEWORK

Technology is dependent upon processes that occur in four interrelated contexts: basic research, applied research, the development of prototypes for testing or experimentation, and ongoing production and utilization. Although it is difficult to pinpoint the path of any specific development, it is clear that most technology (in the form of processes, products, or techniques) in use today was brought about by the interactions of people and findings in these four contexts (25).

Within each context different levels and kinds of resources, or inputs are required—for example, manpower, funds, time, facilities, education, and materials—but large social and economic commitments and irreversible commitments of natural resources are usually made only when the development and experimentation phase is undertaken. These large commitments lend an inevitability to the technological advance, because few courts and federal agencies have been willing to halt major socioeconomic commitments, irrespective of hazards to individuals or society (26).

The technology that emerges subsequently brings about social and environmental effects, or outputs—direct and indirect, primary and secondary, beneficial and detrimental, measurable and unmeasurable. Whether one uses nuclear power or the snowmobile as an example of current applications of technology, several classes of effects are apparent. These include effects on health (mental and physical, somatic and genetic), economy (individual and corporate, local and national, international), environment (pollution, disruptions of ecosystems), resources (availability of materials, land, and waters for competing uses), values (changes that are ultimately reflected in new law and policy), and sociopolitical institutions and processes (structural and substantive changes). As these and other effects are aggregated, they determine the quality of life.

---

25. See, for example, *Technology in Retrospect and Critical Events in Science* (National Science Foundation, Washington, D.C., 1968).
26. B. Portnoy, *Cornell Law Rev.* 55, 861 (1970).

We have no quantifiable information on many of these effects; nor can we accurately predict potential effects, their synergism, or the intervention of exogenous forces such as population migration or natural disasters. We do not have devices sophisticated enough to monitor and assess many of these effects, nor do we have articulated goals or indices to measure progress toward such goals (23). Decisions on goals, indices, and effects are now, and will probably always remain, transscientific.

But we have learned one thing well—that impacts and amenities which are unmeasurable or unquantifiable are nevertheless real and should be as integral to decision-making as quantifiable technical and economic considerations. At the federal level, this has been clearly expressed in the National Environmental Policy Act (NEPA) of 1969 (27), which requires that "unquantified environmental amenities and values" be considered along with technological and economic or quantitative inputs to public agency decision-making on projects, permits, contracts, and other major actions when such actions are likely to result in significant environmental impacts. Agencies are now struggling with this new requirement as they develop environmental impact assessments, which are subsequently exposed to the public for review before agency action. Public response to over 3000 impact statements during the past 2 years has ranged from acquiescence, to intervention in agency proceedings, to political pressure, to extensive litigation (28).

Following this brief discussion of inputs to and outputs of the process of technological advance, a simple model can be developed which relates a specific technological development to resources (inputs) and effects (outputs) (Fig. 1).

The implementation of each program will depend on a variety of decision-makers in both public and private sectors and at varying jurisdictional levels—local, state, regional, and federal. These decision-makers function as controls on any program in essentially two ways (Fig. 2): (i) *by controlling resources* (for example, public and private sources of manpower and funds for research and development; land use and natural resource authorities; federal and state legislatures, whose enactments may be essential to the availability of other program resources; and educators, who determine training programs) and

27. 42 U.S. Code 4321.

28. See *102 Monitor*, the monthly report of the Council on Environmental Quality, for listings of environmental impact assessments and periodic reviews of litigation related to NEPA. Also see (23, pp. 221–267) for a comprehensive survey of NEPA implementation.

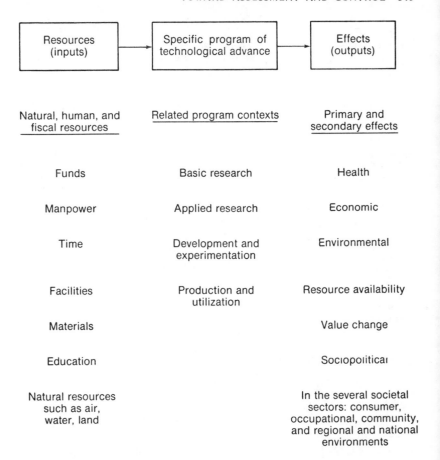

Fig. 1 RESOURCES (INPUTS) AND EFFECTS (OUTPUTS) OF TECHNOLOGICAL DEVELOPMENTS.

(ii) *by controlling the detrimental effects* (for example, the courts by means of preliminary or permanent injunctions or awards of compensatory damages; federal agencies, such as the Food and Drug Administration and the Environmental Protection Agency, and their state counterparts by engaging in standard-setting, regulation, and enforcement; and program managers, corporate management, and insurance rate-setters by bringing about program or product redesign to abate or ameliorate specific effects).

To further develop this model, some of the major influences on decision-

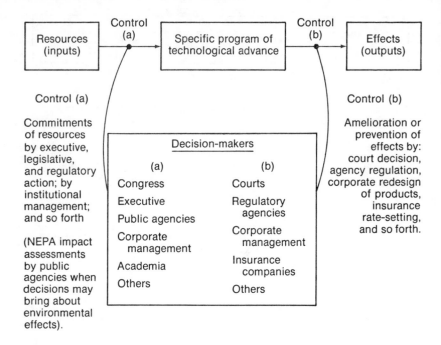

Fig. 2 DECISION-MAKERS

makers who control technological developments must be determined. These influences (Fig. 3) include information on: (i) resource availability; (ii) technical and economic feasibility; (iii) actual and potential effects; and (iv) operational-institutional values, which are comprised of the common law, legislation, economic and social policy, institutional management policies, and other "given" values that have been recognized and accepted by decision-makers as of the time any specific decision is made regarding further program development. These include diverse and often conflicting laws and policies—for example, NEPA (to foster the conservation and rational use of resources) and the oil depletion allowance (to foster rapid exploitation of resources).

To complete this general model, the social dynamics of any program of technological advance must be considered further—specifically, the responses of individual citizens and organized interest groups to perceived resource commitments and program effects (Fig. 4). These responses can be manifested through institutional procedures for changing the laws and policies that influence decision-makers—a lengthy process requiring extensive aggregation of voters or shareholders and generally undertaken in order to influence future decisions, not the particular decision that provoked the response.

Responses can also be manifested through formal, adversarial procedures to challenge decision-making—for example, injured consumers can go to court and disturbed environmentalists can intervene in agency proceedings or seek judicial review of agency decisions. Finally, a variety of informal procedures can be employed to feed back responses to decision-makers—such as demonstrations, employee absenteeism, product boycotts, consumer choice, or quasipolitical campaigns. The environmental and consumer protection movements serve as vivid examples of these new pressures on decision-makers, pressures new only in their intensity.

Citizens responding to perceived detrimental effects or resource misuse comprise a diverse group of consumers, shareholders, unions, crusaders, and citizens' organizations, ranging from those with national objectives (for

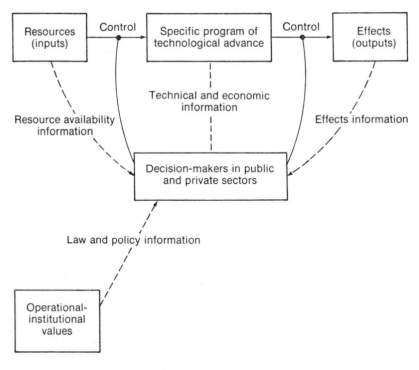

Fig. 3 INFORMATION FLOWS TO DECISION-MAKERS

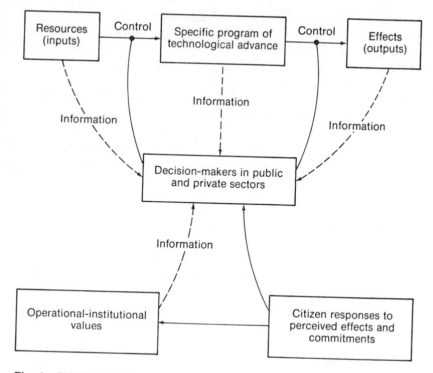

Fig. 4 SUMMARY OF INFLUENCES ON DECISION-MAKING

example, the Sierra Club) to those with local or self-interest objectives (for example, labor unions, airport neighbors). The responses manifested through institutional, formal-adversarial, or informal procedures for exerting pressure on decision-makers may, in time, become so widespread or aggregated that they will be incorporated into the common law or form the basis for new management policy or legislation and, as such, become part of the matrix of operational-institutional values. This has already occurred to a considerable extent with regard to environmental and consumer protection responses.

Although the sector of society that responds adversely to the effects of a specific technological development does not normally constitute a democratic majority in its early stages, the issues raised by such responses deserve serious consideration, and the procedures for eliciting such responses are being strengthened by the courts and legislatures. First, the responses represent new perceptions, new "pieces of the truth" that were either unknown to, ignored, or lightly considered by decision-makers. Second, they represent market and political influence that can be magnified by use of the media. Third, although they may be ignored at first, these responses will continue to appear in various forms and may bring about delays that are more costly after a program has been started (the utilities and the Atomic Energy Commission, for example, are now finding this out as they attempt to further the nuclear power program; plant construction and operation are running more than 2 years behind schedule, with greatly increased costs, because of extensive litigation and hearings (29), which resulted from an earlier failure to consider citizens' concern about thermal and radioactive waste disposal, reactor safety, and related ecological and health issues). Fourth, such responses are based on real concerns, will often find larger public support, and eventually could result in stringent legislation or judicial findings that decision-makers would have to live with (30).

Finally, a citizenry that expresses a diversity of interests is the most effective mode of promoting the accountability of decision-makers to the full social context in which they operate. Too often, decision-makers in all institutions have failed to inform the public about the bases and risks of decisions, thereby precluding feedback of larger social issues and humanistic concerns in their effort to promote institutional or self-interest objectives (31). But the benefits of an informed and responsive public have now been adequately demonstrated. Cars will be cleaner by 1975; the Army Corps of Engineers will not continue to dam rivers and spend public funds without more rigorous analysis of impacts and needs; the Food and Drug Administration will begin informing the public of the chemical contents and quality control criteria of specific consumer products they regulate; maximum permissible exposures of workers and the public to power-plant radiation have been falling. These are some of the recent "accountability" benefits that are being derived from public pressure.

29. No data available at this time. Statement based on conversations with professionals familiar with nuclear power program.

30. See, for example, Calvert Cliffs Coordinating Committee v. Atomic Energy Commission, 449 Fed. Rep., 2nd ser. 1109 (D.C. Cir. Ct. 1971).

31. As Senator Sam Ervin (D–N.C.) has said: "When the people do not know what their government is doing, those who govern are not accountable for their actions—and accountability is basic to the democratic system. By using devices of secrecy, the government attains the power to 'manage' the news and through it to manipulate public opinion. Such power is not consonant with a nation of free men . . . and the ramifications of a growing policy of governmental secrecy is extremely dangerous to our liberty" [The Nation (8 November 1971), p. 456].

Decision-making in both public and private institutions supporting technological programs and applications is becoming more complicated and less efficient, in the institutional, short-term sense; but long-term efficiencies, in terms of larger social interests such as public health, can be expected. In more pragmatic economic and political terms, it has become increasingly apparent that it is in the long-term self-interest of decision-makers and their institutions to be open and responsive to the interests of the public. As David Rockefeller has defined the issue for the private sector (32):

> The question really comes down to this: Will business leaders seize the initiative to make necessary changes and take on new responsibilities voluntarily, or will they wait until these are thrust upon them by law? Some adjustments are inevitable . . . there may have to be new laws to force consideration of the quality-of-life dimension so that more socially responsive firms will not suffer a competitive disadvantage. It is up to the businessman to make common cause with other reformers . . . to initiate necessary reforms that will make it possible for business to continue to function in a new climate as a constructive force in our society.

In the public sector, opposition to projects and the failing credibility of programs have prompted several agencies to increase citizen participation in program planning and design—beyond the environmental impact statement requirements of NEPA (33).

The model I have presented (Fig. 4) does not provide any answers, but it can be used for several purposes: to widen the perceptions of planners, designers, and decision-makers responsible for specific technological advances and applications; to depict the interrelationships of resources, effects, decision-makers, institutions, and citizens; to develop policy, management, or program alternatives in the corporate, congressional, and public agency sectors that support and regulate technological development and utilization; and to assess, with public participation, the impacts of technological developments before they are utilized. Above all, the model articulates an accounting system, or framework, for decision-making that is dynamic and that can be used by all of the decision-makers, irrespective of their interests. The model has also proved helpful in the development of curricula and research: by making possible the ordering and integration of diverse perspectives and events and by providing an understanding of the patterns of technological develop-

---

32. Boston Globe (5 May 1972), p. 17.

33. See Congr. Rec., 5 October 1972, p. 517059, regarding the Corps of Engineers and Policy and Procedure Memorandum 90–1 (Department of Transportation, Washington, D.C., 1972) regarding the federal highway program.

ment, application, and impacts, as well as social responses to technology. This understanding extends to technology in general, as well as to developments in such specific areas as mariculture, housing, and bioengineering (*34*).

REFORMS IN PROCESS

A number of recent legal developments can be related directly to the model, particularly to the sector designated "citizen responses to perceived effects and commitments" of technology. For citizen responses to be responsible, the flow of information to the public about effects and commitments—actual and potential—must be coherent and balanced, and it must present alternatives with their uncertainties in comparable terms. For citizen responses to be meaningful, the processes of planning, design, and decision-making must be accessible to citizens and open to their concerns.

For example, NEPA requires federal agencies to assess environmental impacts before "major actions" are taken. These actions range from the Atomic Energy Commission's approval of a construction license for a nuclear plant to be built by a utility, to the funding of increments of the highway program by the Department of Transportation, to authorization by the Department of Agriculture for the use of herbicides and pesticides. The responsibility for assessment is broad and must include full consideration of five issues (*35*):

1) potential environmental impacts,
2) unavoidable adverse impacts,
3) irreversible commitments of resources,
4) short-term use considerations versus long-term resource needs, and
5) alternatives to the proposed action.

Draft and final impact assessments are made available to other governmental officials and to the public for review and further development under guidelines established by the Council on Environmental Quality (*36, 37*). Although NEPA does not provide veto power to any official, even if the project poses real environmental hazards, the act does provide new informa-

---

34. The model is being used in the presentation of "Law and the social control of science and technology" and "Legal aspects of environmental quality," two graduate courses, and in several research projects at M.I.T. by the author.
35. Public Law 91–190 (1970), sect. 102 (2) (c).
36. *Fed. Reg.* 36, 7724 (23 April 1971).
37. Council on Environmental Quality, "Memorandum for agency and general counsel liaison on NEPA matters" (mimeographed), 16 May 1972.

tion to the public—by exposing the extent to which environmental effects are being considered by the agency—and provides an enlarged record for judicial review of agency decisions. Obvious deficiencies in an agency's procedure, the scope of its statement, or the content of its statement will, on the basis of experience since NEPA was enacted, result in citizen intervention in agency processes, political opposition, and litigation. Many projects proposed and assessed have been delayed, and, in some cases, projects have been abandoned. Other projects have proceeded after being redesigned to ameliorate those effects on the environment that generated controversy (*23*, pp. 221–267).

Most projects involve applications of existing technology, but a few involve the development of new technologies—for example, the Department of Transportation's air cushion vehicle, the Atomic Energy Commission's liquid metal fast breeder reactor, cloud seeding experiments of the National Science Foundation and the National Oceanic and Atmospheric Administration, and the use of polyvinylchloride containers, to be approved by the Internal Revenue Service, for alcoholic beverages *(38)*.

NEPA does not expressly require consideration of social, health, or economic impacts or of secondary effects such as subsequent population migration and land development. These considerations are frequently ignored or treated in cursory fashion, even though they are integral to comprehensive assessment of project impacts and decision-making. NEPA does not impose assessment and exposure processes on industry or the private sector, but, whenever a utility, corporation, or other private institution is the applicant or intended beneficiary of federal agency funds, license, or other "major action," its proposal is subject to the NEPA process. There have been suggestions that NEPA be extended directly to the private sector, but as yet these have not been seriously considered at the federal level. However, variants of NEPA have been adopted by several states, and more states are expected to follow suit (*39*). Because of state and local control of land use, state versions of NEPA have the potential for directly affecting land develop-

---

38. See the *102 Monitor* of the Council on Environmental Quality for abstracts of draft and final impact assessments, some of which grapple with new technological developments.

39. See *102 Monitor 1* (No. 6), 1 (July 1971) for action by six jurisdictions. Since this review, Massachusetts has adopted its version of NEPA; Chap. 781 of Massachusetts Acts of 1972, amending Chap. 30 of Massachusetts General Laws. Connecticut is now considering similar action.

ment activities in the private sector. This potential has been realized in California, where the state supreme court has determined that the state's Environmental Quality Act requires county boards of supervisors to conduct environmental assessments before issuing building permits for housing projects and other land developments to the private sector (40). Similar requirements may apply to the private sector in Massachusetts, where the new environmental assessment requirements are imposed on "political sub-divisions" as well as on state agencies and officials (41).

Therefore, the model can be further developed by adding environmental impact assessments by public decision-makers at the point where resources are to be committed to certain types of projects that apply "old" technology, as well as to certain activities that will involve the further advance or appli-cation of new technology. Concomitantly, the flow of information to citizens has been enhanced.

The development of impact statements is a meaningless exercise unless they are actually used in decision-making (42). It is difficult to use impact statements because of the diversity and the essentially unquantifiable nature of the new factors they present—since most agency decision-making depends on quantification of technical and economic factors (37). The use of impact statements in the last stage of a project, such as the awarding of construction contracts, is deceptive. The earlier stages of planning and design may not have included assessment, thereby precluding citizen inputs at a time when more important changes in project plans and alternatives could have been accom-

40. Friends of Mammoth v. Mono County, 4 Environ. Rep. Cases 1593, Calif. S. Ct. (1972).

41. Chap. 30, Massachusetts General Laws, sect. 62.

42. In Calvert Cliffs Coordinating Committee v. AEC (30), the court's ruling included discussion of the "balancing process" that agencies must undertake in project decision-making to comply fully with NEPA, in addition to procedural compliance in the development of impact assessment: "The sort of consideration of environmental values which NEPA compels is clarified in Section 102(2) (A) and (B). In general, all agencies must use a 'systematic, interdisciplinary approach' to environmental planning and evaluation 'in decision-making which may have an impact on man's environment.' In order to include all possible environmental factors in the decisional equation, agencies must 'identify and develop methods and procedures . . . which will insure that presently unquantified environmental amenities and values be given appropriate con-sideration in decision-making along with economic and technical considerations.' 'Environmental amenities' will often be in conflict with 'economic and technical considerations.' To 'consider' the former 'along with' the latter must involve a balancing process. In some instances environmental costs may outweigh economic and technical benefits and in other instances they may not. But NEPA mandates a rather finely tuned and 'systematic' balancing analysis in each instance."

plished. In other words, effective use of impact assessment techniques and citizen feedback can be more readily achieved in the earlier, less tangible stages of a project—precisely when most agencies prefer to plan and design without public intervention. Hopefully, litigation and subsequent judicial review will impose the NEPA framework earlier in agency processes *(43)*.

Further difficulties with the NEPA process have become apparent. There is an inherent conflict in the requirement that the agency proponent of a project assess it and discuss alternatives. After all, the agency has already selected an alternative and has undertaken the impact assessment essentially to justify its choice. Subsequent discussion of alternatives is too often a superficial process of setting up "straw alternatives" for facile criticism. Clearly, independent review of all the alternatives, including the proposed agency action, would be desirable. However, independent review would also require the structuring of new agency procedures and independent institutions for assessment *(44)*.

Finally, the problem of dealing with unquantifiable impacts remains. The assignment of values and weights to environmental and social amenities may either be arbitrary or intentionally designed to produce decisions that had been predetermined by agency officials.

Despite these difficulties and the numerous conflicts and increased costs that now attend agency programs, NEPA is slowly forcing wiser environmental practices, more sensitive agency bureaucracies, and more effective roles for citizens. It is possible that the NEPA process could eventually

43. See, for example, Stop H-3 Association v. Volpe, 4 Environ. Rep. Cases 1684 (1972), where the U.S. District Court for Hawaii held that highway project design work and further test borings be enjoined until an impact assessment has been developed and used, since such work "would increase the stake which . . . agencies already have in the [project]" and reduce any subsequent consideration of alternatives.

44. M. Baram and G. Barney, *Technol. Rev.* 73 (No. 7), 48 (1971).

45. The "Leopold Matrix" is a useful mechanism for promoting rational discussion and systemic resolution of project impacts by the proponents and opponents of a project in a nonadversarial setting. The matrix disaggregates impacts, calls for designation of probability of magnitude and significance of each impact, and can be completed by each of the interested parties in a project controversy. Comparative analysis of the results reveals important areas of difference of opinion and enables the parties to consider a variety of strategies for reducing these differences, such as design change or the need for concurrent projects to offset specific impacts. For example, waste water from a housing project may be one of the bases for community opposition, yet state and federal funds and programs may be available to reduce the problem. See *A Procedure for Evaluating Environmental Impact,* circular No. 645 (U.S. Geological Survey, Washington, D.C., 1971). Also see P. Bercano (unpublished manuscript, 1971) for application of the "Leopold Matrix" to technology assessment.

provide the basis, not for conflict in the courtroom or at agency hearings, but for negotiation in good faith between interested parties over points of dispute as revealed by the environmental assessment (45). The resolution of labor-management conflicts under the National Labor Relations Board provides useful experience that should be reviewed for possible application to the NEPA context.

A major extension of NEPA practices to the assessment of new technology may have been accomplished with the passage of the Technology Assessment Act of 1972 (46). This law established within the legislative branch an Office of Technology Assessment (OTA) to ". . . provide early indications of the probable beneficial and adverse impacts of the applications of technology and to develop other coordinate information which may assist the Congress. . . . " The office is required to undertake several tasks (46, sect. 3):

1) identifying existing or probable impacts of technology or technological programs;

2) where possible, ascertaining cause and effect relationships;

3) identifying alternative technological methods of implementing specific programs;

4) identifying alternative programs for achieving requisite goals;

5) estimating and comparing the impacts of alternative methods and programs;

6) presenting findings of completed analyses to the appropriate legislative authorities;

7) identifying areas where additional research or data collection is required . . . ;

8) undertaking . . . additional associated activities . . .

Assessments to be carried out " . . . shall be made available to the initiating . . . or other appropriate committees of the Congress . . . [and] may be made available to the public . . . " (46).

The law does not distinguish between technological developments in the public agency and private sectors and presumably includes technology being developed with private funds. Although provided with the authority to subpoena witnesses, OTA " . . . shall not, itself, operate any laboratories, pilot plants, or test facilities." The broad language of the assessment requirements

46. Public Law 92-484 (1972). For the text of the bill and relevant background, see U.S. Senate, Committee on Rules and Administration, subcommittee on computer services, *Office of Technology Assessment for the Congress* (92nd Congr. 2nd sess., 2 March 1972).

and the way in which assessments are used by Congress effectively preclude a substantial replication of the litigation and other conflicts that have characterized the NEPA experience.

Political conditions will inevitably determine the initiation of OTA studies and their use by congressional committees, and it appears that the public will, in general, be unable to secure judicial review to promote accountability of OTA and Congress.

The burden of formulating guidelines to describe when OTA should be called upon by Congress and prescribing procedures for providing information to the public clearly lies with the OTA board and advisory council. Above all, it appears essential that OTA develop and articulate a coherent framework for all technology assessments to be undertaken. Such a framework would prevent OTA assessments from becoming skillfully contrived, ad hoc case studies, which would be essentially closed to the introduction of important information from citizens and interest groups. OTA therefore has the additional burden of laying out a framework that will replace the multiple, partial models employed by different interests, that will promote inputs from interdisciplinary and humanistic sources, and that will clearly present, in a replicable format, the quantifiable and unquantifiable costs and benefits of new technological developments and applications.

Procedures to enhance the flow of balanced information on technological developments to the public will inevitably face the problem of information manipulation and secrecy practices (47).

The public's need for information is especially great in the field of science and technology, for the growth of specialized scientific knowledge threatens to outstrip our collective ability to control its effects on our lives.

Secrecy on the part of public agencies and the executive branch is still common practice to protect decision-making processes from public criticism, despite the 1967 Freedom of Information Act (48). However, sustained public pressures for the release of nonclassified information have made such secrecy more controversial and somewhat more difficult to justify. The recent passage of the Federal Advisory Committee Act may bring about the diminution of another important form of secrecy in the public sector—

47. Soucie v. David, 2 Environ. Rep. Cases 1626 (D.C. Cir. Ct., 1971).
48. 5 U.S. Code 552.

agency advisory committee proceedings and recommendations, which are used in setting standards and other decision processes (*49*).

The common law of trade secrets is similarly invoked to protect corporate information—presumably from the competition (the common law basis for the concept) (*50*), but increasingly from the public and government. The Environmental Protection Agency has been unable to secure information on the quantities of polychlorinated biphenyls (PCB's) made and sold by the one American manufacturer, despite evidence that PCB's are now part of the international pollution problem (*51*). In other industrial technology sectors, however, congressional legislation has provided the government with access to information and procedures normally cloaked by trade secrecy. For example, section 206(c) of the Clean Air Act (*16*) provides that the Environmental Protection Agency may:

. . . enter at reasonable times, any plant or other establishment of such [auto engine]

49. Public Law 92–463 (1972) and Executive Order 11686 (1972). Also see U.S. House of Representatives, Committee on Government Operations, *Advisory Committees* (92nd Congr., 2nd sess., 4 November 1971).

50. M. Baram, *Harv. Bus. Rev.* 46 (No. 6), 66 (1968).

51. *Chlorinated Hydrocarbons in the Marine Environment* (National Academy of Sciences, Washington, D.C., 1971), p. 17: "Recommendation: Removal of obstacles to public access to chemical production data. Among the causes contributing to the lack of available data on the chlorinated hydrocarbons is a legal structure that allows manufacturers of a given material, when there are no more than two producers, the right to hold their production figures as privileged information.* The panel recognizes the economic rationale that deters the release of production figures by such manufacturers and understands that our government is charged by law with the protection of their proprietary interest. Indeed, we approve the principle that governmental action should not artificially affect competition. However, we also feel that there are times when it is not in the public interest for government to maintain as privileged data that are necessary for research into the state of our environment and for an assessment of its condition. In that regard, we recognize the possibility that it is not always competitive concerns alone that determine the less than candid posture assumed by industry concerning production figures. We recommend that the laws relating to the registration of chemical substances and to the release of production figures by the Department of Commerce and the Bureau of the Census be reexamined and revised in the light of existing evidence of environmental deterioration. The protection afforded manufacturers by government is an artificial obstacle to effective environmental management, particularly with reference to the polychlorinated hydrocarbons. In view of other impediments—technological, methodological, and financial—such protection is clearly inappropriate."

*For example, the Monsanto Chemical Company has refused to release its production figures for PCB's, although requested to do so by many scientists and government officials manufacturer, for the purpose of conducting tests of vehicles or engines in the hands of the manufacturer or . . . to inspect . . . records, files, papers, processes, controls, and facilities used by such manufacturer in conducting tests . . . [regarding motor vehicle and engine compliance with EPA regulations].

A similar section in the 1972 Water Pollution Control Act (*15*, sect. 308) also provides the Environmental Protection Agency access to secret information held by water polluters. It appears that Congress is now aware of trade secrecy as an obstruction to pollution control and is willing to begin limiting the antisocial uses of secrecy to some extent.

Finally, trade secrecy, in its present forms, will certainly obstruct the development of meaningful "corporate social audits" that David Rockefeller and other industrial leaders have called for. Legal sanctions for corporate secrecy obviously must be challenged if corporate responsibility and technology assessment are to be realized.

Beyond secrecy lies the problem of corporate advertising for new products and technological processes. Here, too, developments in the courts and regulatory agencies indicate that better information must be provided the public. The rapid evolution of the "Fairness Doctrine" now means that radio and television broadcast licenses must make reasonable and fair presentations of the contrasting sides of a controversial issue, once such issue has been raised (usually by advertising) on licensee broadcast time. As expressed in a recent law review note: "This obligation is incurred even at the licensee's expense if no sponsorship is available . . . [although] the licensee has discretion to determine how the contrasting sides will be presented and who will be the spokesman" (*52*, p. 109).

The doctrine has been applied by federal courts to cases of product advertising (cigarettes, large-engine automobiles, and high-test gasolines) in which it was felt that only one side of a controversial issue—the effect of such products on public health—was being presented by Federal Communications Commission (FCC) licensees in the form of advertisements. In the case of cigarettes, Banzhaff v. FCC (*53*), the court noted that its ruling for equal time for countercommercials or presentations promoted the first amendment policy of fostering the widest possible debate and dissemination of information on matters of public importance. In the case of commercials

52. B. Wiggins, *Natur. Resour. J.* 12 (No. 1), 108 (1972).
53. 405 Fed. Rep. 2nd ser. 1082 (1968); certiorari denied, 396 Supreme Ct. 824 (1969).

for automobiles and high-octane gasolines, the court noted, "When . . . the hazards to health implicit in air pollution are enlarged and aggravated by such products, then the parallel with cigarette advertising is exact . . . " (*54*) and ignored possible impacts on advertising and licensees as it sent the case back to the FCC for redetermination.

The idea that broadcast licensees should present balanced information on advertised but controversial technological processes or products is now a reality. Once again, the flow of information to the public, as indicated on the model (Fig. 5), is being enhanced and new corporate attitudes and advertising practices should follow. (The NEPA, OTA, secrecy, and "Fairness" developments can now be depicted on the model.)

54. Friends of the Earth v. Federal Communications Commission, 2 Environ. Rep. Cases 1969 (D.C., Cir. Ct., 1971).

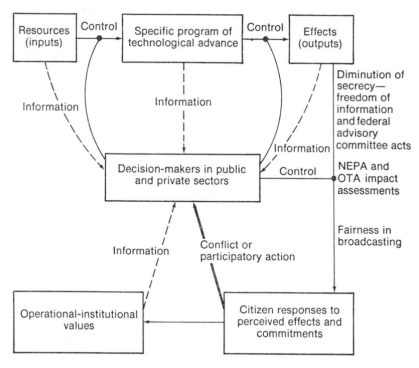

Fig. 5 SUMMARY OF INFLUENCES AND RECENT DEVELOPMENTS FOR DECISION-MAKING

How will this enhanced flow of information be used by citizens responding to the effects of technology? What will be the nature and forms of the resulting new pressures on decision-makers?

On the model, the broad arrow from citizens to decision-makers represents not a flow of information, but adversarial processes in courts and agency proceedings. For decision-makers to learn from an endless series of adversarial processes is a slow, costly, and painful task that benefits only lawyers. The task facing the public sector and corporate decision-makers who are responsible for applications of technology is to transform this relationship from an adversarial one to one of joint decision-making and negotiation of differences in good faith among all interested parties—in short, to establish an ongoing dialogue and joint effort at assessing and planning the uses of technology (55). This effort will require new institutional management procedures, the development of more sophisticated assessment techniques, the articulation of assumptions by decision-makers, an opening up of project or program planning and design stages, and, ultimately, structural and substantive changes in the political system.

"Who speaks for the public?" will become a central issue—one that the federal agencies and the courts are now grappling with in the context of NEPA (56). Perhaps technology itself may provide some assistance here. Citizen-feedback technology exists, has been used experimentally, and has demonstrated a remarkable potential for both informing citizens and eliciting

55. Of course, the achievement of a consensus is not sufficient to ensure responsible decisions; there must also be an integration of technical perspectives on long-term material and individual needs, which may have been ignored by the parties to the consensus. Such needs are usually too remote (for example, teratogenic effects) or hidden (for example, ground water depletion) to be accorded full consideration by project proponents and citizen adversaries.

56. See Sierra Club v. Morton, 45 Supreme Ct. 727 (1972), wherein the Supreme Court provided the latest answer to when " . . . a party has a sufficient stake in an otherwise justiciable controversy to obtain judicial resolution of that controversy . . . . " The court noted that injury other than economic harm is sufficient to bring a person within the zone of standing; that merely because an injury is widely shared by the public does not preclude an individual from asserting it as a basis for personal standing; that injury sufficient for standing can include esthetic, conservational, and recreational injury, as well as economic and health injury. But the court noted that " . . . broadening the categories of injury that may be alleged in support of standing is a different matter from abandoning the requirement that the party seeking review must have himself suffered the injury . . ." and that " . . . a party seeking review must allege facts showing that he is himself adversely affected . . ." in order to prevent litigation by those " . . . who seek to do no more than vindicate their value preferences through the judicial process."

opinions and information useful for decision-making (57). The enhanced process orientation that could result from applications of the recommended model, improved information flow, and new citizen-feedback techniques would ensure continuing recognition in decision-making of the pervasive social impacts of technology.

Can these numerous, fragmented developments in technology and in our legal and political systems be integrated into a coherent framework for the social control of technology? It has been noted that (58, p. 729):

... two major intellectual developments of the 17th century occurred almost simultaneously in law and science. The first was the drive for systematic arrangements and presentation of existing knowledge into scientifically organized categories . . . the second . . . was the concern with degrees of certainty or . . . probability . . . . By the end of the 17th century . . . traditional views . . . had been upset and new methods of determining truth and investigating the natural world had replaced those that had been accepted for centuries . . . there was a strong movement toward arranging both concepts and data into some rational ordering that could be easily communicated and fitted into the materials of other fields so that a universal knowledge might emerge . . . traditions of legal history and legal argumentation that assume the law's autonomous march through history are seriously in need of correction . . . .

It is now time to replicate this experience, develop a coherent framework for the social control of technology, and ensure that forthcoming processes of technology assessment and utilization will be systematic and humane.

57. T. Sheridan, "Technology for group dialogue and social choice," M.I.T. report to the National Science Foundation on grant GT-16, "Citizen feedback and opinion formulation," 1974; and D. Ducsik, N. Lemmelshtrich, M. Goldsmith, E. Jochem, "Class exercise simulating community participation in decision-making on large projects: radiation case study" (unpublished manuscript, 1972).

58. B. Shapiro, *Stanford Law Rev.* 21, 727 (1969).

59. I wish to thank Dennis W. Ducsik, a doctoral candidate in the department of civil engineering at M.I.T. who is pursuing an interdisciplinary program in environmental resource management and technology assessment, for his help as a research assistant in the project and in the development of this article. I also wish to acknowledge the support of the National Endowment for the Humanities (grant No. EO-5809-71-265).

Participatory Technology

JAMES D. CARROLL

In recent decades the idea of the alienation and estrangement of man from society has emerged as one of the dominant ideas of contemporary social thought. While interpretations of the concept of social alienation vary, Etzioni (*1*) has expressed the core of the idea as "the unresponsiveness of the world to the actor, which subjects him to forces he neither comprehends nor guides.... Alienation ... is not only a feeling of resentment and disaffection but also an expression of the objective conditions which subject a person to forces beyond his understanding and control."

There is considerable speculative and observational testimony and some empirical evidence (*2*) that the scope and complexities of science and technology are contributing to the development of social alienation in contemporary society. Keniston (*3*), for example, suggests that technology and its effects have been a factor in the alienation of many young people. At the same time he notes that the attitude of many young people toward technology is ambivalent because a revolt against the effects of technology must inevitably exploit the technology it opposes. In a different vein, de Jouvenel *(4)* has testified to the adverse psychological impact of scientific and technological complexities on sustaining general confidence in one's judgment. "Because science saps such individual confidence, we have a problem, which I feel we can meet but which it would be imprudent to deny." In a more general observation Mesthene (*5*) recently has referred to "the antitechnology spirit that is abroad in the land."

1. A. Etzioni, *The Active Society* (Free Press, New York, 1968), pp. 617–622.

2. The best review is E. Chaszer, *Science and Technology in the Theories of Social and Political Alienation* (George Washington Univ., Washington, D.C. 1969). See also V. C. Ferkiss, *Technological Man: The Myth and the Reality* (Braziller, New York, 1969), and H. M. Sapolsky, *Science* 162, 427 (1968).

3. K. Keniston, *The Uncommitted: Alienated Youth in American Society* (Harcourt, Brace & World, New York, 1968): *Young Radicals* (Harcourt, Brace & World, New York, 1968). See also T. Roszak, *The Making of a Counter Culture* (Doubleday, New York, 1969).

4. B. de Jouvenel, in *Science and Society*. E. Vavoulis and A. Colver, Eds. (Holden-Day, San Francisco, 1966), p. 85.

5. E. Mesthene, *Technology Assessment* (hearings before the Subcommittee on

PARTICIPATORY TECHNOLOGY

In this article I analyze the incipient emergence of participatory technology as a countervailing force to technological alienation in contemporary society. I interpret participatory technology as one limited aspect of a more general search for ways of making technology more responsive to the felt needs of the individual and of society. The term *participatory technology* refers to the inclusion of people in the social and technical processes of developing, implementing, and regulating a technology, directly and through agents under their control, when the people included assert that their interests will be substantially affected by the technology and when they advance a claim to a legitimate and substantial participatory role in its development or redevelopment and implementation. The basic notion underlying the concept is that participation in the public development, use, and regulation of technology is one way in which individuals and groups can increase their understanding of technological processes and develop opportunities to influence such processes in appropriate cases. Participatory technology is not an entirely new social phenomenon, but the evidence reviewed below suggests that its scope and impact may be increasing in contemporary society.

I first analyze several facts of which people are becoming increasingly aware that suggest why participatory technology is emerging as a trend, and I then analyze different forms of this trend. Finally, I evaluate some of its implications.

UNDERLYING REALIZATIONS

One primary reason for the emergence of participatory technology is the realization that technology often embodies and expresses political value choices that, in their operations and effects, are binding on individuals and groups, whether such choices have been made in political forums or elsewhere. In the language of contemporary political science, by "political value choices" I mean choices that result in the authoritative allocation of values and benefits in society. In its most significant forms politics culminates in the determination and expression of social norms and values in the form of public law, public order, and governmental action. To an indeterminate extent, tech-

Science, Research, and Development of the House Committee on Science and Astronautics, 91st Congress, 1st Session) (Government Printing Office, Washington, D.C., 1969), p. 246.

nological processes in contemporary society have become the equivalent of a form of law—that is, an authoritative or binding expression of social norms and values from which the individual or a group may have no immediate recourse. What is at issue in the case of the computer and privacy, the supersonic transport and noise levels, highway development and the city, the antiballistic missile and national security, and the car and pollution is the authoritative allocation of social values and benefits in technological form.

The second realization is a correlative of the first. Technological processes frequently are the de facto locus of political choice. They are often political processes in which issues are posed and resolved in technical terms. In the absence of appropriately structured political processes for identifying and debating the value choices implicit in what appear to be technical alternatives technical processes become, by default, the locus of political value decisions. In the context of a concern for the environment, technical questions of waste disposal systems involve value choices. In the context of a concern for urban development, technical questions of highway location and development involve value choices. In the context of a concern for privacy, technical questions of data collection and retrieval involve value choices. Technological processes often embody significant value questions that are difficult to identify and resolve in public forums because the processes are technically complex and occur in administrative organizations to which citizens do not have easy access.

Third, there is the realization that the public order of industrial society is not particularly well structured for identifying, publicizing, and resolving in public forums political questions implicit in technological processes. The public order of industrial society is founded on, and perpetuates, values, compromises, and perceptions that are being rendered obsolete by transformation of the social and political conditions from which they were derived. The public order of industrial society preeminently expresses perceptions of material need and the values of economic growth—perceptions and values rooted in the experience of material want and economic insecurity of past generations. Because of the development of powerful technologies of production, and because of other factors, these perceptions and values, as embedded and expressed in public institutions and processes, do not encompass the total area of concern, which is expanding to include the quality of the environment, race, urban development, population growth, educational opportunity, the direction of technology, and other matters. Established means of structuring and expressing political concern themselves often border on obsolescence, because they are often based on geographical and functional jurisdictions that are unrelated to the issues on which the public must take action. If these jurisdictions were otherwise defined—for example, were defined to include an entire metropolitan area—they might provide the structure for more effective representation of diverse views and might facilitate public action through bargaining and tradeoffs.

Today, in the face of population growth and technological complexity, legislative bodies, except in unusual cases such as that of the antiballistic missile, delegate to administrative agencies the responsibility for regulating, developing, and controlling technology. The general objectives of these administrative agencies involve mixed questions of value and technique, and the agencies resolve such questions in terms of their bearing on realization of the general objectives. Often the general objectives further the interests of individuals and groups allied with a particular agency. To the Department of Defense the question of the desirability of developing, maintaining, and transporting chemical and biological agents is primarily a matter of national defense policy. It is not primarily a question of the humaneness of such agents, or of their ultimate effects on the environment, or of their value or threat to man in contexts other than that of national defense.

By default, the responsibility for scrutinizing mixed questions of technology and value from the perspective of societal well-being often passes to special-interest groups and to individuals who may or may not be in a position, or be well equipped, to learn of and to influence such decisions. This is one aspect of the more general phenomenon of the devolution of authority from public representatives and administrators to "private" groups and individuals in contemporary society.

Fourth, there is the realization that, in contemporary society, political action directed toward the achievement of political value objectives, such as the production of 2.6 million housing units a year, often depends on the ability to translate the desired objective into technical tasks. Marcuse (6) observes that "the historical achievement of science and technology has rendered possible the *translation of values* into technical tasks—the materialization of values. Consequently, what is at stake is the redefinition of values in *technical terms,* as elements in the technological process. The new ends, as technical ends, would then operate in the project and in the construction of the machinery, and not only in its utilization [emphasis in the original]."

To a considerable extent, the achievement of more effective processes of

6. H. Marcuse, *One Dimensional Man* (Beacon, Boston, 1964), p. 232.

education, housing, delivery of health care, postal service, public safety, and urban development depends on the political and technological capacity of contemporary society to agree on, and to translate, value objectives into technological acts. Traditional legislative declarations of intent are not sufficient. The establishment of a right to a decent home in a suitable environment requires more than a legislative act declaring that such a right exists. It also depends on the development of technical capability to translate the right into reality.

This does not mean that, in the formulation of political objectives, a technological, problem-oriented mode of thought must replace humanistic, intuitive, moral, and other modes of thought. It means that other modes of thought often depend for realization in public life and action on their expression in technical form, and that the development and control of that form is itself a political value-oriented act.

Fifth, there is the realization that the status enjoyed by technology as an agent for both bringing about and legitimatizing social change contributes to the growth of participatory technology. There is a tendency, stressed by Ellul (7), Rickover (8), and others, for contemporary man to accept change in technological form as inevitable and irresistible. In some cases, new technologies probably are accepted because of the specific results they produce for the individual, such as the mobility that, under some conditions, is made possible by the automobile. But there seems to be an additional social, psychological, and economic element at work—what Ellul calls "technological anaesthesia"—that generates acceptance of technological innovation irrespective of the particular effects that may result. Many people seem willing to use cars in urban areas even though such use may contribute little to mobility and may adversely affect the environment and health. It seems paradoxical but true that, while some changes in institutions and behavior are strongly resisted, other changes often are readily accepted when a technological element in the situation is the agent of change.

Participatory technology is one limited way of raising questions about the specific technological forms in terms of which social change is brought about. It is directed toward the development of processes and forums that are consistent with the expectations and values of the participatory individuals, who may resort to them in the absence of other means of making their views known. In participatory technology, however, as in other participatory

7. J. Ellul, *The Technological Society* (Knopf, New York, 1964).
8. H. Rickover, *Amer. Behav. Scientist,* 8, 3 (1965).

processes, the opportunity to be heard is not synonymous with the right to be obeyed.

I here analyze three kinds of activities to illustrate some of the empirical referents of the concept of participatory technology.

LITIGATION

The first is the citizen lawsuit, directed toward the control and guidance of technology. As Sax (9) indicates, "The citizen-initiated lawsuit is . . . principally an effort to open the decision-making process to a wider constituency and to force decision-making into a more open and responsive forum. . . . [The] courts are sought out as an instrumentality whereby complaining citizens can obtain access to a more appropriate forum for decision-making."

The courts, of course, rely heavily on adversary proceedings, various forms of which have been suggested (10) as appropriate for handling scientific and technological issues involving the public interest. Not only can litigation restrict the use of technology, it can also lead to the modification and redevelopment of existing technology and stimulate the development of new technology to satisfy social values expressed in the form of legal norms, such as a right to privacy.

The legal response to cases involving technology has taken two forms. The first is an extension of those aspects of the legal doctrine of standing which determine who has a right to be heard in court on particular issues involving activities undertaken or regulated by public agencies. The second is a search by legal scholars, practicing lawyers, and judges for systems of conceptual correspondence in the terms of which scientific and technological developments and activities can be conceptualized and evaluated as changes in social values and norms that may warrant a legal response. The appropriate role of law in the regulation of genetic experimentation is an example.

An extension of the doctrine of standing has occurred in several recent

9. J. Sax, *Ann. Amer. Acad. Polit. Soc. Sci.* 389, 72 (1970).

10. J. Conant, *Science and Common Sense* (Yale Univ. Press, New Haven, 1961); J. Killian, in *Science as a Cultural Force*, H. Woolf, Ed. (Johns Hopkins Press, Baltimore, 1964); A. Kantrowitz, *Science* 156, 763 (1967); H. Wheeler, *Center Mag.* 2, 59 (1969); H. Green, in *Technology Assessment: The Proceedings of a Seminar Series*, R. C. Kasper, Ed. (George Washington Univ., Washington, D.C., 1969). See also H. W. Jones, Ed., *Law and the Social Role of Science* (Rockefeller Univ. Press, New York, 1966); L. Mayo, *Scientific Method, Adversarial System, and Technology Assessment* (George Washington Univ., Washington, D.C. 1970).

cases involving technology, although the extension is not limited to such cases. In the words of the United States Supreme Court (*11*), "The question of standing is related only to whether the dispute sought to be adjudicated will be presented in an adversary context and in a form historically viewed as capable of judicial resolution." The basic question is "whether the interest sought to be protected by the complainant is arguably within the zone of interests to be protected or regulated by the statute or constitutional guarantee in question" (*12*). The question of standing is a question not of whether a party should win or lose but of whether he should be heard.

The current extension of the doctrine is sometimes called the "private attorney general" concept. Under this concept a private citizen is allowed to present a case as an advocate of the public interest. A leading case is Scenic Hudson Preservation Conference v. Federal Power Commission (*13*), decided by the Second Circuit of the United States Court of Appeals on 29 December 1965. On 9 March 1965 the Federal Power Commission granted a license to Consolidated Edison Company to construct a pumped storage hydroelectric project on the west side of the Hudson River at Storm King Mountain in Cornwall, New York. A pumped storage plant generates electric energy for use during peak load periods by means of hydroelectric units driven by water from a headwater pool or reservoir. The Storm King Project, as proposed by Consolidated Edison, would have required the placement of overhead transmission lines on towers 100 to 150 feet (30 to 45 meters) high. The towers would have required a path some 125 feet wide through Westchester and Putnam counties from Cornwall to the Consolidated Edison's facilities in New York City—a distance of 25 miles (40 kilometers). The petitioners were conservation and other groups and municipalities who claimed that the project, as designed by Consolidated Edison and as approved by the Federal Power Commission, would destroy the character of the land and the beauty of the area.

The Federal Power Commission argued, among other things, that the petitioners did not have standing to obtain judicial review of the legality of the license because they "make no claim of any personal economic injury resulting from the Commission's action."

11. Flast v. Cohen, *United States Supreme Court Rep. No. 392* (1968), p. 83.

12. Association of Data Processing Service Organizations v. Camp, *United States Law Week* 38, 4194 (1970).

13. *Federal Reporter No. 354,* U.S. Court of Appeals, Second Circuit (1965), p. 608; certiorari denied, *United States Supreme Court Rep. No. 384* (1966), p. 941.

The Court of Appeals held that the petitioners were entitled to raise the issue of the legality of the license and the licensing procedure even though they might not have a personal economic interest in the question. The court reasoned that a citizen has an interest in actions that affect the nature of the environment, and that this interest is arguably within the zone of interests that are or should be protected by law. On the merits of the case, the court held that the Federal Power Commission was required to give full consideration to alternative plans for the generation of peak-load electricity, including a plan proposed by one of the petitioners for the use of gas turbines.

The Scenic Hudson case is significant because it set a precedent for the enlargement of the opportunity of citizens, acting as citizens and not as private parties, to secure judicial review of the actions of public agencies, and of actions of the interests these agencies often regulate, in cases involving technology as well as other matters. The decision supports the proposition that, in certain cases, citizens will be recognized in court as advocates of a public interest, on the grounds that, as members of the public, they have been or may be injured by the actions complained of. They need not claim that they have been or will be injured economically or otherwise as private persons *(14)*.

The development of the "private attorney general" concept does not mean that substantive changes will automatically occur in the constitutional, statutory, and common law doctrines that regulate rights and duties pertaining to the development and use of science and technology. The work of analysts in the areas of law, science, and technology—analysts such as Patterson *(15)*, Frampton *(16)*, Cowan *(17)*, Miller *(18)*, Cavers *(19)*, Mayo and Jones *(20)*, Korn *(21)*, Green *(22)*, Ferry *(23)*, Wheeler *(24)*, and others *(25)*—

14. In several recent cases the Scenic Hudson doctrine has been applied to matters such as highway location, the displacement of people by urban renewal projects, the protection of navigable waters, and the protection of lumber preserves. See *Cornell Law Rev. 55* , 761 (1970). The proposed Environment Protection Act of 1970, introduced in the U.S. Senate in early 1970 by Senators Hart and McGovern, would clarify and extend the right of private citizens to bring antipollution suits against government agencies, industries, and private citizens.

15. E. Patterson, *Law in a Scientific Age* (Columbia Univ. Press, New York, 1963).

16. G. Frampton, *Mich. Law Rev.* 63, 1423 (1963).

17. T. Cowan, *George Washington Law Rev.* 33, 3 (1964).

18. A. Miller, *ibid.,* p. 17.

19. D. Cavers, *Mich. Law Rev.* 63, 1325 (1965).

20. L. Mayo and E. Jones, *George Washington Law Rev.* 33, 318 (1964).

21. H. Korn, *Law and the Determination of Facts Involving Science and Technology* (Columbia Univ. Law School, New York, 1965).

indicates the difficulties of developing systems of conceptual correspondence between scientific and technological developments and legal concepts and doctrines. Scientific, technological, and legal systems often further different values and serve different purposes, and the reconciliation of conflicts in these values and purposes is only in part a juridical task. The "private attorney general" concept, however, does invite more active judicial scrutiny of such conflicts and may contribute to substantive changes in legal doctrine in the future (26) in areas such as the computer and privacy; air and water supply and pollution; noise control; medical, genetic, and psychological experimentation; drug testing and use; nuclear energy and radiation; food purity and pesticides; and the control and handling of chemical and biological weapons.

While the legal form of citizen participation in the control and development of technology has severe limitations because it tends to be (i) reactive rather than anticipatory, (ii) controlled by restrictive rules of evidence, and (iii) subject to dilatory tactics, litigation has proven, over time, to be a significant element in the efforts of individuals and groups to influence the processes and institutions that affect them.

TECHNOLOGY ASSESSMENT

A second form of participatory technology comes within the scope of existing and proposed processes of "technology assessment." While the concept of technology assessment can be interpreted to include the kinds of legal

22. H. Green, *Bull. Atom. Scientists* 23, 12 (1967).

23. W. Ferry, *Saturday Rev.* 51, 50 (1968).

24. H. Wheeler, *Center Mag.* 2, 59 (Mar. 1969).

25. See *Vanderbilt Law Rev.* 17, 1 (1963); *Report of a Conference on Law and Science* (David Davies Memorial Institute, London, 1964); *George Washington Law Rev.* 33, 1 (1964); *Mich. Law Rev.* 63, 1325 (1965): *Case Western Reserve Law Rev.* 19, 1 (1967); *George Washington Law Rev.* 36, 1033 (1968); *Univ. of California Los Angeles Law Rev.* 15, 267 (1968); *Cornell Law Rev.* 55, 663 (1970).

26. Suits initiated in recent years to affect the control of technology through new applications of, or substantive changes in, legal doctrines include actions to ban the use of pesticides; to prevent airlines from using jets that pollute the air at the Newark, New Jersey, airport; to enjoin offshore drilling; to order a paper company to provide air pollution controls at a pulp mill; and to prevent a gas company from extending pipelines across a wooded tract. Several of these and similar suits are discussed in J. W. Moorman, "Outline for the Practicing Environmental Lawyer" (Center for the Study of Responsive Law, Washington, D.C. 1969); L. J. Carter, *Science* 166, 1487 (1969); *ibid.*, p. 1601.

action I have discussed (27), the term usually is used to refer to activities that are somewhat more anticipatory in nature and broader in scope.

To some extent "technology assessment" is a new label for an old activity —the attempt to comprehend, and to make informed decisions about, the implications of technological development. The movement to formalize and improve this activity in a public context was initiated in 1967 by Senator Edmund Muskie (28) in the Senate and by Representative Emilio Q. Daddario (29) in the House of Representatives. This movement has successfully directed attention to some limitations in the way technological questions are currently considered in the American system of politics and government.

"Technology assessment" was defined in the bill introduced by Daddario in the House of Representatives on 7 March 1967 as a "method for identifying, assessing, publicizing, and dealing with the implications and effects of applied research and technology." The bill asserted that there is a need for improved methods of "identifying the potentials of applied research and technology and promoting ways and means to accomplish their transfer into practical use, and identifying the undesirable by-products and side effects of such applied research and technology in advance of their crystallization, and informing the public of their potential danger in order that appropriate steps may be taken to eliminate or minimize them."

The strengths and weaknesses of various forms of existing and proposed technology assessment are extensively analyzed in the hearings conducted by the Muskie (30) and Daddario (31) subcommittees; in the studies undertaken

27. See, for Example, B. M. Portnoy, *Cornell Law Rev.* 55, 861 (1970).
28. "Creation of a Select Committee on Technology and the Human Environment," Senate Resolution 68, 90th Congress, 1st Session, 25 January 1967.
29. "Technology Assessment Board," House of Representatives Bill 6698, 90th Congress, 1st Session, 7 March 1967. See also "Technology Assessment" (statement of Emilio Q. Daddario, chairman, Subcommittee on Science, Research, and Development of the House Committee on Science and Astronautics, 90th Congress, 1st Session) (Government Printing Office, Washington, D.C. 1968).
30. *Establish a Select Committee on Technology and the Human Environment* (hearings before the Subcommittee on Intergovernmental Relations of the Senate Committee on Government Operations, 90th Congress, 1st Session) (Government Printing Office, Washington, D.C., 1967).
31. *Technology Assessment Seminar* (proceedings before the Subcommittee on Science, Research, and Development of the House Committee on Science and Astronautics, 90th Congress, 1st Session) (Government Printing Office, Washington, D.C., 1967); *Technology Assessment* (hearings before the Subcommittee on Science, Research, and Development of the House Committee on Science and Astronautics, 91st Congress, 1st Session) (Government Printing Office, Washington, D.C., 1969).

for the Daddario subcommittee by the National Academy of Sciences (*32*), the National Academy of Engineering (*33*), and the Science Policy Research Division of the Legislative Reference Service (*34*); and in related analyses, such as those made by the Program of Policy Studies in Science and Technology of George Washington University (*35*).

In these hearings and reports, citizen participation in technology assessment is both described and advocated. The analysis by Coates (*36*) of 15 case histories of technology assessments identifies one case that involved direct citizen participation—the examination of consumer products undertaken by the National Commission on Product Safety, which was established by Congress on 20 November 1967. In 1968 and 1969, the commission investigated the safety of such products as toys and children's furniture, architectural glass, power mowers, power tools, glass bottles, and aerosol cans. Citizens testified before the commission and directed the commission's attention to various incidents and problems. Coates observes that citizens participated in this particular assessment because the experience of members of the public with various products was itself part of the subject matter of the inquiry. There was no direct citizen participation in the other assessments examined by Coates, but the subject matter of several of the assessment processes suggests that some form of citizen contribution, either direct or through representative intermediaries, would have been appropriate. This is true, for example, of the assessments of environmental noise, and of future public transportation systems of advanced type.

In his written testimony submitted to the Daddario subcommittee, Mayo (*37*) stresses the importance, in assessment processes, of direct participation

32. National Academy of Sciences, *Technology: Processes of Assessment and Choice* (Government Printing Office, Washington, D.C., 1969).

33. National Academy of Engineering, *A Study of Technology Assessment* (Government Printing Office, Washington, D.C., 1969).

34. Science Policy Research Division, Legislative Reference Service, *Technical Information for Congress* (Government Printing Office, Washington, D.C., 1969). See also National Academy of Public Administration, *A Technology Assessment System for the Executive Branch* (Government Printing Office, Washington, D.C., 1970).

35. These analyses are described in *Report; 1967–1968* and *Report 1968–1969* (Geoege Washington Univ., Washington, D.C., 1970).

36. V. Coates, "Examples of Technology Assessments for the Federal Government," (George Washington Univ., Washington, D.C., 1970).

37. L. Mayo, *Technology Assessment* (hearings before the Subcommittee on Science, Research, and Development of the House Committee on Science and Astronautics, 91st Congress, 1st Session) (Government Printing Office, Washington, D.C., 1969), pp. 82–102.

or representation of persons affected by a technology. He emphasizes the fact that technology assessment has a dimension beyond the identification and analysis of the impacts of technology. This is the dimension of evaluation of the social desirability or undesirability of such impacts. Since different segments of the public may view the impacts in various ways, as beneficial or detrimental, comprehensive evaluation is difficult without direct inputs from such segments. While special-interest groups can be relied on to express their views they cannot safely be regarded as representative of the views of all major segments of the public that may be concerned.

Of the various hearings and reports generated by the Daddario subcommittee, the report of the technology assessment panel of the National Academy of Sciences places the greatest emphasis on citizen participation and representation. This panel asserts that legislative authorization and appropriation processes are inadequate as technology assessment processes because legislative processes frequently consider only the contending views of well-organized interest groups and often do not direct attention to long-range consequences. The panel further argues that, while technology assessment occurs in industry and in government agencies, with few exceptions the basic questions considered concern the probable economic and institutional effects of a technology on those who are deciding whether to exploit it. Existing processes fail to give adequate weight to "the full spectrum of human needs" because not enough spokesmen for diverse needs have access to the appropriate decision-making processes.

In the judgment of the panel, extensive citizen participation and representation in the assessment process is necessary both for practical reasons and for reasons of democratic theory. There are two practical reasons. First, citizen participation in the early stages of the development of a technology may help to avoid belated citizen opposition to a technological development after heavy costs have been incurred. Second, "objective evaluation" is impossible unless the diverse views of interested parties have been considered. On the level of political theory, the panel suggests that, in a democratic framework, it is necessary to consider the views of those who will be affected by a particular course of action.

The National Academy of Sciences panel explicitly acknowledges that technology assessment in some of its aspects is a political process because it involves questions of value (32, p. 83); "We can hope to raise the level of political discourse; we must not seek to eliminate it." The panel concludes (32, pp. 84 and 87) that there is a "need to accompany any new assessment mechanism with surrogate representatives or ombudsmen to speak on behalf of interests too weak or diffuse to generate effective spokesmen of their own. . . . Means must also be devised for alerting suitable representatives of interested groups to the fact that a decision potentially affecting them is about to be made. . . . *Whatever structure is chosen, it should provide well-defined channels through which citizens' groups, private associations, or surrogate representatives can make their views known. . . . It is particularly important to couple improved assessment with improved methods of representing weak and poorly organized interest groups"* [emphasis in the original].

As the National Academy of Sciences report states, and as Folk (*38*) stresses, to be effective technology assessment must function as part of the political process. What is at issue is the distribution and exercise of a form of decision-making power over technology. New technology assessment processes and structures probably would open decision-making processes to a wider constituency than now exists, and might change the distribution of power over some decisions involving technology. At the very least, new processes and structures might make it difficult for those accustomed to making technological decisions to do so without the knowledge of many other concerned people. It is doubtful that new assessment processes would be regarded as neutral either by those who now dominate technological decision-making processes or by those who might disagree with the results. Even though every effort were made to analyze questions of value as dispassionately as possible, or to exclude such questions entirely from assessment processes, dissatisfied parties almost certainly would attack the results and seek to offset them by other forms of political action.

Persuasion, bargains, and trade-offs in values are at the heart of political processes. Whether effective assessment can or should attempt to avoid these processes is questionable. Because technology assessment is to some extent a political process, the participation or representation of citizens may be not only desirable from the perspective of democratic theory but also necessary in political practice. Even such participation may not assure the effectiveness of the process in a larger political context.

AD HOC ACTIVITY

A third form of participatory technology encompasses a variety of ad hoc activities of individuals and groups beyond the scope of structured processes

38. H. Folk, paper presented at the Boston meeting of the AAAS, December 1969.

of litigation and assessment. This form includes activist intellectualism of the sort undertaken by Carson (*39*), Nader (*40*), and Commoner (*41*); quasi-official action of the kind undertaken by Congressman R. D. McCarthy concerning chemical and biological warfare (*42*); political and informational activities (*43*) of the sort undertaken by such groups as the Citizens' League Against the Sonic Boom, the Scientists' Institute for Public Information, the Sierra Club, Friends of the Earth, and Zero Population Growth; and sporadic activities of loose coalitions of individuals and groups energized by particular situations and issues.

Rather than attempt to survey such ad hoc activities, I here briefly describe and analyze an example of abortive participation that occurred in 1967 and 1968 in the initial efforts to develop a new town on the site of Fort Lincoln in Washington, D.C. (*44*). In some ways the Fort Lincoln example is typical of problems that often arise in processes of citizen participation in urban development. In other ways the case is distinctive because the primary purpose of the Fort Lincoln project was to demonstrate on a national basis the potentials of technological and administrative innovation for urban development.

On 30 August 1967, President Johnson publicly requested several members of his administration and of the government of the District of Columbia to begin at once to develop a new community on the site of Fort Lincoln, which consists of 345 acres of nearly vacant land in the northeast section of Washington, D.C. The President explained the purpose of the project as the development of a community that would demonstrate the potentials of administrative and technological innovation in urban development. The Fort

39. R. Carson, *Silent Spring* (Houghton Mifflin, Boston, 1962).

40. R. Nader, *Unsafe at Any Speed* (Grossman, New York, 1965).

41. B. Commoner, *Science and Survival* (Viking, New York, 1966).

42. See R. D. McCarthy, *The Ultimate Folly* (Vintage, New York, 1969).

43. See G. DeBell, Ed., *The Environmental Handbook* (Ballantine, New York, 1970); J. G. Mitchell and C. L. Stallings, eds., *Ecotactics* (Pocket Books, Simon & Schuster, New York, 1970); R. Rienow and L. T. Rienow, *Moment in the Sun* (Ballantine, New York, 1967); W. A. Shurcliff, *SST and Sonic Boom Handbook* (Ballantine, New York, 1970).

44. The account given here is derived from a longer study: J. D. Carroll and J. Zuccotti, "The Siege of Fort Lincoln, circa 1969: A Study in Nonparticipatory Technology," paper presented at the Eastern Regional Conference on Science, Technology, and Public Programs, Boston, 1970. See also M. Derthick, *New Towns In-Town* (Urban Institute, Washington, D.C., 1970), and "Fort Lincoln," *The Public Interest*, *No. 20* (1970), p. 3.

Lincoln project was conceptualized as the leading project in a national program to develop "new towns intown" on federally owned land in various cities throughout the country.

On 25 January 1968, Edward J. Logue, who had achieved national recognition as an urban development administrator in New Haven and Boston, was retained as principal development consultant for Fort Lincoln. In the following 10 months, Logue and his associates developed an ambitious and innovative plan (45) that was based on, among other things, a thorough analysis (46) of the potentials for technological innovation in the development of Fort Lincoln and on a proposal (47) for an innovative educational system for the new community.

Fort Lincoln was a federal urban renewal project. Some form of citizen participation in urban renewal projects is required by law. Logue and the government officials involved in the Fort Lincoln project had had extensive experience with citizen participation in other urban development projects, including a model cities project in Washington, D.C. In developing the plans for Fort Lincoln, they made extensive efforts to fashion a participatory structure that would be acceptable to the citizens of the northeast section of Washington. For the most part they failed. Political activists in the area perceived the technical planning process as the locus of political opportunity and choice concerning such questions as the number of low-income families to be housed on the site. Although these activists disagreed over who could speak for the citizens, they agreed that the residents of the area should be granted funds to hire professionals to participate with and for them in the technical planning and development processes. At one point the Department of Housing and Urban Development offered to grant money for this purpose to the council that represented the citizens, but for various reasons the council rejected the offer.

The Nixon Administration suspended development of Fort Lincoln in September 1969, pending further study. One analyst (48) has argued that the

45. *Fort Lincoln New Town Final Planning Report* (District of Columbia Redevelopment Land Agency, National Capital Planning Commission, and Government of the District of Columbia, Washington, D.C., 1969).

46. D. A. Crane, A. H. Keyes, F. D. Lethbridge, D. H. Condon, *Technologies Study: The Application of Technological Innovation in the Development of A New Community* (District of Columbia Redevelopment Land Agency, National Capital Planning Commission, and Government of the District of Columbia, Washington, D.C., 1968).

47. M. Fantini and M. A. Young, "A Design for a New and Relevant System of Education for Fort Lincoln New Town" (New York, 1968).

48. M. Derthick, *New Towns In-Town* (Urban Institute, Washington, D.C., 1970).

project was suspended because neither federal nor local officials believed that the development plan was either technologically or politically feasible. Other analysts (49) have suggested that the project was suspended because members of the Nixon Administration regarded it as a personal undertaking of President Johnson's and as an example of the overly ambitious social engineering activities of "the Great Society."

The struggle over citizen participation diminished support for the project in the neighborhood and among its potential supporters in other areas of the city. No strong political constituency favored the project. The Nixon Administration could and did suspend it without antagonizing any strong or vocal interest group.

Fort Lincoln is one example of the extent to which technical planning and development processes can become the locus of political conflict when these processes are perceived as the de facto locus of political choice. It is also an example of some of the difficulties that can arise in the course of efforts to reconcile the dictates of administrative and technological reasoning with the dictates of the political thinking of participating individuals in particular situations.

PROBLEMS

Like many other participatory processes, participatory technology raises questions about the adequacy of the theory and practice of representative government.

According to traditional theories of American public life, citizens should express their demands for public action to their political and governmental representatives. Conflicting demands should be reconciled by persons elected or appointed to policy-making positions in which they are publicly accountable for their actions. Administrative and technical processes are not, in theory, the appropriate locus for the exercise of political influence and the reconciliation of political conflicts, because these processes are not usually structured as open political forums, and because most administrators and technical people are not directly accountable to electorates.

This theory of government is a prescriptive rather than a descriptive one. It does not correspond well with the realities of the exercise of political

49. J. D. Carroll and J. Zuccotti, "The Siege of Fort Lincoln, circa 1969: A Study in Nonparticipatory Technology," paper presented at the Eastern Regional Conference on Science, Technology, and Public Programs, Boston, 1970.

power in and through administrative and technical activities. Among other things, increases in population, the expansion of the public sector, and the increase in technological complexity have changed the number and, to some extent, the nature of demands and possibilities for governmental action in recent decades. While legislative bodies and individual elected officials continue to respond to some of these demands, many other demands are considered and resolved in administrative processes of limited visibility. The very act of translating most legislation into specific processes usually involves an exercise of political choice. Furthermore, agencies often invite demands upon themselves as a way of expanding the scope of their support and powers.

The politicalization of administration in this century, especially in response to the activities of interest groups, is a widely recognized phenomenon (*50*).

Participatory technology is an attempt to influence public agencies directly, and, through them, the quasi-public and private interests they often influence and regulate. Like other participatory processes, participatory technology in some of its forms circumvents traditional processes of expressing demands through elected representatives and of relying on representatives to take appropriate action.

The hazards of participatory technology are many. On the one hand it can be used by administrative and technical people in a manipulative way to generate the illusion of citizen support of a particular course of action. On the other hand it can degenerate into forums for the exercise of obstructionist, veto-power techniques and paralyze public action. It can generate an overload of demands that agencies are not equipped to handle. It can be used as an instrument by an aggressive minority to capture decision-making processes and to impose minority views on a larger community. It can simply shift the locus for the exercise of "the tyranny of small decisions" (*51*) from one group to another or merely enlarge the core group that exercises control. Finally, it can lead to the dominance of technological know-nothing over the judgments of qualified individuals who are legally responsible for, are dedicated to, and understand processes of public action.

At the same time, as Spiegel and Mittenthal (*52*) observe, "Citizen par-

50. See T. Lowi, *The End of Liberalism* (Norton, New York, 1969); see also J. C. Charlesworth, Ed., *Theory and Practice of Public Administration* (American Academy of Political and Social Science, Philadelphia, 1968).

51. A. E. Hahn, *Kyklos—Int. Rev. Soc. Sci.* 19, 23 (1966).

52. H. Spiegel and S. Mittenthal, in *Citizen Participation in Urban Development*, H. Spiegel, Ed. (National Training Laboratories Institute for Applied Behavioral Science,

ticipation can occur in partnerships with a governmental unit as well as against it. Its nature can be cooperative and integrative or conflicting and oppositional. . . . " Participatory technology, if appropriately structured, can contribute to decision-making processes that take into account alternative points of view, and can help an agency perform its functions in a more effective and open manner. It can provide a means by which the individual who feels powerless in the face of technological complexity can find a forum for the expression of his views.

The basic questions are these: In what cases is citizen participation in technological processes warranted, and according to what rationale? How should participation be structured and conducted? How much weight should participation be given in decision-making processes?

To provide a priori answers to these questions is impossible because of the variety of situations to which they apply. For this reason it is recommended that public agencies, scientific and technical associations, and individual members of the scientific, technological, and political communities undertake analyses of these questions in the various situations for which they have responsibility or to which they have access. No single activity by a particular organization such as the National Academy of Sciences can meet the need. The analysis must be as broad-based as the activities to which these questions apply.

At the same time, the men responsible for policy making in foundations should consider the establishment of an experimental center for responsive technology. Such a center would analyze, on a continuing basis, the question of the ways in which public participation in technological decisions involving a public interest can be structured, and would support such participation in appropriate cases. The center might also support the education of proponents of technology, who would be qualified to recognize alternative conceptions of the public interest in technological matters and to present these conceptions to decision-making bodies.

SUMMARY

The hunger to participate that exists today in various segments of the American public is in part a response to what some people perceive as an

Washington, D.C., 1968), vol. 1, pp. 12, 13. See also P. Davidoff, *J. Amer. Inst. Planners* 31, 331 (1965); E. M. Burke, *ibid.* 34, 287 (1968); S. R. Arnstein, *ibid.* 35, 216 (1969); A. Altshuler, *Community Control* (Pegasus, New York, 1970).

unresponsiveness of institutions and processes to the felt needs of the individual and of society. It is also, in part, an expression of a desire for a redistribution of power in American public life.

Technology is one of the major determinants of the nature of public as well as private life in contemporary society. Participatory technology is an attempt on the part of diverse individuals and groups to influence technological processes through participation in existing or new public processes by which technology is or can be developed, controlled, and implemented. Like other processes of direct citizen participation in governmental decision making, it raises many questions about the adequacy of existing theories and practices of representative government. These questions cannot be answered on an a prior basis. Members of the educational, scientific, technical, and governmental communities should analyze these questions in an effort to develop answers that are appropriate to the particular situations for which they are responsible and with which they are concerned.

On Criticizing Technology

LANGDON WINNER

1. PROLOGUE WITHOUT COMMENT

From the records of I. P. Pavlov comes a story which could well serve as a parable of our time. In his experiments on the conditioned reflex Pavlov found that most of the dogs used as subjects would submit to the laboratory environment without the least sign of anxiety or resistance. There was a significant minority, however, who apparently could not adapt to Pavlov's apparatus. The psychologist wrote of one animal in particular who when brought to the experimental chambers, took a look at the set-up and responded in violent objection. "The longer the session was prolonged, the more excited it became; it wanted to be loose, scratched the floor, gnawed the bench, etc. Dyspnoea and a continuous salivation resulted from the uninterrupted musclar work; the animal became completely unsuitable for our work."

Pavlov pondered this peculiar form of behavior and decided that the dog had shown a "freedom reflex."[1]

2. INTRODUCTION

One of the most remarkable aspects of contemporary social criticism is the frequency with which technology has been isolated as a crucial problem. In a far-reaching debate in both academic circles and the public media, the various faces of modern technology have been continually scrutinized to discover what new promises or difficulties, blessings or nightmares they hold in store.

Unfortunately, much of this discussion has already burned itself to a cinder leaving little positive result. Two technology-oriented popular ideologies of the decade – McLuhanism and the counterculture – seem to have evolved in fulfillment of the idea that there is no source of opposition which the technological society cannot neutralize and transform for its own purposes.[2] Both of these tides of criticism have been absorbed by Madison Avenue and now exist as little more than advertising styles in the service of the polyethylene, throwaway world which they sought to call into question. There is good evidence that exactly the same fate now awaits an even more serious challenge to the technological order – the ecology movement. Noticing how easily the public can lose sight of even the most noble of ideas, manufacturers have gradually changed the "save our environment" arguments into high-powered promotion campaigns for gasoline and disposable bottles.

One can hope that the scholarly discussion of technology-related subjects will meet with a happier end. But it is not at all clear that it will. In the middle 1960s students from a wide range of disciplines found themselves in agreement that there was something uniquely troublesome in the relationship of technology to politics, social life, and human values. They recognized the general neglect of such questions and the need for new research and thinking in this area. Responses to this awakening came in the founding of new programs on technology and society at Harvard, George Washington,

1. Quoted in Maurice Merleau-Ponty, *The Structure of Behavior* (trans. by Alden I. Fisher; Boston: Beacon Press, 1963), p. 123.
2. Marshall McLuhan, *Understanding Media: The Extensions of Man* (New York: McGraw-Hill, 1961): Theodore Roszak, *The Making of a Counter Culture: Reflections on the Technocratic Society and Its Youthful Opposition* (New York: Anchor, 1969).

Purdue, Case Western Reserve, Indiana, and several other universities across the country.

What was envisioned at the beginning of this movement of scholars was a radical departure. Unlike the normal academic fare, technology studies were to place a high premium on innovative approaches, interdisciplinary cooperation, the development of foresight, and utopian speculation. It was held, furthermore, that such work ought to go beyond the long-existing split between objective knowledge and human values. Those awakened to this new range of concerns recognized that their central categories would have to include not only "truth" and "falsity," but "opportunity" and "danger" as well.[3] But as time has passed, it has become less and less certain that the movement of technology-oriented scholars would live up to its original promise. The primary difficulty seems to be that, like McLuhanism, the counterculture, and the ecology movement, the thrust of the activity will be conveniently reabsorbed into the normal flow of things. At exactly the point where the learned discussion about technology and social life should begin to bear new and distinctive fruit, it is entirely possible that it will become merely another parochial wrinkle on the tapestry of social scientific propriety. The recent ruckus will have been for naught.

The question I wish to pose, therefore, is simply whether the current discussion will make any difference at all in the way we think about technology or in the way we act toward it. My emphasis will fall upon certain tendencies in the literature which I find disturbing, their causes, and one possible means of correction. In general, I shall argue that programs of research based on the ideas of *technological change and technology assessment* are insufficient. There is still a pressing need for intensive criticism of our most fundamental ideas concerning the technological character of this civilization. If we proceed with programs of assessment with this work left undone, it is likely that our thoughts and deeds will become trivial and perhaps even supportive of the trends which the enterprise hopes to alter.[4]

3. Works representative of the new concern for technology and the future include: Denis Gabor, *Inventing the Future* (New York: Knopf, 1964); Olaf Helmer, *Social Technology* (New York: Basic Books, 1966); Bertrand de Jouvenel, *The Art of Conjecture* (New York: Basic Books, 1967); Robert Boguslaw, *The New Utopians* (Englewood Cliffs, N.J.: Prentice-Hall, 1965); and many others.

4. It is not my purpose here to look for or offer a definition of technology. The term, it seems to me, has always been a vagrant one in search of a meaning. Lewis Mumford's definition of "technics" as "that part of human activity wherein, by an energetic organization of the process of work, man controls and directs the forces of nature for his own purposes," will serve for now: Lewis Mumford, *Art and Technics* (New York: Columbia University Press, 1952), p. 15.

3. PESSIMISM AND INEVITABILITY

The philosophical literature on man and technology has long been characterized by a pervasive ambivalence which in any other area of thought would
be considered a blatant weakness. Most writers on this theme find it necessary
to speak both as Francis Bacon and as Jean-Jacques Rousseau. They call
attention to both the wonderful possibilities of modern technology and the
sorrowful consequences which follow from its misuse. In this sense, one
finds that over the course of many decades all of the speculative works on
technology have come to exactly the same conclusion. Technology may be
used for good or evil. It depends on how we use it. This embarrassingly
obvious truth conceals an important moral problem which this tradition of
thought has never been able to resolve. For it appears to be true that our
patterns of motivation and judgment are very poorly suited to any effective
way of coping with the negative effects of technological development. The
power of machines, tools, techniques, and large technical systems has a way
of teaming up with the least admirable of human traits to form a combination
which is, at best, difficult to limit.

In recent years there has arisen a large body of literature focusing on this
phenomenon. For a variety of reasons and from a variety of perspectives, a
number of thinkers have decided that the negative possibilities of Western
technological development now deserve the weight of our attention. Their
writings, now widely popular among students in our universities, are of course
well known — Lewis Mumford's *The Myth of the Machine,* Herbert Marcuse's
One-Dimensional Man, Kenneth Keniston's *The Uncommitted,* Hannah
Arendt's *The Human Condition,* Jacques Ellul's *The Technological Society,*
and others.[5] It is not my intention to argue that such works offer the true
light into the problems of technology in our time. What is clear, however,
is that works in this genre offer us the viewpoints of thinkers who have gone
deeply into certain very real problems of modernity. Keniston's theory of
human obsolescence, for example, is one of the best statements of a contemporary dilemma now beginning to plague persons in professions subject

5. Lewis Mumford, *The Myth of the Machine: Technics and Human Development*
(New York: Harcourt, Brace and World, 1966), and *The Myth of the Machine: The
Pentagon of Power* (New York: Harcourt, Brace and World, 1969); Herbert Marcuse,
One-Dimensional Man (Boston: Beacon Press, 1964); Kenneth Keniston, *The
Uncommitted* (New York: Delta, 1964); and *The New Radicals* (New York: Harvest,
1968); Hannah Arendt, *The Human Condition* (Chicago: University of Chicago Press,
1958); Jacques Ellul, *The Technological Society* (trans. by John Wilkinson; New York:
Knopf, 1965).

to rapid change.[6] The perceptions and theories of such thinkers, however far removed from the mainstream of social science they may be, contain much that social scientists would do well to consider.

It is for this reason that I find it distressing to discover that in the recent scholarly writing on technology and society, all of the radical critics in the field are dismissed as merely "pessimistic" or blindly negative. Emmanuel Mesthene, Director of the Harvard University Program on Technology and Society, has apparently decided that there is nothing of real substance in any of the philosophical critics other than a kind of gut-level, Schopenhauerian gloom. In his book *Technological Change,* he lists the so-called pessimists among those who hold "inadequate views" about technology and compares them to the optimists who believe "that technology is a virtually unalloyed blessing for man and society."[7] "Taken together," Mesthene observes, "the two views may be seen as the latest stage of the eternal battle between God and the Devil. In the first view, technology is invested with an omnipotence heretofore reserved to the Almighty. In the second view, technology emerges as the modern counterpart of the Devil, responsible, as the Devil has traditionally been, for man's eternal inhumanity to man."

In his other writings Professor Mesthene makes it clear that the pessimists include, among others, Ellul, Marcuse, Mumford, Arendt, and so on.[9] In the Harvard Program's research the task of studying these supposed prophets of doom has been assigned to the young sociologist Manfred Stanley. In the course of his investigations, Stanley has uncovered several themes in the literature which he strongly recommends for further research.[10] In Professor Mesthene's *Fifth Annual Report,* however, Stanley's work is spoken of as if it were merely an attempt to classify some ancient mummies and dry bones. The Director of the Harvard Program seems to feel that writers with any access to philosophy have a "demonic vision" and that their ideas are at best glimmerings of rhetorical gloss.

Roughly similar opinions dot the pages of the *Technology Assessment Hearings before the Subcommittee on Science, Research and Development*

---

6. Kenniston, *op. cit.,* pp. 209–240.

7. Emmanuel G. Mesthene, *Technological Change: Its Impact on Man and Society* (New York: Mentor, 1970), p. 16.

8. *Ibid.,* p. 18.

9. *Fifth Annual Report, Harvard University Program on Technology and Society* (1968, 1969), pp. 1–4, 14–17.

10. Manfred Stanley, "The Technicist Projection: A Study of the Place of Social Theory in Moral Rhetoric" (unpublished manuscript).

of the U.S. House of Representatives of December [1969]. A collection of prestigious academic spokesmen felt obliged to chide the "technophobiacs" and "bleeding heart humanists" for what are alleged to be bleak and even nihilistic views of technology. After offering a remarkably shallow summary of the ideas of Ellul, Mumford, and Marcuse, historian Melvin Kranzberg concludes: "While such wholesale indictments may stimulate nihilistic revolutionary movements, they really tell us very little about what can be done to guide and direct technological innovation along socially beneficial lines."[11]

The fact that an alleged pessimism or nihilism is frequently chosen as the ground for rejecting the radical critics is a revealing one. For it is not so much that the critics are wrong in what they say, but that the style of what they are saying is found to be unacceptable. The requirement of rosy optimism in thinking about technology appears to have become something of an addendum to a revised Ockham's Razor: "State your theory in as economical a way as possible, while at the same time avoiding negative overtones."

The influence of this need for optimism has even begun to play a role in some of the significant books recently published in this area. In both Amitai Etzioni's *The Active Society* and Victor Ferkiss' *Technological Man* there occurs a peculiar use of the affirmative future tense "will" at exactly those points where matters seem most problematic. "Since the active society will be a post-nationalist one, the active citizen will be a cosmopolitan one."[12] "Technological man will be man in control of his own development within the context of a meaningful philosophy of the role of technology in human evolution."[13] "Technological man will be his own master."[14] Such language tends to obscure the fact that the conditions of Etzioni's active society and Ferkiss' technological man *will not,* in all probability, be realized. The question that needs to be addressed is why this is so and what might be done about it. But in order to avoid the uncomfortable feelings which they believe will follow from any kind of deep-seeking critical analysis of the technological society, scholars in our field presently pass such questions by.

11. Melvin Kranzberg, "Historical Aspects of Technology Assessment," in *Technology Assessment Hearings before the Subcommittee on Science, Research and Development of the U.S. House of Representatives* (Washington, D.C.: Government Printing Office, 1970), p. 385.

12. Amitai Etzioni, *The Active Society* (New York: Free Press, 1968), p. 11.

13. Victor C. Ferkiss, *Technological Man: The Myth and the Reality* (New York: George Braziller, 1969), p. 246.

14. *Ibid.,* p. 272.

From all appearances, they would prefer to whistle in the dark rather than risk the perils of philosophy.

The matter of optimism versus pessimism and hope versus despair are in the end simply irrelevant to the discussion at hand. Lewis Mumford's *Technics and Civilization,* written forty years ago, was a profoundly optimistic work about a society about to escape the misery of the industrial revolution. In recent years Mumford has published the two volumes of *The Myth of the Machine,* a somewhat unhappy account of how the earlier prophecy has been falsified by the unchecked growth of "megatechnics." The point of interest here is not that Mumford's mood somehow changed, but rather that a substantive shift took place in his analysis of the technological society. It is indeed a shame that scholars would rather brand Mumford a pessimist than consider the reasons for his change of mind.[15]

The prevailing notion seems to be that to recognize the negative side of technological development is to yield to a paralysis of thought and action. Speaking of Ellul's influence, Victor Ferkiss concludes, "By exaggerating the situation, he creates a despair so profound as to render resistance hopeless, leaving many who accept what he has to say with the conviction that the only dignified thing to do is to await the end, savoring one's knowledge of its inevitability, like a figure in a Greek tragedy."[16]

But why is it that Ellul's book should not be the source of an invigorating challenge rather than a dark shroud over our spirits?

As F. Scott Fitzgerald once pointed out, "One should be able to see that things are hopeless and yet be determined to make them otherwise."[17]

At the heart of the controversy between the radical critics and more orthodox scholarship lies an idea which has plagued European and American authors for the last two centuries — the notion that technology has gotten out of control. In its contemporary form the issue is usually stated as follows: that in some very significant ways our physical technologies and the social systems that support them have developed and continue to develop without adequate guidance by man's rational, moral, and political agency. One of the major faults which American scholars find in the radical critics is that they include in this idea a conception of historical inevitability. Ellul and the others are said to bow before the specter of autonomous technology, whereas

15. Mumford, op. cit.
16. Ferkiss, *op. cit.,* p. 87.
17. F. Scott Fitzgerald, *The Crack-Up* (New York: New Directions, 1956), p. 69.

intelligent and hopeful men know that there is still a wide range of options open to us.

Unfortunately, there stands an implicit paradox in the arguments against autonomous technology. As one reads the writings in this field, he cannot help noticing that the respectable spokesmen grant just as much of the nightmare and its essential unchangeability as the thinkers they reject. In a statement before a U.S. Senate hearing [in 1969], Harvey Brooks took care to deny the proposition that "technological progress" is a "largely autonomous development."[18]

While this pessimistic view of technology is not without evidence to support it, I believe it represents only a partial truth. Furthermore, it is an essentially sentimental and irrational view, because man in fact has *no choice* but to push forward with his technology. The world is already *irrevocably committed to a technological culture.* (Emphasis added.)

Especially when one notices that Professor Brooks has in mind the size, scope, general character, and rate of development of the kinds of technological systems which this culture already has, there is little to distinguish his denial of technological autonomy from Ellul's affirmation. Both believe that man is inextricably caught up in exactly the forms of technology he now has and that the future holds no significant alteration of existing technological trends. The idea of autonomous technology and the idea of progress are at present merely two sides of the same coin. Both sides are satisfied in the belief that "man in fact has no choice." In the statement mentioned earlier, Melvin Kranzberg sought to refute Ellul and Marcuse by saying, "Twentieth century man will never divorce himself from technology nor even consent to a moratorium on further advances."[19] But this is exactly the case that Ellul and Marcuse argue in the first place.

The fact of the matter is that the current literature on technology, man, and society assumes as given and unchangeable many of the conditions that one might hope could be called into question, at least for purposes of speculation and research. In Herman Kahn and Anthony J. Wiener's *The Year 2000* we discover an Ellulian list of the determinants of the future in the form of a "Basic, Long Term Multifold Trend."[20] The list includes the

18. Reprinted in *Technology Assessment Hearings,* op. cit., p. 331.

19. Kranzberg, op. cit., p. 385.

20. Herman Kahn and Anthony J. Wiener, *The Year 2000: A Framework for Speculation on the Next Thirty-Three Years* (New York: Macmillan, 1967), pp. 1–65.

continued growth of bureaucracy, the rise of megalopolis, the world-wide spread of industrialization and modernization, the increasing tempo of change, the increasing capability for mass destruction, and so forth. Kahn and Wiener do not attempt to evaluate or judge the merits of the social and technological conditions which engender these trends. Neither do they speculate on alternative socio-technical configurations which might serve as alternatives. Apparently, history has saddled man with these basic, long-term multifold trends and the best an intelligent man can suggest is that we ride it out. The possibility of altering a trend here and there does not enter into our ability to think, criticize, judge, and act. Instead, the true possibilities can be found in certain unexpected future occurrences, usually the development of a new technology, which provide the opportunity for change. As Kahn and Wiener put it, "Our most important caveat . . . is that almost any day has some chance of bringing up some new crisis or unexpected event that becomes a historical turning point, diverting current tendencies so that expectations for the distant future must shift."[21]

Similar qualities of thought mark the writings of the Commission on the Year 2000. While Daniel Bell and the others involved in the project talk about producing new alternatives and widening the area of choice, most of their work has focused on (1) the extrapolation of existing social, political, and technological tendencies and (2) speculation about the impact of new technological innovations. One important consequence of this approach is to encourage a conception of the world in which man is a passive adapter rather than an active master of his fate. Since the world of the future will be determined by such marvels as biomedical engineering, weather modification, and the computer, it is incumbent upon man to anticipate these inevitable changes and adjust his pattern of living to them.[22]

The intrinsic limitations of this manner of thinking are compounded by the fact that Commission members are generally agreed that the existing political, social, and economic institutions of American society and the elites which govern them are also in some sense "given" and do not stand in need of any serious questioning or re-evaluation. The research of the Commission is, for this reason, directly geared to existing policymaking structures. Like so many of the programs ostensibly established to study technology and the future, the Commission on the Year 2000 in the end offers little more than a new mask for old and highly conventional kinds of inquiry.

---

21. *Ibid.*, p. 13. The passage is placed in italics in the authors' original.
22. "Toward the Year 2000: Work in Progress," *Daedalus* (Spring 1967).

The acceptance of the conditions of the technological society as basic and unchangeable is often justified as a necessary step in becoming practical or realistic about the problems of our time. Indeed, such practicality and realism is a virtue in most forms of political thought. But when the mind in its reflections yields too early to the brute facts of the present and the ineluctable trends of the future, the consequences can be regrettable. Often it places the thinker in the position of giving tacit endorsement to conditions which he might otherwise vigorously seek to oppose.

Two poignant examples of this situation are to be found in Warren Bennis and Philip Slater's interesting work, *The Temporary Society*. In the first chapter of the book, the authors survey the conditions of our rapidly changing organizational society and weigh them against the idea that in such an environment, democracy is no longer possible. They conclude that exactly the opposite conclusion can be drawn. Democracy is not only still possible, but in point of fact inevitable. "Our position is, in brief, that democracy (whether capitalistic or socialistic is not at issue here) is the only system that can successfully cope with the changing demands of contemporary civilization."[23] "Democracy becomes a functional necessity whenever a social system is competing for survival under conditions of chronic change."[24]

The difficulty with this appealing argument is that Bennis and Slater define democracy in a highly peculiar way. For them, democracy is "a climate of beliefs governing behavior" which includes the following values: full and free communication, reliance on consensus, the idea that influence is based on technical competence and knowledge, an atmosphere that permits and even encourages emotional expression, and so on.[25] Their description is an interesting definition of something. But it accords with virtually nothing in the common-sense, historical, or political theoretical meanings of the word *democracy*. Missing from their definition is any reference to such important matters as the nature of participation, voting, majority rule, the public, and so forth.

The process which has taken place is clear. Bennis and Slater have examined the conditions of modern organizations, particularly the attempt of such organizations to be more and more open and humane. Calling upon a traditional and much revered concept, they attempt to show that the course of

23. Warren G. Bennis and Philip E. Slater, *The Temporary Society* (New York: Harper, 1969), p. 2.
24. *Ibid.*, p. 4.
25. *Ibid.*

organizational evolution is definitely "democratic." But if, for example, they had applied the criteria of Dahl's *Preface to Democratic Theory* to the same organizations, it is probably safe to predict that their findings would have been exactly the opposite. By adapting their concepts to the existing state of affairs, Bennis and Slater have rendered an important category for thinking about human conduct in large-scale organizations totally meaningless.

A second example of the willingness to yield to the lamentable inevitabilities of the technological society can be seen in Bennis and Slater's discussion of the ephemerality of the "temporary society." The world they describe, one all too familiar to urban-dwelling academics, is one of "temporary systems, nonpermanent relationships, turbulence, uprootedness, unconnectedness, mobility, and above all, unexampled social change. . . ."[26] Bennis and Slater recognize that this way of living is in many ways a source of torment for individuals in our time. Persons tend to feel more atomized, narrowly specialized, bewildered, alienated, and insecure. All personal relationships, especially those of the family, are subject to severe strain. The "temporary society" is a world in which nothing of any value lasts for more than a fleeting instant.[27]

At one point Bennis pauses to ponder whether or not it would be possible to curb the source of the difficulty at its roots – the rapid pace of social change caused by technological and organizational innovation. He decides that all alternatives in this vein are impossible.[28]

Whereas it is too late to slow down the pace of temporary societies, it is not too late (and it becomes necessary) to examine ways that may be more adaptive in coping with temporary systems, ways that could both realize our full human potentialities and extract whatever benefits modernization can bring.

The solution Bennis suggests derives from his research into the dynamics of the T-group technique. "We should help our students develop the necessary interpersonal competencies, which would include at least the following . . . learning how to develop intense and deep human relationships quickly – and learning how to 'let go.' In other words, learning how to get love, to love, and to lose love. . . ."[29] In Bennis' temporary society the whole spectrum of human relationships will be reduced to a never-ending series of one-night

26. *Ibid.,* p. 124.
27. For a descriptive account of how the ephemerality of modern life affects city-dwellers, see Alvin Toffler, *Future Shock* (New York: Random House, 1970).
28. Bennis and Slater, *op. cit.,* p. 125.
29. *Ibid.,* p. 127.

stopovers. Once again man becomes a sophisticated adapter, the dependent variable which fluctuates helplessly in response to the development of an anonymous and ineluctable process. One would hope that Bennis and Slater could indicate at least some small means of resisting the spread of this ephemeralization of human existence. But they do not.

In summary, it is characteristic of many contemporary studies of technology and the future to deny historical inevitability on the one hand while smuggling in the substance of that inevitability with the other. If one goes to the literature seeking radically new possibilities, he finds that, alas, they have been precluded by certain necessary facts of modernity beyond our control.

4. CHANGE AND ASSESSMENT

In the six or seven years since technology became a popular problem for social scientists, there has evolved a tacit understanding among scholars concerning the proper way this subject should be handled. It is now widely agreed that what we are studying is *technological change* and its effects upon society and the environment. This approach accords very well with the available tools of natural and social science, with the commitment to objectivity and with the aforementioned need for optimism. It is not my intention to suggest that there is anything wrong with this approach in and of itself. I do wish to point out, however, that the perspective systematically excludes certain crucial problems which also deserve our attention, an attention which the original ferment in this field seemed to promise.

The commitment to change as the primary theme in the technology studies is evident in the *Fifth Annual Report* of the Harvard University Program on Technology and Society. As Professor Mesthene points out in his introduction, "Our four major areas of concentration continue to be: the effect of technological change on (a) the life of the individual, (b) social and individual values, (c) the political organization of society, and (d) the structure and process of social institutions."[30] The report goes on to summarize the work in progress of Harold Wilensky, Michael Maccoby, Harvey Cox, Alan Westin, and others — all of which is described in terms of the impact of technological change on various areas of human existence. At least as Mesthene describes these studies, the majority of them take changes in a specific technology or in technology generally as the independent variable. This approach is also evident in Mesthene's *Technological Change: Its Impact*

30. Harvard Program on Technology and Society, *op. cit.*, p. 1.

on Man and Society and in much of the published research sponsored by the Harvard Program.[31]

The purely scientific objects of the Harvard Program and of similar programs are admirable ones. If research in this area succeeds, we will have at our disposal a new body of knowledge with wide ranges of possible uses. But the technological change research is already much more than just an interesting new branch of scientific information. Many of its aspects are closely allied with and often explicitly tailored to a specific moral and political purpose — an enterprise which has come to be called *technology assessment.* With the support of certain amenable segments of the U.S. Congress, the executive branch and the federal bureaucracy, many social scientists have recently become full-time or part-time technology assessors intent on influencing public policy.

The philosophy of technology assessment is perhaps best set forth in two reports, one from the National Academy of Sciences, the other from the National Academy of Engineering, prepared at the request of the Committee on Science and Astronautics of the U.S. House of Representatives.[32] While the two documents differ on many points, their most fundamental orientation is the same. Since the N.A.S.'s *Technology: Processes of Assessment and Choice* is the more eloquent of the two, I shall draw on it for purposes of quotation.

The N.A.S. panel's position begins with an affirmation of the idea that what is problematic about modern technology is that it continually changes or "advances." The difficulty is that such advances create not only beneficial consequences for society, but also "deleterious side effects."[33] In the past, too little attention was given to these side effects and how they weigh against the benefits of technological development. A corrective response to this shortcoming has appeared in recent years as "concern has mounted over society's seeming inability to channel technological developments in directions that sufficiently respect the broad range of human needs."[34] The panel cites a list of problems — "the specter of thermonuclear destruction; the tensions

31. *Ibid.,* Appendix A, pp. 57-71.
32. National Academy of Sciences, *Technology: Processes of Assessment and Choice* (Report to the Committee on Science and Astronautics, U.S. House of Representatives, Washington, D.C.: Government Printing Office, July 1969); National Academy of Engineering, Committee on Public Engineering Policy, *A Study of Technology Assessment* (Report to the Committee on Science and Astronautics, U.S. House of Representatives; Washington, D.C.: Government Printing Office, July 1969).
33. N.A.S., *op. cit.,* p. 12.
34. *Ibid.,* p. 1.

of congested cities; the hazards of a polluted and despoiled biosphere; the expanding arsenal of techniques for the surveillance and manipulation of private thought and behavior; the alienation of those who feel excluded from power in an increasingly technical civilization" — which are now widely believed to have been influenced by "the ill-considered exploitation of technology."[35]

Early in its discussion the panel makes a fundamental decision which very largely determines the nature of its subsequent effort. "At the outset we set aside as beyond the scope of this report those ultimately philosophical issues that seem to be posed by any increasingly technical civilization."[36] The footnote to this sentence lists Jacques Ellul and Victor Ferkiss. Apparently, the philosophical problem of autonomous technology and human mastery is an issue which the panel felt it necessary to avoid. In the pages that follow, however, the panel makes some interesting judgments, the philosophical premises of which are left unexamined. "Our panel starts from the conviction that the advances of technology have yielded and still yield benefits that, on the whole, vastly outweigh all the injuries they have caused and continue to cause."[37] The challenge, it believes, is to "discipline technological progress."[38] The panel assures the reader, furthermore, that its "purpose is not to conceive of ways to curb or restrain or otherwise 'fix' technology...."[39]

With these commitments in mind the panel outlines what it considers to be the appropriate objectives and methods of technology assessment. In the future, society must be able to anticipate the full range of consequences of technological innovation and to make more adequate decisions about how new technological developments are employed. Decisions of this sort must take into account such considerations as the public interest and the interests of persons who may have no immediate awareness of how a new technology will affect their lives. New conceptual tools such as social indicators should be developed as aids to thinking on these matters. In addition, means must be found to provide new and sophisticated knowledge to all parties potentially concerned with the impact of a given technological innovation. This must be done, the panel urges, early enough to make a difference in the policymaking process. The report goes on to suggest a variety of ways in

35. *Ibid.*
36. *Ibid.*, p. 9.
37. *Ibid.*, p. 11.
38. *Ibid.*, p. 12.
39. *Ibid.*, p. 15.

which technology assessment could be institutionalized within the context of American political pluralism.

Given the panel's self-imposed limitations, the N.A.S. report stands as an impressive and innovative piece of political thinking. Particularly in its suggestion of new and broader criteria for judging new technologies, the panel has taken a substantial step forward. It suggests, for example, that "The reversibility of an action should . . . be counted as a major benefit; its irreversibility a major cost."[40]   It also recommends that much of the burden of uncertainty be shifted to those who presume that technological developments are harmless until proven otherwise.[41]   Since the costs of this presumption have been unusually high of late, the panel suggests that more rigorous requirements of proof be placed on those who maintain that such things as off-shore drilling and supersonic transports are an unmixed boon to mankind.

But despite its many strengths, the N.A.S. report contains a fundamental weakness of perspective which limits the impact of its analysis. If one takes this mode of technology assessment at its word, *the only opportunities for positive action lie with future developments in technology.* Existing technologies and the social systems which support them are not a subject of concern. As in the other writings I have mentioned, such things are taken to be inevitable and unchangeable characteristics of modern times. The panel admits at one point that the new sensitivity to technology-related problems "does not necessarily imply that the deleterious side-effects of technological change are worse today than they were a century or two ago."[42]   But does this mean that the panel is willing to survey the last two centuries of technological developments in order to assess them? Obviously not. This is water under the bridge.

The inherent weakness of this way of looking at the world becomes evident in an admission which the panel makes late in the report. After presenting all of its conclusions and recommendations, the panel points out that its work has failed to cover a problem area which includes a large and extremely significant portion of the nation's advanced socio-technical systems — military technology. It accounts for this notable omission by calling attention to the unusual conditions which limit inquiries into this sphere, e.g., the fact that much of the information is classified. The panel goes on to say that "the present system for the assessment of military technology violates most

40. *Ibid.,* p. 32.
41. *Ibid.,* pp. 33–39.
42. *Ibid.,* p. 42.

of the canons suggested by the panel . . ." and that it would be "remiss in its responsibility if it did not point out what appears to be almost the most glaring gap in our present technology-assessment mechanisms."[43]

These comments seem rather bizarre if one considers the nature of contemporary criticisms of the place of military technology in American life. The issues posed by Seymour Melman, Richard Barnet, and others are only partially that the socio-technical systems of warfare are changing rapidly and that they need to be assessed more adequately.[44] The startling realizations here have to do with the very existence of a large-scale military technology and of its extraordinarily disproportionate role in modern American civilization. At the most basic level, therefore, such matters as change, development, and advance in this area are simply beside the point.

The same observation can now be made of our study of advanced technology generally. The phenomenon of change is, or should be, merely one focus of our attention. For if the world never saw another change, advance, development, breakthrough, or startling new innovation, there would still be a great number of crucial issues which we would have to face. By itself, the technological change/technology assessment mode of looking at things is drastically and systematically one-sided. It directs the mind of the researcher to only one problem area while purporting to encompass the whole field. Neglected is any attempt to inquire into a range of deeper questions with genuine relevance to the decisions now at hand — questions involving the basic relationships between man and technology and the nature of modern technological civilization. In the absence of such inquiries, our probable course will be to fall back upon conventional assumptions, e.g., that the progress of mankind is inextricably linked to new technological apparatus. If our preliminary investigations have shown us anything, it is certainly that the conventional assumptions lie at the heart of the trouble. They, above all, now require rigorous scrutiny.

The shortcoming I have described in the technological change/technology assessment approach is, I believe, a serious one. It has profound implications for the direction our research takes in the coming years. It could also have a significant influence on the modes of action which this society chooses in governing technology. As I have already suggested, *the bias of the approach is to find opportunities for making judgments and taking action at only those points in which a new development in technology occurs.*

43. *Ibid.*, pp. 111–114.
44. Seymour Melman, *Pentagon Capitalism* (New York: McGraw-Hill, 1970); Richard J. Barnet, *The Economy of Death* (New York: Atheneum, 1970).

An example of the debilitating effects the change/assessment approach might have can be seen in the drift of current research on technology and values. The original demand for more attention to human values in studies of technology has met with an interesting response. Instead of bringing about an open and reasoned discussion about the values and criteria we employ or might employ in making choices in this area, the discussion about values has itself become a problem of "change" subject to empirical research. In most studies of this sort the aim is to discover how changes in technology influence changes in human values. As Professor Mesthene views the matter, the crucial problem is to gain an understanding of value accommodation:[45]

What does happen is that values change through a process of accommodation between the system of existing values and the technological and social changes that impinge on it. Understanding of the effects of technological change on our values, therefore, depends on discovering the specific ways in which this process of accommodation occurs, on identifying the trends implicit in it, and on tracing its consequences for the value system of contemporary American society.

I am not saying that knowledge of this sort is worthless and that research in this area ought to be discontinued. Neither am I saying that there is something pernicious about the fact that values are changing in the modern world. What seems to me clear, however, is that a program of inquiry which views matters of value as just another dependent variable for objective research is sorrowfully insufficient. By implication, it raises the image of man as a passive adapter to technological change to a positive virtue. If the change/ assessment research is not accompanied by a thorough discussion of the world we have made and the world we would like to make, the task we have undertaken will surely fail.

5. TECHNOLOGY CRITICISM

It is safe to assume that persons currently working on problems of technological change and technology assessment will find my remarks somewhat surprising. They rightfully maintain that their efforts make a substantial improvement over the ways that judgments about technology were made in the past. A probable reason why the term "assessment" was selected rather than "evaluation" was that such activities as "program evaluations" had traditionally come to the conclusion that everything was just fine. The word

45. Mesthene, *op. cit.*, p. 48.

"assessment" has a sharper edge to it. It implies that the good will now be sifted carefully from the bad.

But the edge, it seems to me, is still not sharp enough. A standard dictionary definition of the word "assessment" indicates that it means "the setting of an estimated value" on something. The implication is that the subject in question can be rated in terms of explicit standards which are known in advance. But the point of the matter seems to be that the standards themselves must be open to question. There are now adequate signs that many of our existing ideas and premises of judgment are themselves pathological. Our beliefs concerning the inherent beneficence of economic and material "growth," our unquestioning acceptance of all technological innovation, our tendency to seek technical solutions to every variety of human problem, our accustomed notions as to how technologies "serve" human needs — all of these are matters which ought to be re-examined in light of twentieth-century experience.

The early literature of the technology and society movement recognized the need for an inquiry of this sort. But as time has gone on, the matter has been pushed aside and forgotten. Given the tone and substance of the best writings in this field, it is no longer conceivable to look forward to any significant questioning of the dominant technological trends in our society. The enterprise of assessment, even if it succeeds in becoming institutionalized, will be at best a very superficial process. The assessors will apply rigorous empirical data to the most obvious and least troublesome of criteria. Their recommendations will alter the present course of events in relatively minor, incremental, and politically prudent ways. The nation might, for example, be induced to build a modest twenty-billion-dollar anti-ballistic missile system rather than the outrageous thirty-billion-dollar model. We would, no doubt, then congratulate ourselves on having taken a bold step forward.

If one were looking for evidence of the power of Ellul's "autonomous technique," he need go no further than the futility of our technology assessors. They are engulfed by the very problems they hoped so bravely to confront.

What is required, therefore, is not so much technology assessment, but *technology criticism.* I mean by this that we must begin an intensive and thoroughgoing examination of the role of technology in this culture and its role in our own identities. The territory here is much more uncertain than that which we usually tread. It is also less likely to produce a quick social scientific payoff. But if we are to avoid the triviality of thought and insignificance of political impact which follow from the course we are now taking, the critical capacity must be reintroduced into the way we define problems.

Limitations of space prevent me from offering anything but a brief outline of what such a study would include.[46] We must, for example, re-evaluate the fundamental questions involved in any attempt to build a social science. This would certainly entail an inquiry into what we can claim to know about the nature of man and social and political life as they relate to various kinds of technology. Which of our "needs" and habits appear to be natural and inborn? Which of them are determined by the specific conditions of our environment? How do such things as tools, machines, and the technical processes of work influence the character of human beings in the world and the way they manage to live together?

The study I am suggesting at this level amounts to a philosophical anthropology. For what is necessary to advance the discussion is nothing less than a sweeping reappraisal of the identity of Western man as he appears in the technological society. An example of how this kind of inquiry might begin is to be found in Lynn White's article, "The Historical Roots of Our Ecological Crisis."[47] In White's analysis, the excesses in our present use of science and technology are rooted in certain cultural obsessions which began in early Christian theology. Another possible starting point would be to follow a peculiar clue present in much of the literature: the conclusion that we are actually "soft determinists."[48] Closer scrutiny might reveal that the determinism is considerably more than "soft" and might lead to a more acute awareness of the ways in which technology plays a formative role in social and political life.

A second branch of the process of technology criticism would be a practical re-examination of the specific socio-technical configurations which this society contains and their consequences for the way we life. How and why, for example, do we organize production and consumption, labor and leisure as we do? Given the diverse capacities of modern technology, what *alternative forms* are available to us? Although one would never know it from the contemporary writing, the technologies of production, transportation, and communication of today's America are not necessarily indelible facts of life. This

46. My own contribution will be found in an article, "Complexity and the Limits of Human Understanding," in Todd R. Laporte (ed.), *Organized Social Complexity: A Challenge to Politics and Policy* (Princeton, N.J.: Princeton University Press, 1975), and a book, *Autonomous Technology* (in preparation).

47. Lynn White, "The Historical Roots of Our Ecological Crisis," *Science, CLV* (1967), 1203–1207.

48. See, for example, Robert L. Heilbroner, *Between Capitalism and Socialism* (New York: Vintage Books, 1970), pp. 147–164.

society now encourages the expansion of living patterns which decrease the possibility of meaningful work, decrease the possibility of fulfilling human contact, and increase the level of psychological punishment. Are we bound to such patterns by the operation of what many now call the "technological imperative?" Or are there other possibilities, other structures that we might devise?

This aspect of the critical approach would require the rebirth of two faculties which have largely vanished from social scientific thinking — imagination and the ability to conceive of utopias. In this regard, one example from which we can still draw inspiration is Paul Goodman — a man who has never given up on the idea that modern technology should be able to give us a much better world than the one we now have. Not intimidated by the alleged inevitabilities of his times, Goodman has spent several decades writing about more sensible ways of integrating technical processes with social and economic life.[49]

Beyond the measures already suggested, technology criticism requires a third essential characteristic currently lacking from the assessment mentality — a definite and declared willingness to say "no." The hollow optimism and tendency to yield to the "inevitable" found in much of our thinking must find a corrective in the courage to recognize and call attention to the untenable. Most of the problems we confront, of course, will continue to require us to weigh long, complicated lists of "pro's" and "con's." But there are some important occasions facing us in which such delicate weighing can only be an abdication of responsibility. There are times when conscience will require us to say, "Well, if nothing else, this must not continue. And this must not begin at all."

Anyone whose interests have led him to read thus far already knows what is at stake here. There exist in our present and in our probable future a significant number of technological configurations which bode little if any good for mankind. Inherent in our system of production, information, and defense are numerous possibilities for the degradation of human existence, the loss of personal and political freedom, and the extinction of life on this planet. Left uncriticized and unchecked, our military and corporate technologists could very likely give us a world which would make Kafka seem naive and light-hearted — a world of increasingly insane weaponry, danger-

49. Paul Goodman, *Utopian Essays and Practical Proposals* (New York: Random House, 1962), *People or Personnel and Like a Conquered Province* (New York: Vintage Books, 1968), and *New Reformation: Notes of a Neolithic Conservative* (New York: Random House, 1970).

ously efficient national data banks, increasingly large and anonymous organizations, senselessly expanding megalopolises, wild experimentation with human genetics, increasingly intimidating tools of police technology, hopelessly polluted biospheres, and so on. Such developments, I agree, are not inevitable. But neither are they self-limiting. If the persons best able to foresee the dangers refuse to speak out, who will?

I am well aware of the fact that the sentiments I am expressing here may be interpreted as anti-technological and anti-modern. Any person who seriously suggests that the word "no" be uttered in the face of technological "progress" is now commonly believed to be a prime example of that most hateful of ogres – the Luddite.

But remember that the much-maligned Luddites merely sought the repeal of a single set of advances in textile manufacturing which had made them irrelevant to the British economy.[50] They did not advocate an end of technology or the smashing of all machinery. Similarly, my suggestion that critical voices now begin to say "no" to certain kinds of technological development is not a request that we call a halt to modernity and return to the Middle Ages. It is a request that the notion of improving the human condition be clearly distinguished from technological innovation and removed from the contemporary fascination with technique and extraordinary apparatus.

By comparison, we would not find it odd that a business consultant advising a company might decide that certain of the firm's activities be halted altogether or that the technical means to some of its major ends be radically altered. But a person who begins making similar recommendations for the technical structure of this civilization is immediately branded a dangerous heretic.

If the conviction that much of this culture's socio-technical complex ought to be discontinued, dismantled, or reconstructed in favor of something better is a Luddite belief, then I will admit to being a Luddite. As a contemporary poet once remarked, "Given the world I see about me every day, I think *more* is really *less*."[51]

The need for technology criticism beyond technology assessment is manifest in the nature of many of the crucial dilemmas which the future places in our path. The possibility of altering the character of man through genetic surgery, for example, is hardly a subject for the assessment of "costs" and

50. For an interesting discussion of the Luddites, see George Rude, *The Crowd in History* (New York: Wiley, 1964), pp. 79–92.
51. Don Van Vliet, an American poet.

"benefits." What will be in question here is the very definition of the human species. In making choices to implement or limit such powers, we will want to have a firm grasp on the idea of who we are, how we got that way, and what we would like to become.

Recognition of the need for a more profound perspective on technology and the world has begun to appear in the assessment literature itself. In the National Academy of Engineering's *Study of Technology Assessment,* there is a peculiar passage in which the reporting committee admits the limitations of its approach. Its own methodology, largely that of cause-effect model-building and systems analysis, stops short of illuminating all of the problems which the committee feels are important. To remedy this lack, the report calls for "intuitive contributions" to the assessment process.[52]

Applying only cause-effect methods to technology initiated studies produces a mass of data but few broad conclusions. An improved approach is to organize the assessment effort so as to obtain supplementary contributions of talented individuals or groups who can intuitively perform analysis and evaluation, and thus illuminate additional potential areas of social impact. This approach demands an integrated combination of information and value judgment that cannot always be formulated explicitly.

The candor of the N.A.E. committee is most admirable. But its confidence in the "supplementary contributions of talented individuals" is misplaced. Why must the capacity for intuition and judgment be sought in *other* persons? Is it not possible that these qualities can be nurtured in one's own thinking? Technology criticism must at the outset be self-criticism. Rather than wait for miraculous assistance from some external source, it is self-criticism that the technology assessors might attempt in their quest for a deeper under-standing.

What I have been saying here can be summarized as follows: If students of technology and society continue to moderate their conversations in the debilitating ways they now use, their possible contribution will surely be lost. As they continue their work, it would be well for them to remember an ancient challenge to those who underestimate themselves and their calling:

Ye are the salt of the earth: but if the salt have lost his savor, wherewith shall it be salted?   — St. Matthew 5:13

52. N.A.E., *op. cit.,* p. 17.